Electronics Projects
for Beginners

Using Easily Available Electronic Components

with

a Primer on BASIC ELECTRONICS

Thoroughly Revised and Enlarged Edition

A.K. Maini
B.E. (Electronics) F.I.E.T.E.
Scientist, Defence R&D Organisation

PUSTAK MAHAL®

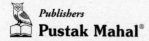
Publishers
Pustak Mahal®

Administrative office and sale centre

J-3/16 , Daryaganj, New Delhi-110002
☎ 23276539, 23272783, 23272784 • *Fax:* 011-23260518
E-mail: info@pustakmahal.com • *Website:* www.pustakmahal.com

Branches
Bengaluru: ☎ 080-22234025 • *Telefax:* 080-22240209
E-mail: pustakmahalblr@gmail.com
Mumbai: ☎ 022-22010941, 022-22053387
E-mail: unicornbooksmumbai@gmail.com
Patna: ☎ 0612-3294193 • *Telefax:* 0612-2302719
E-mail: rapidexptn@gmail.com

© **Pustak Mahal, New Delhi**
ISBN 978-81-223-0152-6
Edition: 2017

Printed at : Radha Offset, Delhi

Dedicated to

Nupur and Nakul

Salient Features

* All projects use easily available electronic components.

* All projects assembled and tested.

* Study material on choosing, using and testing electronic components.

* Guidelines to making your own PCBs.

* A large variety of projects covering HOME/UTILITY projects, MUSICAL AND ENTERTAINMENT projects, EDUCATIONAL projects and TEST AND MEASUREMENT GADGETS.

* Comprehensive and fully illustrated book, ideal for students in schools and colleges looking for suitable projects, Amateurs and Hobbyists.

* Daily-use Electronics data.

Preface

There are plenty of books on the subject of building your own electronics projects in print from both Indian as well as foreign publishers. Various electronics magazines and journals also carry one or two construction projects in every issue. Majority of the books dealing with the subject carries projects suggesting to use electronics components that are not easily available. Usually, these books do not furnish information on the equivalents that could have been used in case the suggested type number is not available. The projects are not fully illustrated, the circuit description is too brief and the PCB layouts are not clear with the result that those seriously interested in building a project selected from one of these books or journals have to think twice before attempting one.

Although the present book is one more added to the list, yet it is different in content, presentation style and choice of projects. It begins with illustrated study material of great practical relevance in the form of the three introductory chapters. The first chapter focuses on the operational aspects of different types of electronics components and devices including Resistors, Capacitors, Coils, Transformers, Diodes, Transistors, LEDs, SCRs, FETs, Opamps, IC timers and 3-Terminal regulators. General application information on digital ICs is also given. Comprehensive colour code charts, component testing and fault finding guidelines and component selection tables are the other highlights of this chapter. The second chapter in the study material section outlines guidelines to make your own PCBs. The art of PCB layout and component layout has been illustrated with examples. The third chapter, which is the new addition to the present edition of the book, contains application information on both linear as well as digital integrated circuits in terms of selection guides and major performance specifications.

The project section contains fifty projects in all. Ten new projects have been added to the existing forty projects in the previous edition. Each project is complete with detailed circuit description, parts list, PCB and components layout and also practical data such as lead identification of components, alternative type numbers etc. wherever needed.

The fifty projects contained in the book cover a large variety of topics. There are projects with an educational value that would be highly appreciated by students mainly at plus-2 and diploma levels looking for one to build as a part of their curriculum. The test and measurement-oriented projects such as *Opamp Tester*, *Digital IC Tester* etc. would certainly interest hobbyists and electronics enthusiasts. Then, there are musical and entertainment projects and there are projects that have utility value such as *Kitchen Timer*, *Auto Switch on/off for TV/ VCR*, *Laser-based intruder alarm* and so on.

The present edition of the book is a thoroughly revised and enlarged version of the previous edition, both in terms of the technical matter contained in the first part of the book as well as the projects given in the second part.

I do hope that the book in the present form with all these features will clearly standout amongst other books dealing with same subject and that it will be well received by students, hobbyists, amateurs and electronics enthusiasts. I acknowledge with gratitude the invaluable contribution of my colleagues Ms. Varsha Agrawal and Ms. J. Kavitha in conceptualization and subsequently circuit design validation/testing of the ten new projects included in this enlarged edition of the book. I am grateful to my publishers for giving the book a nice production get-up and an affordable price tag. Suggestions, if any, will be welcome. All such correspondence should be addressed to the publishers and marked for the attention of the author.

—Author

CONTENTS

CHAPTERS

PROJECTS

CHAPTER-1

CHOOSING, USING AND TESTING ELECTRONIC COMPONENTS

General purpose electronic components like Resistors, Capacitors, Transformers, Diodes, Transistors, Thyristors etc. and the hardware components like Fuses, Relays, Switches etc. are the backbone of any electronics construction project. Before we get on to the task of building electronics projects and doing some construction activity, a brief introduction to these components with particular emphasis on topics like **lead identification**, **colour coding schemes**, wherever applicable, **troubleshooting methods** and so on will certainly be a very good starting point. Other topics that would be of interest to a serious electronics hobbyist and a construction enthusiast, particularly those who have just begun to try their hands at this fascinating hobby are the tips to good soldering practice, PCB layout making guidelines, PCB etching techniques and so on. All the above mentioned aspects of electronics construction are covered in the first two introductory chapters of this book. Electronics components and the relevant practical aspects are covered in the first whereas the construction guidelines are outlined in the one to follow. This is followed by detailed application-related information on the whole range of general-purpose linear and digital integrated circuits in the third chapter, which is a new addition to the present edition of the book.

1.1 RESISTORS

SOME USEFUL FACTS ABOUT RESISTORS

1. A resistor is an electronic component whose resistance value tells us about the opposition it offers to the flow of electrical current. Resistance is measured in ohms (Ω), kilo-ohms (KΩ) and mega-ohms (MΩ) with 1 MΩ = 1000 KΩ = 1000000Ω. Current (I) flowing through a resistance (R), voltage (V) across the resistance (R), and the power dissipated as heat (W) are interrelated by $P = I^2R = (V^2/R)$. Also, $V = IR$.

2. More than one resistors are often connected in series or in parallel to get a resistance value that is not available as a standard value (standard resistance values will be discussed a little later) or to even enhance the wattage rating of what is available. Equivalent resistance (Rs) of more than one resistors connected in series is given by $Rs = (R1 + R2 + R3 + ...)$. Equivalent resistance (Rp) of more than one resistors connected in parallel is given by.

$$Rp = \cfrac{1}{\left(\dfrac{1}{R_1}\right) + \left(\dfrac{1}{R_2}\right) + \left(\dfrac{1}{R_3}\right) + ...}$$

TYPES OF RESISTORS

Carborn composition, Carbon film, Metal film and **Wirewound resistors** are the popular types of fixed resistors. In carbon composition resistors, the resistive element is a slug of carbon. These are usually made in the resistance range of 2.7Ω to 22MΩ and percentage tolerance specification of ±20%, ±10%, ±5%. In carbon film resistors, the resistive element is a relatively thin layer of carbon film painted or deposited on a ceramic or glass tube. These are usually available in the resistance range of 1Ω to 100M and percentage tolerance specification of ±5%, ±2%, ±1% and ±0.5%. In metal film resistors, the resistive element is a flim of metal, metal alloy or metal oxide. These are available for tolerance specification of ±5%, ±2%, ±1%, ±0.5%, ±0.25, ±0.1%, ±0.05%, ±0.01%. In wire wound resistors, the resistive element is a length of wire wound in one or more than one layers on an insulating core. Typical resitance range is 0.1Ω to 200KΩ. These are available in both general purpose as well as precision tolerance categories. Different types of fixed resistors are shown in Fig. 1.1.

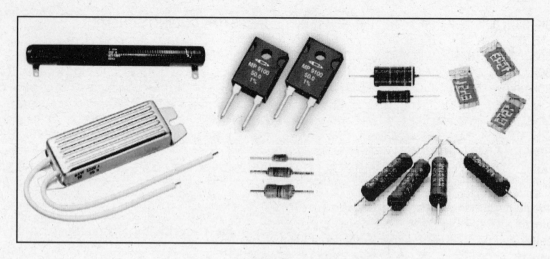

Fig. 1.1

IMPORTANT RESISTOR SPECIFICATIONS

Resistance Value, Percentage Tolerance and the **Wattage Rating** are the more popular specifications of fixed resistors. For all practical purposes, a resistor is almost completely defined with these three specifications. Less common specifications include the **Voltage rating,** the **Temperature co-efficient of resistance** and **Voltage co-efficient of resistance**. We have already talked about the resistance value. It is expressed in ohms, kilo-ohms or mega-ohms. **Tolerance** of a resistor is the permissible plus or minus deviation in the resistance value. For example, the actual resistance value of a 100K, ±10% resistor could be anywhere between 90K and 110K. Resistors with tight tolerance (usually ±1% or better) are referred to as precision resistors. Metal film resistors are an example. **Wattage rating** is the maximum power in watts that the resistor can safely dissipate. The wattage rating of a resistor should be so chosen that it is about twice the power that is likely to be dissipated when used in the circuit.

FIXED RESISTORS—STANDARD VALUES

There is an internationally accepted standard for the resistance values available in a given range for a given tolerance specification. The number of different resistance values available in case of ±1% carbon film resistors is far more than the number of ±10% tolerance carbon film resistors in the same range.

The standard resistance values in ±20% and ±10% tolerance categories are:

2.7, 3.3, 4.7, 5.6, 6.8, 8.2, 10, 12, 15, 18, 22, 27, 33, 39, 47, 56, 68, 82, 100, 120, 150, 180, 220, 270, 330, 390, 470, 560, 680, 820, 1000, 1200, 1500, 1800, 2200, 3300, 3900, 4700, 5600, 6800, 8200, (all in ohms) 10K, 12K, 15K, 18K, 22K, 27K, 33K, 39K, 47K, 56K, 68K, 82K, 100K, 120K, 150K, 180K, 220K, 270K, 330K, 390K, 470K, 560K, 680K, 820K, 1M, 1.2M, 1.5M, 1.8M, 2.2M, 2.7M, 3.3M, 3.9M, 4.7M, 5.6M, 6.8M, 8.2M, 10M, 12M, 15M, 18M, 22M. The list of industrial grade resistors in these tolerance categories have five additional values namely 1, 1.2, 1.5, 1.8, 2.2 (all in ohms).

Standard resistance values in case of ±5% and ±2% tolerance resistos are:

2.7, 3.0, 3.3, 3.6, 3.9, 4.3, 4.7, 5.1, 5.6, 6.2, 6.8, 7.5, 8.2, 9.1, 10, 11, 12, 13, 15, 16, 18, 20, 22, 24, 27, 30, 33, 36, 39, 43, 47, 51, 56, 62, 68, 75, 82, 91, 100, 110, 120, 130, 150, 160, 180, 200, 220, 240, 270, 300, 330, 360, 390, 430, 470, 510, 560, 620, 680, 750, 820, 910, (all in ohms) 1K, 1.1K, 1.2K, 1.3K, 1.5K, 1.6K, 1.8K, 2.2K, 2.4K, 2.7K, 3.0K, 3.3K, 3.6K, 3.9K, 4.3K, 4.7K, 4.7K, 5.1K, 5.6K, 6.2K, 6.8K, 7.5K, 8.2K, 9.1K, 10K, 11K, 12K, 13K, 15K, 16K, 18K, 20K, 22K, 24K, 27K,

30K, 33K, 36K, 39K, 43K, 47K, 51K, 56K, 62K, 68K, 75K, 82K, 91K, 100K, 110K, 120K, 130K, 150K, 160K, 180K, 220K, 240K, 270K, 300K, 330K, 360K, 390K, 430K, 470K, 510K, 560K, 620K, 680K, 750K, 820K, 910K, 1M, 1.1M, 1.2M, 1.3M, 1.5M, 1.6M, 1.8M, 2.0M, 2.1M, 2.4M, 2.7M, 3M, 3.3M, 3.6M, 3.9M, 4.3M, 4.7M, 5.1M, 5.6M, 6.2M, 6.8M, 8.2M, 9.1M, 10M, 11M, 12M, 13M, 15M, 16M, 18M, 20M, 22M. In the industrial grade, 1, 1.1, 1.2, 1.3, 1.5, 1.6, 1.8, 2, 2.2 and 2.4 (all in ohms) are available in addition to this list.

Standard resistance values in case of ±1% tolerance resistors for one decade (i.e. resistors greater than or equal to 1Ω and less than 10Ω) are:

1.00, 1.02, 1.05, 1.07, 1.10, 1.13, 1.15, 1.18, 1.21, 1.24, 1.27, 1.30, 1.33, 1.37, 1.40, 1.43, 1.47, 1.50, 1.54, 1.58, 1.62, 1.65, 1.69, 1.74, 1.78, 1.82, 1.91, 1.96, 2.00, 2.05, 2.10, 2.15, 2.21, 2.26, 2.32, 2.37, 2.43. 2.49, 2.55, 2.61, 2.67, 2.74, 2.80, 2.87, 2.94, 3.01, 3.09, 3.16, 3.24, 3.32, 3.40, 3.48, 3.57, 3.65, 3.74, 3.83, 3.92, 4.02, 4.12, 4.22, 4.32, 4.42, 4.53, 4.64, 4.75, 4.87, 4.99, 5.11, 5.23, 5.36, 5.49, 5.62, 5.76, 5.90, 6.04, 6.19, 6.34, 6.49, 6.65, 6.81, 6.98, 7.15, 7.32, 7.50, 7.68, 7.87, 8.06, 8.25, 8.45, 8.66, 8.87, 9.09, 9.32, 9.53 and 9.76 (all in ohms). The resistance values for subsequent decades i.e. 10Ω to 100Ω, 100Ω to 1000Ω, 1000Ω to 1K, 1K to 10K, 10 K to 100K, 100K to 1M and 1M to 10M can be obtained multiplying the given resistance values respectively by 10, 10^2, 10^3, 10^4, 10^5 and 10^6.

RESISTOR CODING SCHEMES

There are various coding and marking schemes used to express the major specifications of fixed resistors on the component itself. We are all familiar with the colour coding of resistors. Other marking schemes include the use of a straight numerical value indication, certain numerical codes that can be easily translated and numerical codes that can be understood only with the help of the data sheet supplied by the manufacturer.

The coding schemes used usually indicate the resistance value and the percentage tolerance of the resistor and the wattage rating is indicated only by the physical dimensions. In some industrial type designations, wattage rating is also expressed by the code itself in addition to the resistance value and the percentage tolerance. The coding schemes used to designate MIL-qualified resistors are quite elaborate and will not be discussed here.

COLOUR CODING OF ±5%, ±10% AND ±20% RESISTORS

Fig. 1.2 illustrates the EIA/MIL colour code for ±5, ±10 and ±20 percent resistors. A wider first band indicates a wirewound resistor. Starting from the extreme left, the first two bands represent the first two significant digits of the resistance value and the third band represents the decimal multiplier. The band on the extreme right represents percentage tolerance. Absence of tolerance band implies ±20% tolerance. The digits and the decimal multipliers and the percentage tolerances represented by various colours are listed in Table 1.1

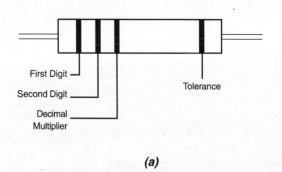

First Digit
Second Digit
Decimal Multiplier
Tolerance

(a)

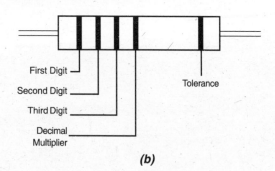

First Digit
Second Digit
Third Digit
Decimal Multiplier
Tolerance

(b)

Fig. 1.2

Table : 1.1

Colur	Digit Represented	Decimal Multiplier	Percentage Tolerance
Black	0	10^0	-
Brown	1	10^1	±1%
Red	2	10^2	±2%
Orange	3	10^3	-
Yellow	4	10^4	-
Green	5	10^5	-
Blue	6	10^6	-
Violet	7	10^7	-
Grey	8	10^8	-
White	9	10^9	-
Golden	-	10^{-1}	±5%
Silver	-	10^{-2}	±10%

INDUSTRIAL TYPE DESIGNATION

In the industrial type designation, the first two digits represent the significant figures and the third digit gives the number of zeros to follow. For resistance values less than 10 ohms, letter (G) substituted in place of the third digit signifies a decimal multiplier of 0.1. For instance, 27G represents a resistance of 2.7 ohms. Another digit following the resistance value code gives the percentage tolerance. Digits used to represent tolerances of ±5%, ±10% and ±20% respectively are 5, 1 and 2. The wattage rating is expressed by two letters preceding the resistance value code. These letters are BB, CB, EB, GB, HB, GM and HM respectively for 1/8, 1/4, 1/2, 1, 2, 3 and 4 watt resistors. We have been talking about commercial grade resistors and industrial grade resistors and the coding methods generally used to indicate major specifications on the component.

It may be mentioned that it is the operational temperature range that distinguishes commercial grade components from industrial grade components. It is 0°C to +70°C for commercial grade and −25°C to +85°C for industrial grade components. Industrial type designation scheme is further illustrated with the help of a few examples in Fig. 1.3.

1.2 CAPACITORS

Next to resistors, capacitor is perhaps the most abundantly used electronic component. In the most basic form where a capacitor is constituted by two parallel plates separated by an insulating medium called dielectric; today, capacitors are fabricated in a large variety of different types, each type having its own characteristics making it more suitable for a certain specific area of applications. Capacitors find use in circuits for a variety of purposes. They are used in time delay generation R-C circuits, in power supplies for filtering and power supply decoupling, as blocking capacitors, for power factor correction and motor starting, in LC tank circuits and so on.

CAPACITOR SYMBOLS
Circuit symbols of different types of capacitors are shown in Fig. 1.4.

SOME USEFUL FACTS ABOUT CAPACITORS
1. Reactance offered by a capacitor to AC of radian frequency (ω) is given by

$$X_c = \frac{1}{\omega C}$$

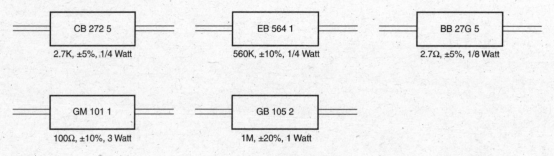

CB 272 5
2.7K, ±5%, 1/4 Watt

EB 564 1
560K, ±10%, 1/4 Watt

BB 27G 5
2.7Ω, ±5%, 1/8 Watt

GM 101 1
100Ω, ±10%, 3 Watt

GB 105 2
1M, ±20%, 1 Watt

Fig. 1.3

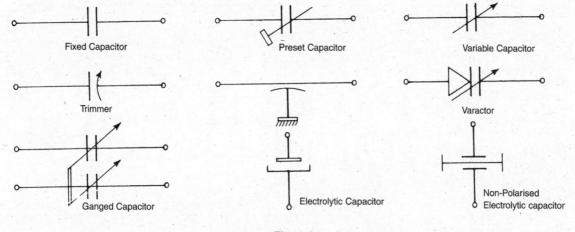

Fixed Capacitor

Preset Capacitor

Variable Capacitor

Trimmer

Varactor

Ganged Capacitor

Electrolytic Capacitor

Non-Polarised Electrolytic capacitor

Fig. 1.4

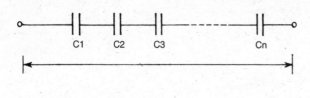

Fig. 1.5

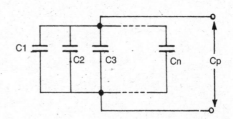

2. An ideal capacitor does not dissipate any energy. Energy stored in a capacitor (C) charged to a voltage (V) is given by $(1/2 \, CV^2)$.

3. Voltage across a capacitor can not change instantaneously.

4. In an ideal capacitor, current leads the voltage by an angle equal to 90°. In a practical capacitor, this phase angle (θ) is less than 90°. The power factor and dissipation factor of a capacitor are respectively given by $(\cos \theta)$ and $(\tan \delta)$ where $\delta = (90 - \theta) =$ Loss angle.

5. The Equivalent Series Resistance (ESR) of a capacitor is the sum of all internal series resistances concentrated or lumped at one point and treated as a single resistance. The Insulation resistance is the DC resistance measured across the capacitor terminals. Greater the value of this resistance, lesser is the leakage current.

6. The equivalent series capacitance (Cs) for a number of capacitors connected in series is given by (Fig. 1.5).

$$Cs = \cfrac{1}{\left(\cfrac{1}{C_1} + \cfrac{1}{C_2} + \cfrac{1}{C_3} + ... + \cfrac{1}{C_n} \right)}$$

The equivalent parallel capacitance (Cp) for a number of capacitors connected in parallel is given by (Fig. 1.5)

$$Cp = C1 + C2 + C3 + ... + Cn$$

CAPACITOR COLOUR CODE

Earlier, colour coding of capacitors was more extensively used for different types of capacitors. Today, majority of the capacitor types are plainly marked with the major specifications of the capacitors like the nominal capacitance value, the tolerance and the working voltage. The polarity is also marked in case of polarised capacitors. A numerical code indicating the nominal capacitance is also quite popular in case of small ceramic disc capacitors used mainly for decoupling purpose. Some types are still colour coded. Colour coding of tubular ceramic capacitors and molded mica capacitors is given ahead.

NUMERICAL CODE FOR CERAMIC DISC CAPACITORS

The ceramic discs of nominal values of less than 1000pF are usually plain marked. For instance, for a 220pF capacitors, it will be marked 220 only. For capacitance values of 1000pF or more, a three digit code is used. The first two digits represent the two significant digits and the third digit represents the decimal multiplier. For instance, 102 represents a capacitance of 10×10^2 = 1000pF and 104 represents a capacitance of 10×10^4 = 100000pF = 100kpF = 0.1µF.

Fig. 1.6

COLOUR CODING OF MOLDED MICA CAPACITORS

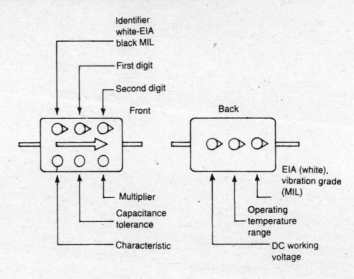

Colour	Significant digits	Multiplier	Capacitance tolerance	Characteristic	DC working voltage	Operating temperature	EIA/ Vibration
Black	0	1	±20%	-	-	–55°C to +70°C	10-55Hz
Brown	1	10	±1%	B	100		
Red	2	100	±2%	C	-	–55°C to +85°C	-
Orange	3	1,000	-	D	300	-	-
Yellow	4	10,000	-	E	-	–55°C to +125°C	10-2000Hz
Green	5	-	±5%	F	500	-	-
Blue	6	-	-	-	-	–55°C to +150°C	-
Violet	7	-	-	-	-	-	-
Grey	8	-	-	-	-	-	-
White	9	-	-	-	-	-	EIA
Gold	-	-	±0.5%*	-	1000	-	-
Silver	-	-	±10%	-	-	-	-

* Or ±0.5 pF, whichever is greater.

Fig. 1.7

14

COLOUR CODING OF TUBULAR CAPACITORS

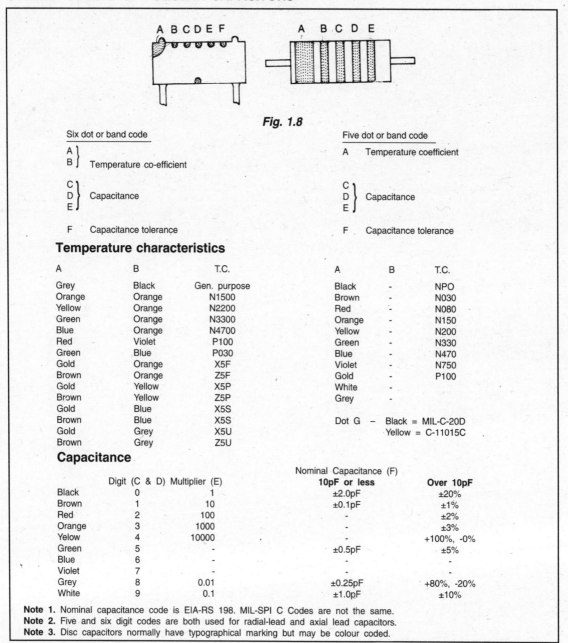

Fig. 1.8

Six dot or band code

A ⎫
B ⎬ Temperature co-efficient

C ⎫
D ⎬ Capacitance
E ⎭

F   Capacitance tolerance

Five dot or band code

A   Temperature coefficient

C ⎫
D ⎬ Capacitance
E ⎭

F   Capacitance tolerance

Temperature characteristics

A	B	T.C.
Grey	Black	Gen. purpose
Orange	Orange	N1500
Yellow	Orange	N2200
Green	Orange	N3300
Blue	Orange	N4700
Red	Violet	P100
Green	Blue	P030
Gold	Orange	X5F
Brown	Orange	Z5F
Gold	Yellow	X5P
Brown	Yellow	Z5P
Gold	Blue	X5S
Brown	Blue	X5S
Gold	Grey	X5U
Brown	Grey	Z5U

A	B	T.C.
Black	-	NPO
Brown	-	N030
Red	-	N080
Orange	-	N150
Yellow	-	N200
Green	-	N330
Blue	-	N470
Violet	-	N750
Gold	-	P100
White	-	
Grey	-	

Dot G – Black = MIL-C-20D
Yellow = C-11015C

Capacitance

	Digit (C & D)	Multiplier (E)	Nominal Capacitance (F) 10pF or less	Over 10pF
Black	0	1	±2.0pF	±20%
Brown	1	10	±0.1pF	±1%
Red	2	100	-	±2%
Orange	3	1000	-	±3%
Yelow	4	10000	-	+100%, -0%
Green	5	-	±0.5pF	±5%
Blue	6	-	-	-
Violet	7	-	-	-
Grey	8	0.01	±0.25pF	+80%, -20%
White	9	0.1	±1.0pF	±10%

Note 1. Nominal capacitance code is EIA-RS 198. MIL-SPI C Codes are not the same.
Note 2. Five and six digit codes are both used for radial-lead and axial lead capacitors.
Note 3. Disc capacitors normally have typographical marking but may be colour coded.

COLOUR CODING OF MOLDED MICA CAPACITORS
Fixed Capacitors—A Comparative Study

Depending upon the type of dielectric used, Fixed capacitors can be broadly categorised as (i) Paper capacitors (ii) Plastic film capacitors (iii) Mica capacitors (iv) Ceramic capacitors (v) Electrolytic capacitors (vi) Oil filled capacitors (vii) Air-dielectric capacitors (viii) Vacuum and Gas filled capacitors. Fig. 1.9 shows picture of some of the more popular types of capacitors. A comparative study of these basic types is a presented in the tabular form ahead.

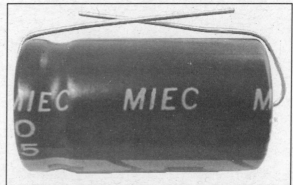

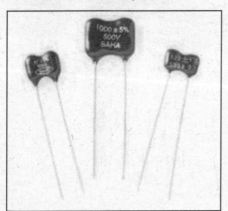

Fig. 1.9

Table : 1.2

Fixed Capacitors—A Comparative Study

CAPACITOR TYPE	DIELECTRIC USED	ADVANTAGES/APPLICATIONS	DISADVANTAGES
1	2	3	4
Paper Capacitors			
(i) Paper Capacitors	Paper or oil impregnated paper	Extensively used for high voltage and high discharge current applications.	Large size. Paper being extremely hygroscopic, it absorbs moisture from atmosphere despite plastic enclosures and impregnants thus increasing its power factor and decreasing its insulation resistance.
(ii) Metalized paper Capacitors	Paper.	Comparatively smaller size and higher voltage rating.	Suitable only for low current applications.
Plastic-Film Capacitors			
(i) Polyester (MYLAR)	Polyester-film	Smaller in size as compared to paper capacitors of comparable specifications. These have almost completely replaced paper capacitors for most DC electronic applications with operating voltages upto 1600VDC and operating temperatures upto 125°C. Moisture pick-up is lesser.	Temperature stability is poorer as compared to that of paper capacitors.
(ii) Polystyrene	Polystyrene	Best general purpose plastic-film capacitor. Excellent stability, low moisture pick-up and a slightly negative temperature co-efficient that can be used to match the positive temperature co-efficient of other components.	Maximum operating temperature is only about +85°C. Comparatively bigger in size.

17

1	2	3	4
(iii) Polycarbonate	Polycarbonate	The insulation resistance, the dissipation factor and dielectric absorption are superior to polyester capacitors. Moisture pick-up is less and these have almost zero temperature co-efficient.	—
(iv) Polypropylene	Polypropylene	Extremely low dissipation factor, very high dielectric strength, low moisture pick-up and high insulation resistance.	—
(v) Polysulfone	Polysulfone	These can withstand voltage at comparatively higher temperatures. Moisture pick-up is typically 0.2% and it limits its stability.	—
(vi) PTFE-Fluorocarbon (TEFLON)	Polytetrafluoro-ethylene	Operating temperature of upto 170°C, extremely high insulation resistance and good stability.	Large size and high cost.
(vii) Polyimide	Polyimide	Operating temperature of upto 200°C. High insulation resistance, good stability and a low dissipation factor.	Large size and high cost
(viii) Metalized Film	Polyester or Polycarbonate	Reliable and significantly smaller in size.	These have limited current carrying capability like the metalized paper capacitors.
Mica Capacitors			
(i) Stacked plate mica capacitors	Mica	Advantages of mica capacitors arise from the fact that the dielectric material in this case (i.e. mica) is inert. It does not change physically or chemically with age and it has good temperature stability.	Unless properly sealed in a case, mica capacitors are susceptible to moisture pick-up which will increase the power factor and the insulation resistance.

18

1	2	3	4
(ii) Metalized mica or Silver mica	Mica	These have the above mentioned advantages of mica capacitors. In addition, these have much reduced moisture infiltration.	—
Glass Capacitors	Glass	Similar to mica capacitors. Stability and frequency characteristics are better than mica capacitors but the cost is higher.	—
Ceramic Capacitors (i) Class-I Temperature compensating type capacitors	Mixtures of complex titanate compounds	These are low cost and small size capacitors. These have excellent high frequency characteristics and have good reliability. Also called temperature compensating ceramic capacitors, these have predictable linear capacitance change with operating temperature.	The capacitance changes with change in applied voltage, with frequency and with ageing effects.
(ii) Class-II High dielectric strength type ceramic capacitors	Barium titanate based dielectrics	Comparatively much smaller than the class-I type due to higher dielectric strength of the ceramics used.	These are not as stable as the class-I ceramic capacitors.
Aluminium Electrolytic Capacitors	Aluminium Oxide	Very large capacitance to volume ratio, inexpensive.	Direct current leakage is high, large inherent internal inductances limit the high frequency performance, poor low temperature stability and loose tolerances. These have been found to burst open when overloaded.

1	2	3	4
Tantalum Electrolytic Capacitors	Tantalum Oxides	Large capacitance to volume ratio, smaller size, good stability, wide operating temperature range, long reliable operating life. Extensively used in miniaturised equipment and computers because of the above reasons. Available in both polarised as well as unpolarised varieties. Solid tantalums have much better characteristics than their wet counterparts.	—
Alternating Oil Capacitors	Oil impregnated paper	Primarily designed to provide very large capacitance for industrial AC applications where these are required to withstand large currents and high peak voltages at power line frequencies. The applications include AC motor starting and running, phase splitting, power factor correction, voltage regulation, control equipment etc.	—
Direct Current Oil Capacitors	Paper or Paper Polyester-film combination	Primarily designed for DC applications such as Filtering, Bypassing, Coupling, Arc suppression, Voltage doubling etc.	Operating voltage rating must be derated as per the curve supplied by the manufacturer if the DC contains ripple.
Energy Storage Capacitors	Kraft capacitor paper impregnated with electrical grade castor oil	These are designed specifically for intermittant duty discharge applications. These are charged normally in milliseconds and made to discharge through a resistive or other critically damped load in a time period ranging from a few nanoseconds to hours. Typical applications include Biomedical equipment, high intensity flash tubes, masers, lasers and welders.	—

20

1.3 COILS AND TRANSFORMERS

INDUCTANCE OF DIFFERENT COIL CONFIGURATIONS

Three commonly used coil configurations are shown in Figs. 1.10(a), (b) and (c). In case of single layer multi-turn coil configuration of Fig. 1.10(a).

$$L \text{ (in } \mu H) = \frac{r^2 N^2}{9r + 10l}$$

where r = Outer radius of the coil in inches

l = Length of the coil in inches

N = Number of turns

In case of multi-layer, multi-turn coil configuration of Fig. 1.10(b)

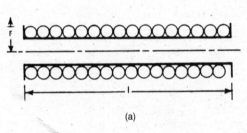

BUILDING YOUR OWN MAINS TRANSFORMER

Although mains transformer for a wide range of secondary voltages and current capabilities are commercially available in both single ended as well as center tapped varieties, yet in some cases, you may like to build one yourself either due to non-availability of transformer with desired rating or due to the fact that you want to have a transformer with multiple secondary windings producing different voltages. The steps to follow while building your own transformer are outlined below.

1. The first step is to determine the required cross-sectional area of the core. The optimum core cross-section can be determined from the empirical formula:

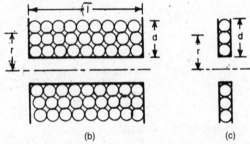

Fig. 1.10

$$L \text{ (in } \mu H) = \frac{0.8 r^2 N^2}{(6r + 9l + 10d)}$$

where r = Mean radius of coil in inches
 d = Depth of coil in inches
 l = Length of coil in inches
 N = Number of turns

In case of spiral coil configuration of Fig. 1.10(c),

$$L \text{ (in } \mu H) = \frac{r^2 N^2}{(6r + 11d)}$$

where r = Mean radius of coil in inches
 d = Depth of coil in inches
 N = Number of turns

Note: **In all the three coil configurations shown in Fig. 1.10 and their respective inductance formulae, an air core has been assumed.**

Fig. 1.11

21

$$A_c = \frac{\sqrt{W}}{5.6}$$

where A_c = Core cross-section in sq. inches

W = Required wattage to be delivered by transformer secondary.

2. Having determined the required (A_c), the stamping size should be so chosen that the ratio of stack thickness (t) to the centre limb width (b) is between 1 and 1.5.

3. The turns per volt can be calculated from

$$\text{Turns/Volt} = \frac{1}{4.44 \times 10^{-8} \times f \times A_c \times B}$$

Where f = 50 Hz

A_c = Core cross-section in sq. inches

B = Flux density in lines/sq. inch

(B) in this expression can be taken to be 50,000 lines/sq. inch which is a reasonably accurate value for 'Stalloy' or other similar materials used for mains transformer core laminations.

4. Having computed turns/volt, both primary and secondary windings' turns can be calculated from known primary and secondary voltages.

5. Primary current can be calculated by assuming an efficiency of about 80 to 85 percent from the known values of output wattage and primary voltage.

$$\text{Primary Current} = \frac{\text{Output Wattage}}{\text{Efficiency} \times \text{Primary Voltage}}$$

6. From the known values of primary and secondary currents, the wire gauge number can be determined from the standard wire gauge table (Table 1.3).

Table: 1.3
SWG Table

SWG No.	Dia. in inch	Wire cross-section (Sq. inch)	Current at 1000Amps per Sq. inch	SWG No.	Dia. in inch	Wire cross-section (Sq. inch)	Current at 1000Amps per Sq. inch
1	0.30	0.07	71.0	26	0.00025	0.018	0.25
2	0.27	0.06	60.0	27	0.00020	0.017	0.21
3	0.25	0.05	50.0	28	0.00017	0.015	0.17
4	0.23	0.04	42.0	29	0.00014	0.013	0.15
5	0.21	0.03	35.0	30	0.00012	0.012	0.12
6	0.19	0.028	29.0	31	0.00011	0.011	0.10
7	0.17	0.024	24.0	32	0.00009	0.0108	0.09
8	0.16	0.020	20.0	33	0.00008	0.010	0.07
9	0.14	0.016	16.0	34	0.00007	0.009	0.06
10	0.12	0.013	13.0	35	0.00006	0.008	0.05
11	0.11	0.010	11.0	36	0.00005	0.007	0.04
12	0.10	0.008	9.0	37	0.00004	0.0068	0.03
13	0.09	0.007	7.0	38	0.00003	0.006	0.028
14	0.08	0.005	5.0	39	0.00002	0.005	0.021
15	0.07	0.0047	4.0	40	0.000018	0.0048	0.018
16	0.06	0.0030	3.0	41	0.000015	0.0044	0.015
17	0.05	0.0025	2.0	42	0.000012	0.004	0.012
18	0.048	0.0020	1.8	43	0.000010	0.0036	0.010
19	0.040	0.0013	1.3	44	-	0.0032	0.008
20	0.036	0.0010	1.0	45	-	0.0028	0.006
21	0.034	0.0008	0.8	46	-	0.0024	0.004
22	0.028	0.0006	0.6	47	-	0.002	0.003
23	0.024	0.0005	0.5	48	-	0.0016	0.002
24	0.022	0.0004	0.4	49	-	0.0012	0.001
25	0.020	0.0003	0.3	50	-	0.001	0.0007

FUSE ELEMENT SELECTION

If you don't have the fuse of right rating for your application or if your fuse had blown off due to some reason or the other and you want to replace the fuse element, Table 1.4 will enable you to choose the right wire size (in terms of wire diameter and SWG number) for a known fuse current rating.

1.4 DIODES

A SEMICONDUCTOR DIODE is a polarity sensitive device comprising a semiconductor junction formed by a P-type semiconductor material and an N-type semiconductor material. Such a semiconductor junction restricts the flow of current to only one direction. The current flows when the diode is forward biased and the applied voltage is more than the cut-in voltage (Vg) of the diode. The cut-in voltage is 0.7 V in case of silicon diodes and 0.3 V in case of germanium diodes. In the reverse biased mode, the small current that flows is the reverse leakage current. This current is independent of the applied reverse bias voltage till the semiconduct or junction breaks down at a voltage known as the BREAKDOWN VOLTAGE or the PEAK INVERSE VOLTAGE resulting in a sudden rise of current that ends up in damaging the device. Fig. 1.12 shows the circuit symbol and the elctrical equivalent circuit of a semiconductor diode. Fig. 1.13 shows the V-I characteristics.

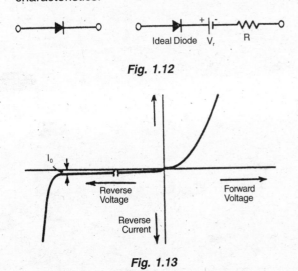

Fig. 1.12

Fig. 1.12

Ideal Diode V_r R

Fig. 1.13

The V-I characteristics of the semiconductor diode are expressed by the universal diode equation given by:

$$I = I_o(e^{qv/nKT}-1)$$

q = Electronic charge = 1.6×10^{-19} Coulombs

k = Boltzmann's constant = 1.38×10^{-23} Coulombs — Volts/kelvin

T = Temperature in kelvin

V = Applied voltage

I_o = Reverse saturation current

n = 1 (for Germanium), 2 (for silicon at low current levels) and 3 (for silicon at higher current levels).

MAJOR ELECTRICAL SPECIFICATIONS OF DIODES

1. FORWARD VOLTAGE (V_F) : It is the voltage across a forward biased diode. It is not a specification in itself. It is given along with the corresponding forward current value to indicate diode's static resistance.

2. FORWARD CURRENT (I_F) : It is the direct current flowing in a forward biased diode.

3. REVERSE VOLTAGE (V_R) : It is the voltage across a reverse biased diode. It is specified alongwith corresponding reverse current value to indicate diode's reverse biased resistance.

4. REVERSE CURRENT (I_R) : It is the direct current flowing through a reverse biased diode.

5. REVERSE BREAKDOWN VOLTAGE ($V_{br,}$ PIV) : It is the maximum reserve voltage that a diode can withstand without breaking down. It is one of the most important diode specifications when it is being used as a rectifier. It is often expressed in a number of ways. Some manufacturers give the PIV rating; others specify the PEAK REPETITIVE REVERSE VOLTAGE (V_{RRM}) and the PEAK NON-REPETITIVE REVERSE VOLTAGE (V_{RSM}). The latter is slightly greater than the former.

6. REVERSE RECOVERY TIME (t_{rr}) : When the diode is switched from the forward biased condition to the reverse biased condition, it is the time taken by the reverse current or voltage to

Table: 1.4
Approximate Size of Fuse Elements

Fuse Current Rating (Amp.)	Approx. Fusing Current (Amp.)	Tinned Copper Wire		Aluminium Wire Diameter (mm)
		SWG	Diameter (inch)	
1.5	3	40	0.0048	-
2.5	4	39	0.0052	-
3.0	5	38	0.0060	0.195
3.5	6	37	0.0068	-
4.5	7	36	0.0076	-
5.0	8	35	0.0084	-
5.5	9	34	0.0092	-
6.0	10	33	0.0100	0.307
7.0	11	32	0.0108	-
8.0	12	31	0.0116	-
8.5	13	30	0.0124	-
9.5	15	-	-	0.400
10.0	16	29	0.0136	-
12.0	18	28	0.0148	-
12.5	20	-	-	0.475
13.0	23	27	0.0164	-
13.5	25	-	-	0.560
14.0	28	26	0.0180	-
15.0	30	25	0.0200	0.630
17.0	33	24	0.0220	-
18.0	35	-	-	0.710
20.0	38	23	0.0240	-
21.0	40	-	-	0.750
22.0	45	-	-	0.850
24.0	48	22	0.0280	-
25.0	50	-	-	0.900
29.0	58	21	0.0320	-
30.0	60	-	-	1.000
34.0	70	20	0.0360	1.120
37.5	80	-	-	1.250
38.0	81	19	0.0400	-
40.5	90	-	-	1.320
43.0	98	-	0.0440	-
43.5	100	-	-	1.400
45.0	106	18	0.0480	-
55.0	120	-	-	1.600
62.0	130	-	-	1.700
65.0	135	17	0.0560	-
66.0	140	-	-	1.800
69.0	150	-	-	1.850
73.0	166	16	0.0640	-
75.0	175	-	-	2.000
78.0	197	15	0.0720	-
80.0	200	-		-2.240
102.0	230	14	0.0800	-
130.0	295	13	0.0920	-

24

reach a specified value. The reverse recovery time is a very significant parameter in fast recovery rectifiers used in switched mode power supplies.

7. FORWARD RECOVERY TIME (t_{ff}) : It is the time required by the forward current or voltage to reach a specified value after the diode has been switched from reverse biased state to the forward biased state. This parameter too is significant in switching applications.

8. POWER DISSIPATION (P, PTA, P_D) : It is the maximum power that can be safely dissipated in a diode.

9. MAXIMUM JUNCTION TEMPERATURE (T_j) : It is the maximum allowable junction temperature. It is significant in case of power diodes and helps in finding the size of the heat sink to be used for a given diode current and the chosen diode type.

10. NOISE FIGURE (NF_o) : It is the ratio of noise power of receiver in which the diode is used to that of an ideal receiver of same gain and bandwidth. It is significant in case of diodes used as detectors and mixers.

11. CONVERSION LOSS (L_c) : It is the power lost in the mixer diode when an RF signal is converted into an IF signal.

12. VIDEO RESISTANCE (R_v) : It is the low level impedance of the detector diode.

13. DIODE CAPACITANCE (C_d, C_o) : It is the inherent capacitance of the diode junction and plays a very significant role in the functioning of switching diodes. Switching diodes have very small inherent capacitance values.

14. MAXIMUM AVERAGE FORWARD RECTIFIED CURRENT $\{I_o, I_F (av)\}$: It is the maximum average forward rectified output current. It is useful in selecting diodes for rectification applications.

15. MAXIMUM FORWARD CURRENT (I_{FM}) : It is the maximum forward current of the diode when

it is forward biased. It is also denoted by (I_{FSM}) by some manufacturers. In that case, it means the maximum surge current. It is always specified for a given time duration. For instance, a surge rating or an I_{FSM} of 10 A for 10 ms implies that the diode can handle a maximum of 10A of forward current for a time duration not exceeding 10 ms.

DIODE PACKAGE STYLES

General purpose discrete electronic devices like Diodes, Transistors, Thyristors etc. are usually made in a large variety of package styles which in turn mainly depend upon current and voltage specifications of the device. For example, there are more than twenty package styles adopted for fabrication of bipolar transistors alone, TO-72, TO-18, TO-39, TO-5, TO-220, TO-66 and TO-3 being some of the popular ones. Same can be said about diodes, thyristors and so on. Thus, there is always a need for comprehensive information on lead identification of these devices in different package styles. While terminal identification is important for using a given electronic device, it is often necessary to test the device for its health before considering it fit for use.

LEAD IDENTIFICATION OF DIODES

For the purpose of lead identification guidelines to be presented here, we have classified semiconductor diodes as (i) SEMICONDUCTOR JUNCTION DIODES (ii) ZENER DIODES and (iii) LIGHT EMITTING DIODES. Majority of the semiconductor diodes are fabricated in one of the following package styles namely DO-7, DO-27, DO-35 and DO-41. The anode (P-side) and cathode (N-side) of the diodes in these package styles are marked in several ways. One of the methods is to indicate the anode with a positive and the cathode with a negative sign (Fig. 1.14a). The most commonly used method is however to put a circular band near the cathode (Fig. 1.14b).

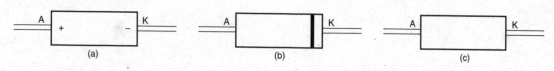

Fig. 1.14

25

The terminal without the band is of course the anode. Yet another popular style of marking diodes' leads is to put an arrow along the length of the diode with the arrow pointing towards the cathode (Fig. 1.14c).

In case of zener diodes too made in these package styles, a band is put near the cathode. In some zener diode types, a (+) sign is put near one of the leads with the other lead unmarked. Here, (+) sign indicates cathode and not anode as stated in case of conventional diodes. Remember that in the usual mode of operation of a zener diode, cathode is made positive with respect to the anode.

High current versions of diodes are usually made in stud mounted metal packages like DO-4, DO-5 (Fig. 1.15). The stud mounted diodes are made both with stud as the anode or cathode. The stud mounted diodes are marked either by putting (+) and (−) signs respectively on the anode and the cathode or by showing the diode symbol with anode pointing towards anode terminal and cathode pointing towards cathode terminal.

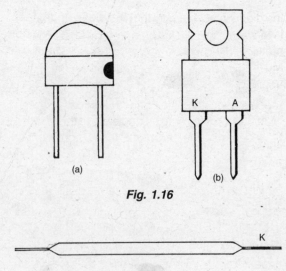

Fig. 1.16

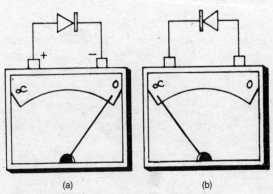

Fig. 1.17

the two terminals. Another less common package is the sealed, axially leaded glass package shown in Fig. 1.17, usually used for making EHT rectifiers and other high voltage diode varieties. The cathode in these diodes is indicated by a coloured band on the lead.

TESTING DIODES

Both P-N junction and zener diodes can be tested with a multimeter. To do so, select the diode check position which is invariably there in all digital multimeters. If you are using an analog multimeter, select one of the lower resistance ranges. The multimeter leads are connected to

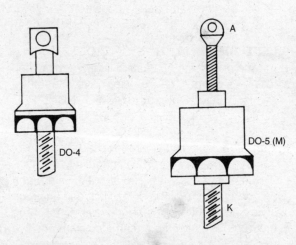

Fig. 1.15

The less common package styles for the diodes include the transistor like TO-106 and TO-220 packages (Fig. 1.16). The diodes in TO-106 package usually have a dot placed near the cathode (Fig. 1.16a).

Whereas in the case of diodes in TO-220 package (Fig. 1.16b), the diode symbol usually indicates

Fig. 1.18

the diode in such a way that the diode under test is forward biased. This is done by making anode more positive with respect to cathode. The Multimeter in this position shows a very low resistance (Fig. 1.18a) confirming that the diode is okay in the forward baised mode. Now, interchange the multimeter leads in an attempt to reverse bias the diode. The multimeter would show an open circuit (Fig. 1.18b) if the diode under test is healthy.

An open circuit in both the tests and a low resistance or a short in both the tests respectively indicate an open and shorted diode. Zener diodes can also be tested in the same fashion. Another important parameter one would like to check in case of zener diodes is the zener breakdown voltage. The breakdown voltage of a zener diode can be ascertained by rigging up a small test circuit as shown in Fig. 1.19. Resistance (R) here can be typically 100 ohms. The input DC voltage being fed from a regulated power supply is gradually increased while continuously monitoring the voltage across the zener diode with a

carrying out this test, remember not to exceed the input excitation voltage to a point that forces the zener diode under test dissipate more power than it can safely handle. Typically, current through the diode should not be allowed to exceed 10 mA while carrying out this test.

LIGHT EMITTING DIODES

Light Emitting Diodes are today available in a large variety of package styles to suit different types of display applications. They are available in the usual dome shaped package in different sizes and shapes (Fig. 1.20), in the rectangular package (Fig. 1.21) and so on. Arrays of LEDs are used to construct bar displays (Fig. 1.22), seven segment display (Fig. 1.23) and many more display types.

Two colour LEDs with two anodes and one cathode (Fig. 1.24) are also becoming increasingly popular. Cathode with one anode emits light of one colour and the same cathode with the other anode emits light of the other colour.

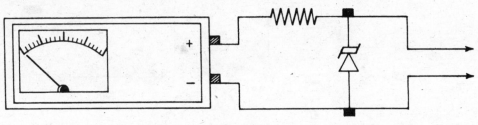

Fig. 1.19

multimeter. The voltage across the zener diode is observed to increase along with the input being equal to the input voltage till it reaches the breakdown voltage. Beyond that, the output voltage. After having reached the breakdown voltage, the current through the zener diode is always given by the input-output differential voltage divided by the resistance (R). The power dissipated in the zener diode in that case would be equal to the product of the breakdown voltage and the current flowing through the circuit. So, while

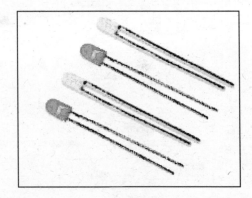

Fig. 1.20

27

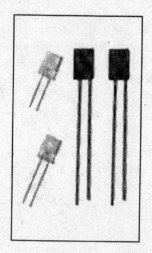

Fig. 1.21

Fig. 1.23

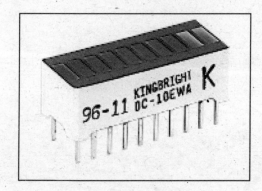

Fig. 1.22

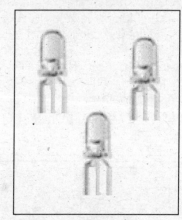

Fig. 1.24

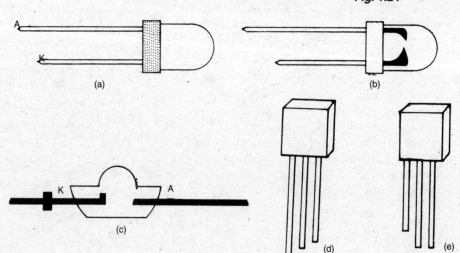

Fig. 1.25

28

Identifying the leads of an LED is quite straightforward. You would observe that the two leads of an LED are of different lengths (Fig. 1.25a). The shorter of the two leads always represents the cathode. Other identification signs are (i) in the dome shaped LED, the dome is slightly flattened near the cathode (ii) the cathode has a peculiar shape that can be easily seen through the transparent housing (Fig. 1.25b) (iii) in case of axial leads, the cathode lead usually has an identification tab (Fig. 1.25c). In case of two colour LEDs, the longest and the shortest leads represent the two anodes. The lead of intermediate length is the cathode (Fig. 1.25d). In some types of bicolour LEDs, two leads have identical length while the third lead is shorter. In these types, the center lead is always the cathode (Fig. 1.25e).

TESTING THE LED

The simplest method of testing an LED is to connect it across a DC voltage source through an appropriate resistance so as to bias it at say 5 mA and check if it glows (Fig. 1.26a). You can even do away with the resistance if you have the tiny 9V battery. Touch the leads of the LED under test to the battery terminals with anode positive and the cathode negative (Fig. 1.26b). A healthy LED would glow. Two series connected 1.5V pencil cells also be used in place of the battery.

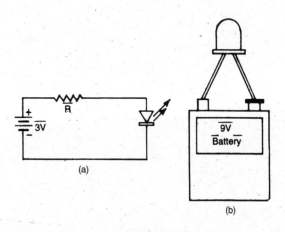

(a)

(b)

Fig. 1.26

1.5 TRANSISTORS

It is a three terminal semiconductor device having two junctions. For the sake of explanation, it can be thought of to be composed of two P-N junction diodes connected back to back (Fig. 1.27). **Remember that two P-N junction diodes connected back to back will not yield a device equivalent of a transistor.** There are NPN transistors where a thin P-type semiconductor layer is sandwiched between two thick N-type semiconductor layers (Fig. 1.28a) and the PNP transistors where a thin N-type semiconductor layer is sandwiched between two thick P-type semiconductor layers (Fig. 1.28b). The three transistor terminals are designated as Emitter (E), Base (B) and Collector (C). The circuit symbols for the two transistor types are shown in Fig. 1.28(c) for NPN and 1.28 (d) of PNP transistors.

In an NPN transistor, when the emitter-base junction is forward biased, normal P-N junction diode action takes place. Electrons from N-type emitter and holes from P-type base move towards the emitter junction and tend to recombine. Since the base region is extremely thin, there are only a small number of holes available for recombination. All those electrons that do not recombine may be powerfully attracted towards N-type collector if the collector junction (Collector-Base junction) is reverse biased. This constitutes current. The process is illustrated in Fig. 1.29(a). It is apparent that number of electrons flowing in the base lead is much smaller than the number of electrons flowing in the collector lead. In other words, there is a large current gain from base to collector. This current gain is still larger from base to emitter and almost unity from emitter to collector. The action in a PNP transistor is similar to that in an NPN transistor with the difference that it is the boles that act as charge carriers. to summarise, current flow in an NPN transistor is due to flow of electrons outside the device and both electrons and holes inside the device, in a PNP transistor, both electrons and holes flow inside the device but it is only the holes that flow outside the device (Fig. 1.29).

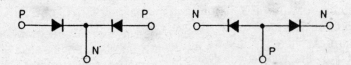

Fig. 1.27

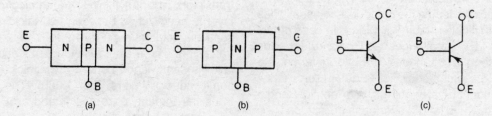

(a)   (b)   (c)

Fig. 1.28

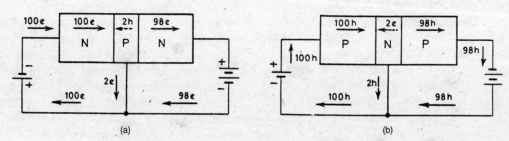

(a)   (b)

Fig. 1.29

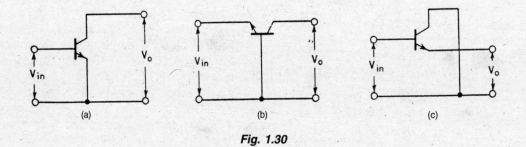

(a)   (b)   (c)

Fig. 1.30

30

BASIC TRANSISTOR CONFIGURATIONS

Transistors are usually connected in either of the following three circuit configurations. Now (*i*) The Common Emitter (*CE*) configuration as shown in Fig. 1.30(a) in which emitter terminal is common to both input and output circuits.

(*ii*) The Common Base (*CB*) configuration as shown in Fig. 1.30(b) in which base terminal is common to both input and output circuits.

the lead arrangement of different types of transistors with varying current and voltage specifications and also manufactured by different companies is identical if only these devices happen to have same package style with the exception of some plastic packages like TO-92, TO-106 where different lead arrangements are possible for different type numbers having same package configuration. For instance, 2N3055 and BU205 have same lead arrangements as both

Table: 1.5

Configuration	Current Gain	Voltage Gain	Input Impedance	Output Impedance
Common Emitter (CE)	HIGH	HIGH	MEDIUM	MEDIUM
Common Base (CB)	Approx. Unity	VERY HIGH	VERY LOW	VERY HIGH
Common Collector (CC) or Emitter Follower	VERY HIGH	Approx. Unity	VERY HIGH	VERY LOW

(*iii*) The Common Collector (CC) configuration also known as Emitter follower in which collector terminal is common to both input and output circuits. The configurations shown in Fig. 1.30 are the basic ones and only show the mode or connection of the transistor. The associated circuitry to be used in these configurations for providing required biasing to the two junctions has been intentionally omitted for the sake of simplicity. A qualitative comparison of these configurations in terms of current and voltage gains, input and output impedances is given in Table 1.5

IDENTIFYING TRANSISTOR LEADS

Transistors are made in a large variety of package styles. Some of the more popular ones include TO-5, TO-18, TO-39, TO-66, TO-72, TO-92, TO-3, TO-202 and TO-220. It is interesting to note that

these transistors are made in TO-3 package though they have widely different electrical specifications and application areas. Similarly transistor type numbers SL/CL 100 and 2N2218 too have same terminal identification though the former is an audio transistor and the latter is a low power switching transistor. On the other hand, transistors 2N3704, 2N5401 and BC558 are all made in TO-92 (Plastic) package but have different lead arrangements.

Another interesting point to note here is that the terminal identification does not change with change in polarity of the transistor (i.e. whether it is an NPN or a PNP transistor) as long as the package is the same. For instance transistor type numbers 2N2222 and 2N2907 have same lead arrangements though the former is an NPN and the latter a PNP transistor.

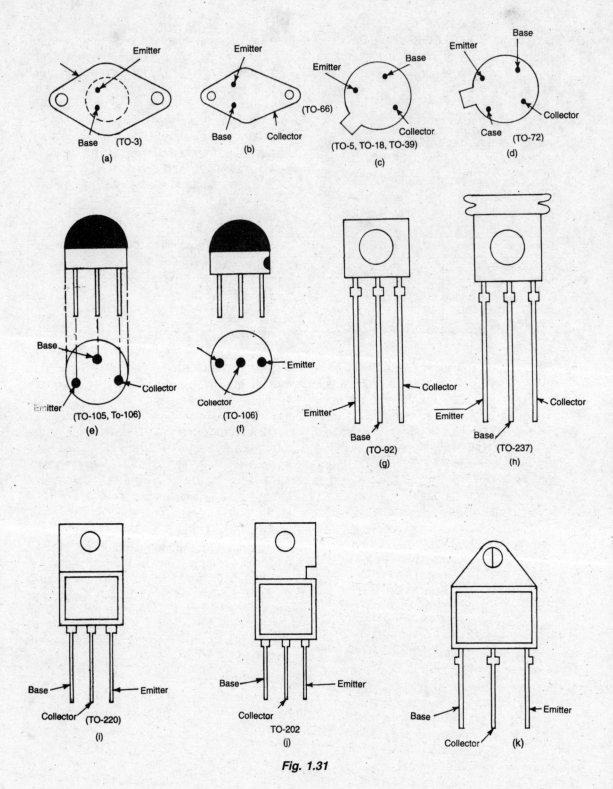

Fig. 1.31

The lead arrangements for different types of transistor package styles are shown in Figs. 1.31(a) to 1.31(k). Some useful tips to remembering the lead arrangment in different package styles are given below:

(i) The metal can transistor packages (TO-5, TO-18, TO-39) invariably have a notch and the lead adjacent to this notch is always the emitter.

(ii) The collector is usually connected internally to the metal can in such packages. One can easily identify the lead that is common with the body through careful observation and even a continuity check with a multimeter is not needed.

(iii) In some of the plastic packages like TO-106 for instance, there is a dot placed near the emitter lead.

(iv) The lead configurations of TO-66 and TO-3 package styles are identical when both types are viewed in the same way. The metal body in both the cases is the collector and there is no separate lead for the collector.

(v) TO-72 package transistors have four leads with the fourth lead connected to the case internally. The package has a notch near the emitter lead and the leads are identified as emitter, base and collector starting from emitter and moving clockwise, just like other similar packages with a notch but having three leads.

Another widely used package designation scheme for transistors is 'SOT' designation, which has much larger number of package styles than the more popular 'TO' designation. But there is no cause for panic. For most of the popular transistor type numbers, there is a corresponding TO-designation for a given SOT-designation and vice-versa. For example, SOT-18 is nothing but TO-72 and SOT-54 is same as TO-92 (Plastic). Also, there are some popular SOT packages which are only slight variations of some popular TO-packages. SOT-93 is similar to TO-220 with a slightly larger width. As far as the lead identification is concerned, for a given SOT package, it is same as the one for the corresponding or even similar TO-package.

LEAD IDENTIFICATION USING MULTIMETER

Multimeter is a very effective tool for identifying the leads of most semiconductor devices like Diodes, Transistors, Thyristors and so on. Its use for identifying the leads of bipolar transistors is similar to the one used for diodes. With the background that in an NPN transistor, emitter and collector are N-type and base is a P-type material, the base-emitter and base-collector junctions can be checked with the multimeter to identify the leads. But such a test gives correct results only if the device under test is healthy. A PNP transistor can also be identified in the same fashion. Also, whether NPN or PNP, the meter shows an open circuit between emitter and collector leads in both the directions.

In the multimeter identification of transistor leads, if either the emitter or the collector lead is known, the other two leads are identified without any problem with a single junction test. If the emitter terminal is known (emitter is the terminal adjacent to the notch in TO-5, TO-18, TO-39 and TO-72 packages), then the base and collector leads can be identified by making collector-base diode junction check. If the collector terminal is known (it is usually connected to the body in case of TO-5, TO-18, TO-39 and TO-72 package styles and is infact the body in case of TO-66 and TO-3 packages), the base and emitter can be identified by making base-emitter junction diode check.

The multimeter tests for identifying the leads of a transistor are illustrated in Figs. 1.32(a) to 1.32(f) for an NPN transistor and Figs. 1.32(g) to 1.32(l) for a PNP transistor. The test arrangements depicted in these figures are self explanatory.

TESTING TRANSISTORS

Transistors can be tested by checking their base-emitter and collector-base junctions. The junctions must be tested both in the forward biased as well as reverse biased modes. In addition, collector-emitter terminals should show an open condition in both directions.

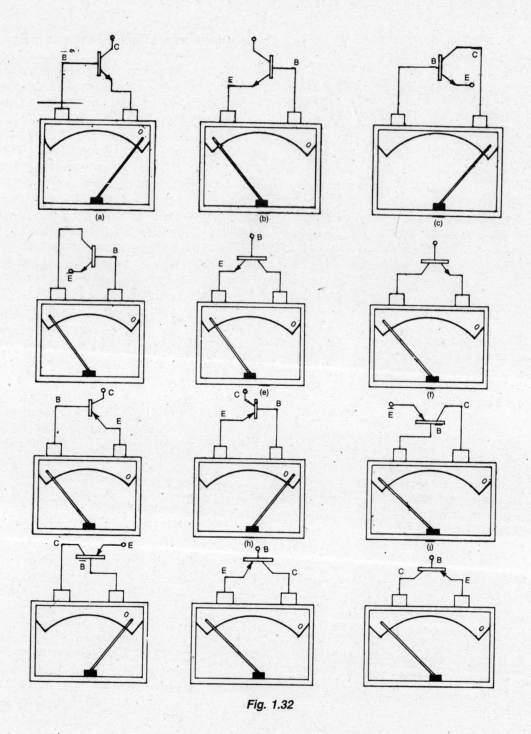

Fig. 1.32

1.6 THYRISTORS

The word thyristor should not be associated exclusively with the silicon controlled rectifier. It is infact a general name given to all the four layer PNPN devices including the commonly used SCR. The diac, the triac and the SCS are the other popular devices belonging to the family of thyristors.

An SCR is a four layer PNPN device with three semiconductor junctions (Fig. 1.33). An SCS also works like an SCR with the difference that it has relatively smaller current and voltage specifications and is usually a four terminal device (Fig. 1.34). Both have I-V characteristics of the type shown in Fig. 1.35. When the anode-cathode voltage is less than the breakover voltage and there is no signal at the gate, the device is in the forward blocking state exhibiting a very high resistance (typically hundreds of kilo-ohms). A trigger pulse of appropriate amplitude and width switches it to the high conduction state. Unlike a conventional junction transistor which conducts only as long as there is a drive at the base, the SCR or the SCS remains in the conducting state even after removal of the gate trigger pulse. The only way to bring it back to the forward blocking state is to reduce the anode current below a certain minimum value known as the holding current usually by temporarily removing the anode supply voltage. A triac on the other hand is a bi-directional thyristor. It can be considered equivalent to two SCRs wired in inverse parallel (Fig. 1.36). Obviously, the triac would behave in the same fashion in first and third quadrants of its I-V characteristics as does an SCR only in the first quadrant (Fig. 1.37). These sort of characteristics pave the way for the use of a triac to control AC power through a given load in both the halves of AC input. While the terminals of an SCR are designated as the anode, the cathode and the gate, they are MT-1 (Main Terminal-1), MT-2 (Main Terminal-2) and the gate in case of triacs.

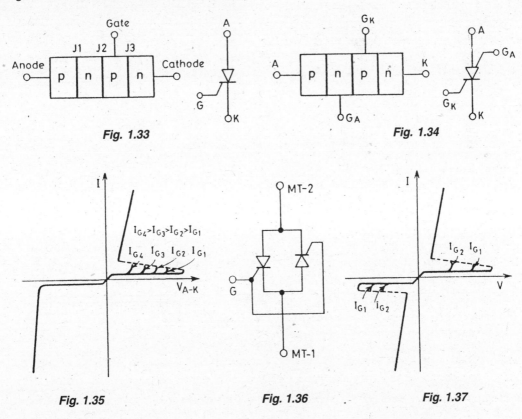

Fig. 1.33   Fig. 1.34

Fig. 1.35   Fig. 1.36   Fig. 1.37

The less common devices in the thyristor family are the SUS (silicon unilarteral switch) which is a 2-terminal four layer diode without the gate contact, the SBS (silicon bilateral switch) which is a triac like device without the gate contact. SUS and SBS have relatively smaller breakover voltage and forward current specifications. SUS and SBS can be used for gate triggering of SCRs and triacs respectively but then they have a limitation that they cannot supply larger gate currents which is often essential for fast turn on of SCRs and triacs. Diac, which has symmetrical bi-directional characteristics like an SBS, works quite well in such cases with its relatively larger breakdown and peak forward current specifications.

LEAD IDENTIFICATION

There is a common standard followed internationally for the terminal designation of thyristors. Fig. 1.38 shows the schemes used for lead identification for the different package styles in case of SCRs. **It is very easy to remember the**

lead identification in case of SCRs by comparing different package styles with the same package styles in case of bipolar transistors and considering cathode, anode and gate terminals in case of SCRs as analogous to emitter, collector and base in case of transistors. This statement holds good for almost all packages with the exception of TO-92, TO-220 and other packages similar in appearance to TO-220. So, if you are familiar with the lead arrangement scheme of bipolar junction transistors, you can easily infer the lead arrangement for these packages when they represented SCRs.

Triacs have a lead arrangement similar to the one in case of SCRs with terminals MT-1, MT-2 and gate in case of triacs respectively representing cathode, anode and gate in case of SCRs. Fig. 1.39 shows the triac lead arrangement in different package styles.

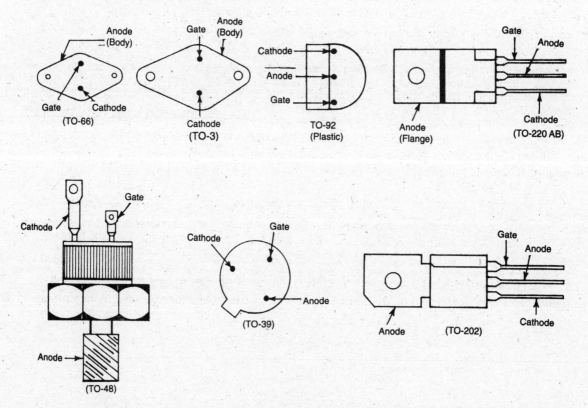

Fig. 1.38

36

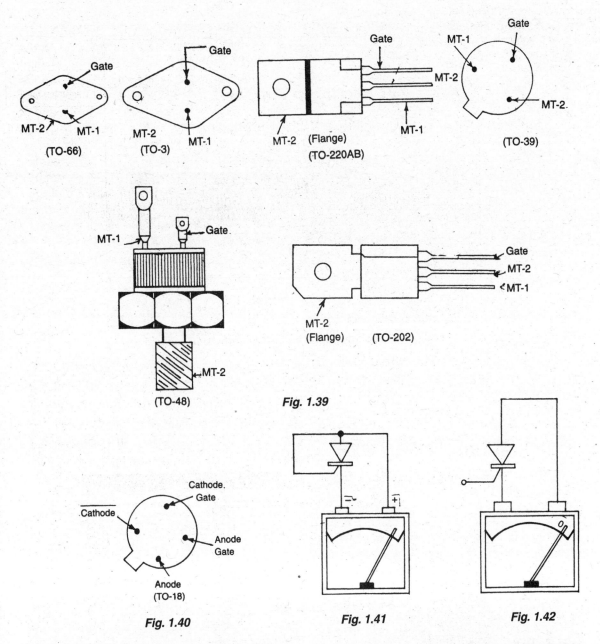

(TO-66)   (TO-3)   (Flange) (TO-220AB)   (TO-39)

(TO-48)

Fig. 1.39

(TO-202)

Fig. 1.40

Fig. 1.41

Fig. 1.42

Silicon controlled switches (SCS) are usually fabricated in TO-18 and other similar low current packages. Fig. 1.40 shows the typical lead arrangement for an SCS in TO-18 package style.

TESTING THYRISTORS
Troubleshooting procedures in case of thyristors are not as straightforward as they are in case of diodes or bipolar transistors. A multimeter or an ohm-meter can be used to check the health of an SCR. The first test to be done is to verify diode action between gate and cathode terminals in both forward biased as well as reverse biased directions. In case of some SCR types, particularly those having higher dv/dt ratings, a low value resistance (typically between 50 and 300 ohms) is made internally to bypass any current resulting from any rapid rate of rise of anode-cathode

voltage thus avoiding any premature triggering of the device. In such devices, the multimeter test of gate-cathode junction would not show a junction property. In fact, it will show a fixed low value resistance in both the directions. The second test is to see an open circuit between anode and cathode and then between anode and gate. The test should be performed in both directions.

The functional test of the SCR can be carried out by connecting the positive of the multimeter to the anode and the negative to the cathode. The multimeter would show an open circuit. Momentarily touch the gate lead to the anode (Fig. 1.41). The multimeter shows a very low resistance. You would notice that the multimeter continues to show a low resistance even after removal of the gate lead (Fig. 1.42). This is due to the fact that an SCR once triggered stays in the conduction state even if trigger is removed. Here the multimeter battery is usually able to supply current more than the holding current of the SCR. Momentarily disconnect the multimeter leads and reconnect the same. The multimeter shows a very high resistance indicating that the device has gone back to the forward blocking state.

OPERATIONAL AMPLIFIERS

Amongst the general purpose linear integrated circuits, the integrated circuit operational amplifier, popularly known as opamp is undoubtedly the most widely used IC. An introduction to different categories of opamps, selection criterion, lead identification and major performance specifications of the popular type numbers and a brief description of a wide range of opamp application circuits are the topics covered in this part of the chapter on linear integrated circuits.

OPERATIONAL AMPLIFIERS

An opamp is basically a high gain differential amplifier capable of amplifying signals right down to DC, which has been possible due to use of direct coupling mechanism. That is why it is also called a DC amplifier. The other main attributes of an opamp are a very high input impedance, very low output impedance, very high bandwidth,

extremely high value of open loop gain and so on. **It is called an operational amplifier at it was originally conceived as an analog computation building block and could be used conveniently to perform mathematical functions like Addition, Subtraction, Integration, Differentiation and so on.** Today opamps have unlimited applications. An opamp fits in any conceivable circuit application from analog computation to building amplifiers and oscillators, from active filters to phase shifters, from comparators to voltage regulators, from function generators to gyrators and so on and so forth. **It is worthwhile mentioning here that an opamp becomes a true operational amplifier to perform all those above listed circuit functions only when negative feedback is introduced around the opamp with the exception of oscillator, multivibrator and other similar regenerative feedback circuits.**

The key parameters of an opamp like Open loop gain, Input impedance, Output impedance, Common mode rejection ratio (CMRR), Bandwidth and Offsets should ideally be infinity, infinity, zero, infinity, infinity and zero respectively. They do approach these values in case of high performance opamps. These parameters which often form the basis of selection criteria are described in little more detail in subsequent paragraphs. **Not all the key parameters are equally important while deciding the right opamp type number for a given application. When the opamp is to be used as a comparator, the response time specification is perhaps the first priority and CMRR a don't care one whereas if we are building a differential amplifier with a high gain accuracy, CMRR and Open loop gain would be among the first few specifications to be paid more attention to.** Today we have different categories of opamps, each one suiting best a particular range of applications. Different categories of opamps are briefly introduced here to expose our readers to what else is being offered beyond the famous 741 under the heading of opamp.

SELECTION CRITERIA-KEY PARAMETERS

Like any other component, the key parameters of an opamp too decide its suitability for a particular application. For instance, an opamp with a CMRR of 120 dB is much better suited for building a differential amplifier than another opamp having CMRR of 80 dB. Also, on the basis of slew rate or response time specifications, we cannot evaluate the performance of a precision opamp. A brief description of the key parameters of an opamp along with their practical implications is given in the following paragraphs.

The **Bandwidth** of an opamp tells us about the range of frequencies it can amplify for a given amplifier gain. The frequency response curve of an opamp looks like the graph of Fig. 1.43 (a). It is nothing but the frequency response of the general purpose opamp 741 and the graph has been reproduced from the data sheets of the said opamp. When the opamp is used in the closed loop mode, the bandwidth increases at the cost of the gain as indicated by the dotted lines. The bandwidth is usually expressed in terms of the unity gain crossover frequency (or in other words, the Gain-Bandwidth product). What is expressed by the curve is the small signal bandwidth of the opamp. That is, the output signal amplitude and the signal frequency are such that the rate of change of output is less than the slewing rate of the opamp. If it is not so, the signal is termed as the large signal and the large signal bandwidth is slew rate limited.

Slew Rate is one of the most important parameters of an opamp. It gives us an idea as to how well the opamp output follows a rapidly changing waveform at the input. It is defined as rate of change of output voltage with time. It is determined by applying a step input and monitoring the output. [Fig. 1.43 (b)]. The step input simulates the large signal conditions. The incapability of the opamp to follow rapidly changing input is due to the minimum charging and discharging time required by an internally connected capacitor across the output. This capacitor has a value that guarantees stable operation of the opamp down to a gain of unity, which means that the amplifier will give a stable

operation and will not get into oscillations for any gain value as unity gain happens to be the worst condition. Now if it is so, then the amplifier is said to be fully internally compensated. Opamp 741 is an example. In case of uncompensated opamp, this capacitor needs to be connected externally. There we have a control on the slew rate specification. We can sacrifice stability to achieve a higher slew rate. For instance, if we know that we are never going to use our opamp for a gain less than 10, we could afford to connect a smaller capacitor and thus get a higher slew rate. But all this is possible only when we decide to use an uncompensated opamp. In internally compensated opamps also, higher slew rate versions provide a larger charging current internally for the compensation capacitor. Opamp 741 has a slew rate of 0.5V/microsecond. Slew rates of upto 10V/microsecond are available in general purpose opamps.

The **Open Loop Gain** is the ratio of single ended output to the differential input. This parameter has a great bearing on the gain accuracy specification of the opamp wired as an amplifier. The ratio of the open loop gain to the closed gain (which depends upon the application circuit) is called the loop gain. Accuracy at any given frequency depends heavily on the magnitude of this loop gain at that frequency [Fig. 1.43 (c)]. As a thumb rule, the gain error at any given frequency is given by the ratio of the closed loop gain to the open loop gain. Thus a higher open loop gain gives a smaller error for a given closed loop gain.

Common Mode Rejection Ratio (CMRR) is a measure of the ability of the opamp to suppress common mode signals. It is the ratio of the desired differential gain to the undesired common mode gain. The ratio CMRR is usually expressed as CMR given by 20 Log (Ad/Ac) dB. A lower CMRR or CMR reflects in terms of variation in the output of a differential amplifier due to variation in the common mode input even if the differential input stays put. The common mode input is the average value of the two inputs. CMR is always specified for a given input voltage range. Exceeding that input voltage range would degrade the CMR specification. In some opamps, the input voltage range is specified separately which implies that the given CMR is guaranteed over the listed input voltage range. Fig. 1.43 (d) shows the degradation that occurs in CMR specification as a result of exceeding the input voltage range. The given curve is drawn for an opamp with an input voltage range of ±10V.

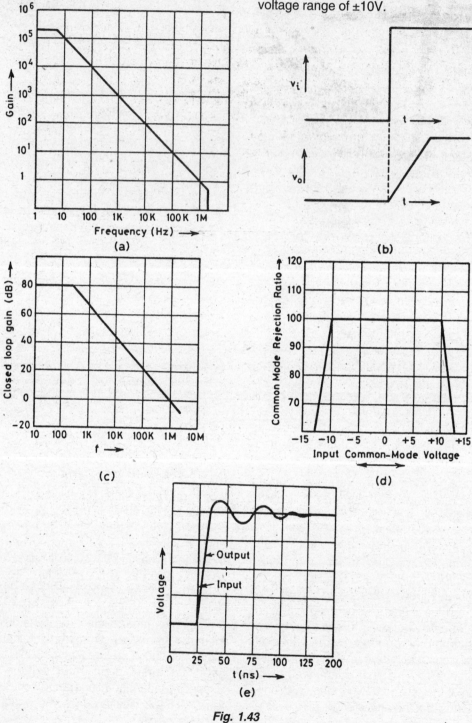

Fig. 1.43

Offset is a commonly used term with reference to opamps. An ideal opamp should produce a zero output for a zero differential input. But this is not so in case of actual opamps. It is observed that we need to apply a DC differential voltage externally to get a zero output. This externally applied input is then the **Input Offset Voltage**. This parameter may be as large as 5 mV in general purpose opamps like 741 and as small as 200 microvolts in low offset opamps. The input offset voltage is often a function of power supply voltages. This variation is expressed in terms of another parameter called **Power Supply Rejection Ratio (PSRR)**. PSRR is expressed in microvolts per volt. Another offset parameter is the **Input Offset Current**. It is the difference between the two bias currents flowing towards the inputs of the opamp. The listed values of input offset voltage and input offset current tend to drift with temperature. This drift is also specified in the datasheets. Some general purpose opamps (741 for instance) have a provision for externally nullifying the input offset voltage by usually connecting the fixed terminals of a potentiometer of a given resistance value across the designated terminals and connecting center terminal to the negative supply voltage.

The **Input Impedance** is the impedance looking into the input terminals of the opamp and is mostly expressed in terms of resistance only. The effective input impedance is however different from what is specified in the data sheet when it is used in the closed loop mode. In the inverting amplifier configuration, the effective input impedance equals the input resistance connected externally from source of input signal to the inverting input of the opamp. In the non-inverting amplifier configuration, it equals the product of loop gain and the specified input impedance.

Settling Time is a parameter specified in case of high speed opamps or the opamps with a high value of gain-bandwidth product. It gives the response of the opamp to large step inputs. It is expressed as the time taken by the opamp output to settle within 0.1 per cent or 0.01 per cent of its final expected value in response to a step at its input. The settling time is usually specified for opamp wired as a unity gain amplifier and it worsens for a closed loop gain greater than 1 [Fig. 1.43 (e)]. This parameter is very important when the opamp is being used as a sample and hold circuit or at the ouput of a high speed digital to analog converter.

Having briefly described the key parameters in respect of different categories of opamps, the operational amplifier selection should be no problem. Based on the circuit objectives, the first thing to be decided is the opamp category that would do the required job economically. Having made up our mind on the broad class of opamps, that is, whether we need a general purpose opamp or a high speed opamp or for that matter an instrumentation amplifier, we can go through the specifications of the devices available in the chosen category to choose a device that suits our needs the best. We should give due attention to both AC as well as DC considerations. One of the major AC considerations for instance is the desired loop gain. As an example, if we wanted the opamp to yield an accuracy of 0.1 per cent while amplifying an AC signal of 10kHz by a gain of 10, then the opamp must have an open loop gain of 10,000. And opamp 741 will certainly not serve the purpose here. The open loop gain for a given frequency can be verified from the gain *vs* frequency plot.

Similarly, slew rate must be high enough to follow the fastest signal input without causing distortion. It is always good as a thumb rule to choose an opamp that has a minimum slew rate of 25 per cent larger than the fastest expected rate of change in the signal.

Input offset voltage and the input bias current are the important DC considerations bsides open loop gain when it comes to choosing the right opamp in the precision category. Input bias current is particularly important when the source of input signal has a relatively higher impedance. FET-input opamps or instrumentation amplifiers deserve an attention in such cases.

GENERAL PURPOSE OPAMPS— APPLICATION DATA

The integrated circuit operational amplifier (opamp as it is popularly known) is basically a very high gain DC amplifier. It has normally a signle ended output and a differential input with the output proportional to the difference between the two inputs. We will not go into other theoretical details of this device as that is not the aim of this presentation. But nevertheless, it is worthwhile stating here once again that due to its versatility, the opamp today is present in any conceivable circuit application. You think of an application and you find that the opamp fits in. Volumes have already been written on opamp applications. All of us are familiar with the opamp 741. Keeping in mind the application potential of this versatile building block, it is all the more important that we are at home with the technical specifications and the precautions, if any, to be observed while using these devices. Familiarity with the technical specifications enables you to think of many more

circuit ideas which you otherwise might not be able to conceive.

SINGLE OPAMPS (741, 748, 709, MC1439, OP-02, LM201, LM318)

Opamp 741/741C is a high performance general purpose operational amplifier. High value of common-mode range and absence of any latch-up tendencies make them a very good choice as voltage followers. They are internally compensated, have external offset nulling facility and a very high open-loop gain. 741 is identical to 741C in all respects except for the operating temperature range which is 0°C to 70°C in case of 741C and −55°C to +125°C in case of 741.

Opamps 741/741C are direct plug-in replacements for the opamp types LM709/709C, LM201, MC1439, Opamp 748, OP-02 and LM318. OP-02 gives a better performance when low offsets are important. LM318 is a high speed replacement for 741. It has a slew-rate of 50V/µS as against

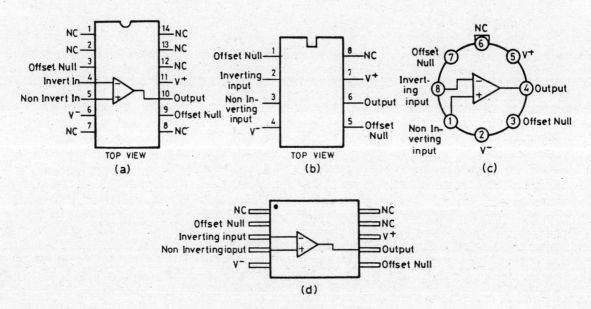

Fig. 1.44

Absolute Maximum Ratings

Parameter	Rating	Unit
Supply Voltage		
741C	±18	V
741	±22	V
Power Dissipation	500	mW
Differential Input Voltage	±30	V
Input Voltage	±15	V
Operating temperature range		
741	−55 to +125	°C
741C	0 to +70	°C
Storage temperature range	−65 to +150	°C
Lead temperature (soldering 60s)	300	°C

0.5V/μS for 741. Opamp 741 and its plug-in replacements are available in variety of packages. Refer to Figs. 1.44 (a) to 1.44 (d).

APPLICATION HINTS

1. Opamp 741 and its plug-in replacements have external offset nulling facility. Offset nulling for these opamps is depicted in Figs. 1.45 (a) and 1.45 (b) for 8-pin and 14-pin packages respectively.

2. The supplies, both positive as well as negative, should preferably be decoupled with say 0.1μF ceramic capacitors near the V_{CC} pins on the PCB.

DUAL OPAMPS (747/747C, OP-03, OP-04, LM1458/1558)

747/747C is a general purpose dual opamp with two independent opamps sharing only a common supply and biasing network. The technical specifications for each of these opamps are same as those of opamp 741 or its equivalent. 747/747C is a direct plug-in replacement for OP-04. OP-04 is also pin-to-pin compatible with OP-03 with the difference that the positive supplies for the two opamps in OP-03 are connected internally. Figs. 1.46 (a) and (b) give the pin configurations in the 10-pin metal can and 14-pin DIP packages respectively. Another popular dual opamp is LM1458/1558 available in either 8-pin metal can or 8-pin mini DIP. LM1458 is same as LM1558

except for the operating temperature range, which is 0°C to 70°C for LM1458 and −55°C to +125°C for LM1558. For configurations, refer to Figs. 1.46 (c), (d) and (e).

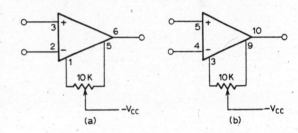

Fig. 1.45

QUAD OPAMPS (LM148/248/348, LM124/224/324, NE/SE 5514, OP-11, RM4156, HA 4741)

LM148 series is a true Quad 741. It consists of four independent, high gain internally compensated opamps. LM148, LM248 and LM348 are identical except for their operating temperature ranges–LM148 (−55ºC to +125ºC), LM248 (−25°C to +85°C) and LM348 (0°C to 70°C). They are pin-to-pin compatible with NE/SE5514, LM124 series opamps, RM4156 and HA4741. NE5514 is same as SE5514 except for operating temperature range, which is 0°C to +70°C for NE5514 and −55°C to +125°C for SE5514. For pin configuration, see Fig. 1.47.

OPAMP COMPARATORS

General purpose opamps due to their slower response times (typically 1 ms) do not make ideal or for that matter even reasonably good comparators. Comparators, in which one of the inputs is normally a reference voltage, switch between two states at the output depending upon whether the other input is higher or lower than the reference. In case of general purpose opamps being used as comparators, the output switches between two levels that are fixed and depend upon supply voltages. These output levels may not be compatible with the load requirements which in most of the applications is a logic circuit. There might, therefore be a requirement to have output levels compatible with TTL logic, CMOS logic and so on. Comparator is the basic building block in circuits, like SCHMIT TRIGGERS, ZERO CROSSING DETECTORS, VOLTAGE LEVEL DETECTORS, SQUARE AND TRIANGULAR WAVE GENERATORS, etc. In all such applications, one would appreciate that a comparator should have as small a response time as possible in addition to having lower input

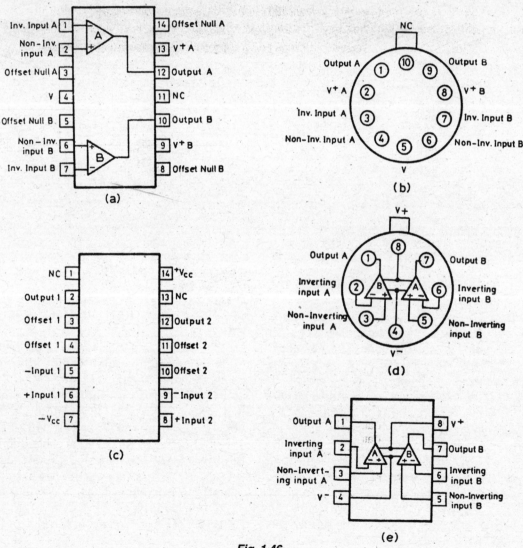

Fig. 1.46

44

bias and offset currents, high voltage gain etc. We shall go on to discuss Single, Dual and Quad comparators of the popular types as regards their pin-configurations, absolute maximum ratings and electrical characteristics with some typical applications. A comparative study of the salient features of some more opamp comparators plus the ones to be discussed in detail has been given in a tabular form at the end.

SINGLE COMPARATORS (LM111/211/311, LM710/μA710)

LM111 series voltage comparators have input currents approximately a hundred times smaller

than the LM710 comparator. Also, these have been designed to operate over a wider range of supply voltages from standard ±15V to single 5V supply. Their outputs are compatible with RTL, DTL, TTL as well as MOS logic circuits.

However, the response time of LM111 series comparators is significantly higher than that of LM710 (200 ns versus 40 ns). Thus LM710/μA710 is a very fast comparator, much faster than LM111 series comparators. LM111 series comparators (LM111/211/311) are pin-to-pin compatible with LM710/μA710.

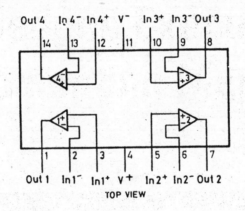

Fig. 1.47

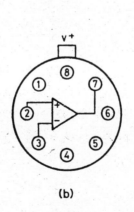

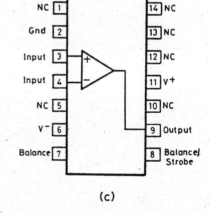

Fig. 1.48

45

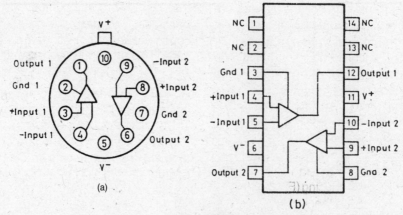

Fig. 1.49

PIN CONNECTIONS (LM111, SERIES, LM710/μA710, LM106 SERIES)

Refer to Fig.1.48 for pin connection diagrams.

DUAL COMPARATORS (LM119/219/319 series, LM711)

In case of LM119 series dual comparators, the response time is typically 80 ns as against 200 ns in case of LM111 series comparators. It is still worse than 40 ns offered by LM710. LM711/μA711 is basically dual LM710/μA710. Due to extremely low input currents and a high voltage gain, LM119 series dual comparators are considered superior than LM711/μA711. Otherwise they are pin-to-pin compatible. For pin configuration refer to Figs. 1.49 (a) and (b)

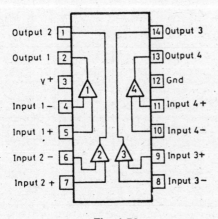

Fig. 1.50

QUAD COMPARATORS (LM139/239/339)

LM139 series consists of four independent comparators with an offset voltage specification as low as 2mV (max.) for each of the comparators. They have been designed specifically to operate from a single power supply over a wide range. The series is pin to pin compatible with MC3302 and LM2901 which have more or less similar characteristics. Fig. 1.50 shows pin configuration.

SINGLE IC TIMERS (555/555C)

IC timer 555/555C are identical in their specifications execpt that the performance specifications of 555 are guaranteed over a temperature range of −55°C to +125°C. Manufactured by various manufacturers, these are available as LM555/555C, SE/NE555. SE555 corresponds to LM555 and NE555 corresponds to LM555C (with reference to operating temperature range).

PIN CONFIGURATIONS

IC timer 555 is available in a variety of packages like 8-pin metal can, 8-pin DIP and 14-pin DIP. Refer to Figs. 1.51 (a), (b) and (c) for pin configurations and internal block schematic.

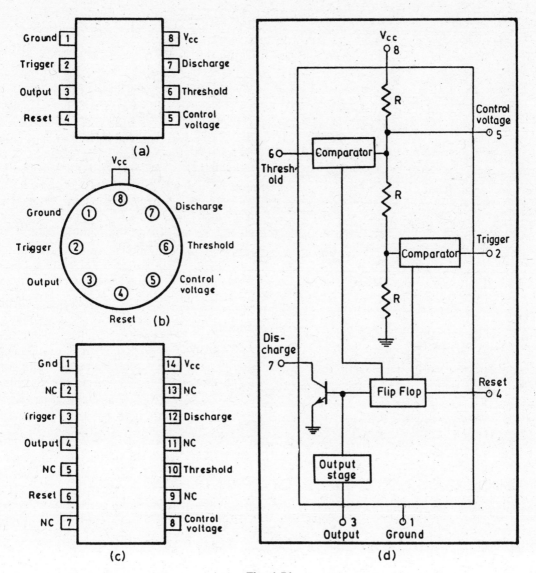

Fig. 1.51

DUAL TIMER (556)

IC timer 556 is basically a dual 555.

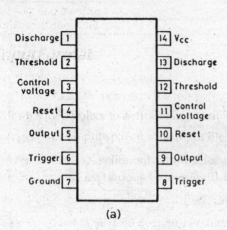

(a)

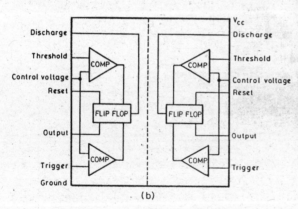

(b)

Fig. 1.52

PIN CONNECTIONS AND INTERNAL BLOCK SCHEMATIC

Refer to Figs. 1.52 (a) and (b) for pin connections and internal block schematic respectively.

QUAD TIMER (558)

IC timer 558 is a Quad timer. The pin connections are shown in Fig. 1.53.

THREE TERMINAL VOLTAGE REGULATORS

Three terminal regulators, which in their basic operational mode require virtually no external components, are available in both fixed voltage as well as adjustable voltage varieties. These are available in the current ratings of 100mA, 500mA and 3.0A. Due to their ready availability, low cost, convenience of operation and host of other practical advantages, the trend today is to have localised regulation for each subsystem of the main system. The earlier convetion of using single point regulation suffered not only from the unequal voltage drops in the impedance of the lines connecting the main regulator to various subsystems, it also resulted in unwanted coupling between different subsystems constituting the main system. The concept of localised regulation using 3-Terminal regulators is free from all these drawbacks.

Application data on some of the popular types of 3-terminal positive regulators, both fixed and adjustable, is presented here. A similar treatise on 3-terminal negative regulators will follow.

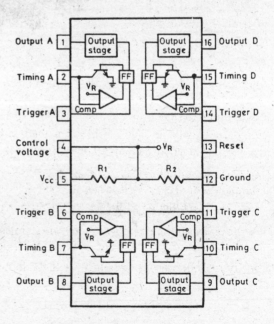

Fig. 1.53

48

THREE TERMINAL POSITIVE VOLTAGE REGULATORS

FIXED: LM78XX/MC78XX,LM78MXX/ MC78MXX, LM78LXX/MC78LXX, LM140XX/340XX

ADJUSTABLE: LM117/217/317

This is the most popular variety of 3-terminal fixed regulated output positive voltage regulators. These are available in various voltage and current specifications. A two digit number in place of "XX" signifies the regulated output voltage. For instance, LM7805 and LM78L05 are both 5V regulators.

Similarly, LM7812, LM78M12 and LM78L12 are all 12V regulators.

LM78XX/MC78XX series has a maximum output current capability of 1.5 A; LM78MXX/MC78MXX series has a maximum output current rating of 0.5A whereas LM78LXX/MC78LXX series' maximum ouput current rating is 0.1A These regulators from National Semiconductors are available in the voltage ratings of 5V, 12V and 15V whereas Motorola devices are available in the voltage ratings of 5V, 6V, 8V, 12V, 15V, 18V, 20V and 24V. Different package types along with their lead identification are depicted in Fig. 1.54.

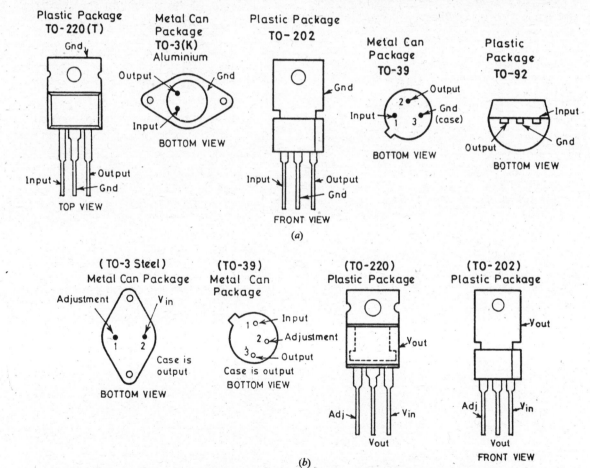

Fig. 1.54 (a) : Lead identification for LM78XX series, LM78MXX series, LM78LXX series, LM109/209/309, LM123/223/323, LM330 & LM140-XX/340-XX series.

(b) : Lead identifications for LM117/217/317, LM138/238/338.

49

LM140-XX/LM340-XX SERIES

LM140-XX/LM340-XX series regulators are again fixed output voltage regulators available in a variety of output voltage and output current specifications.

LM117/LM217/LM317

These are adjustable 3-terminal positive Voltage regulators and are available in the current ratings of 0.1A, 0.5A and 1.5A. The output voltage is adjustable from 1.2V to 37V. In the high voltage version of this series, LM117HV/LM217HV/LM317HV, the output voltage is adjustable from 1.2V to 57V. LM117, LM217 and LM317 are identical in all respects except for their operational temperature ranges. LM117 has an operational temperature range of −55°C to +125°C. It is −25°C to +125°C for LM217 and 0°C to +125°C for LM317.

LM117/LM217/LM317 have built-in current limit and thermal overload protection. Their performance specifications are much better than those of fixed voltage regulators. Since these regulators are floating and see only the input-to-output differential voltage, supplies of several hundred volts can be regulated as long as the input-output differential is not exceeded.

APPLICATION GUIDELINES

Although 3-terminal regulators of LM78XX series and LM340-XX series have been designed primarily as fixed voltage regulators, these devices can be used with external components to obtain adjustable voltages and currents.

(1) Fig. 1.55 shows the basic operational mode of these regulators. Capacitor C_1 is required only if the regulator is located far away from the power supply filter. Typically a 0.22μF ceramic disc capacitor serves the purpose. Use of capacitor C_2 is not an essential requirement. It does however improve transient response. If needed, use 0.1μF ceramic disc.

(2) Fig. 1.56 demonstrates their use as an adjustable output voltage regulator. Fig. 1.57 shows the application of a fixed regulator to obtain an output voltage greater than the Vreg.

(3) Fig. 1.58 shows the application of 78XX/LM340-XX series regulators as current regulators.

(4) Although the regulators in 78XX/LM340-XX series have built-in internal short circuit current limit and thermal overload protection yet it is advisable to take the following precautions while using them.

  (i) If a large output capacitor is used (>10μF), the momentary short circuit at the input can damage the regulator as in that case the output capacitor will discharge through the regulator and the stored charge may be large enough to damage the regulator. A fast diode connected as shown in Fig. 1.59 in that case protects the regulator by bypassing bulk of the discharge current through it.

  (ii) Sufficiently strong transients exceeding the maximum V_{in} rating or going sufficiently below ground level are likely to damage the regulator. The solution is to use a large input capacitor, a choke or a transient suppresser or a combination of these.

  (iii) In case ground terminal becomes disconnected, the output approaches the unregulated input causing possible damage to the other circuits connected to the output of regulator.

(5) Fig. 1.60 shows the application of LM117/LM217/LM317 as an adjustable regulator. Vref is typically 1.25V for LM117/LM217/LM317 and ladj is typically 50μA. C_1 should preferably be 0.1uF ceramic disc or a 1.0uF tantalum. Cadj provides ripple rejection. Cadj of 10μF provides typically 80dB rejection.

(6) Fig. 1.61 shows a constant current battery charger. The constant charging current in this case will be 50mA.

Three Terminal Negative Voltage Regulators

Fixed: LM79XX/MC79XX series, LM79XX/ MC79XX series, LM79LXX/MC79LXX series, LM120-XX/LM320-XX series

Adjustable : LM137/LM237/LM337 series

The merits of the concept of localised regulation as compared to the practice of single point regulation were outlined in brief in the previous section and the three-terminal regulator, which is the most important building block for the implementation of the concept of localised regulation, was introduced followed by technical data and application hints on some of the most popular fixed and adjustable output three-terminal positive regulators. In this section, we shall cover negative regulators.

LM79XX/MC79XX, LM79MXX MC79MXX, LM79LXX/MC9LXX

These are the most commonly used types of three-terminal fixed voltage regulators. These are available in various voltage and current ratings. A two digit number in place of the suffix "XX" indicates the regulated output voltage. For instance, LM7912 and LM79M12 and LM79L12 are all –12V regulators.

LM79XX/MC79XX series has a maximum output current capability of 1.5A. LM79MXX/MC79MXX series has a maximum ouput current capability of 0.5A whereas LM79LXX/MC79LXX series has a maximum output current rating of 0.1A. The regulators from National Semiconductors are available in the voltage ratings of –5V, –12V and –15V whereas Motorola devices are available in the voltage ratings of –2V, –3V, –5V, –5.2V, –6V, –8V, –12V, –15V, –18V and –24V. Different fixed voltage negative regulator package types along with respective lead identifications are shown in Fig. 1.62. These regulators employ internal current limiting safe area protection and thermal shutdown for protection against virtually all overload conditons.

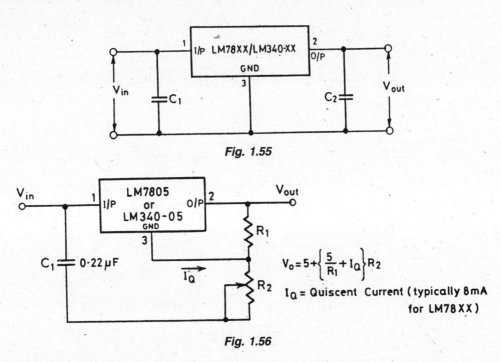

Fig. 1.55

$$V_o = 5 + \left\{ \frac{5}{R_1} + I_Q \right\} R_2$$

I_Q = Quiscent Current (typically 8mA for LM78XX)

Fig. 1.56

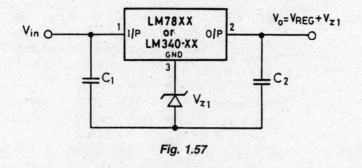

Fig. 1.57

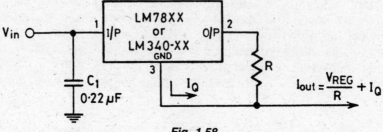

Fig. 1.58

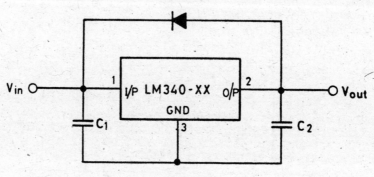

Fig. 1.59

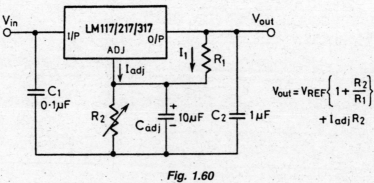

Fig. 1.60

52

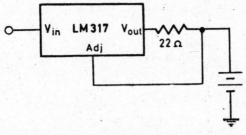

Fig. 1.61

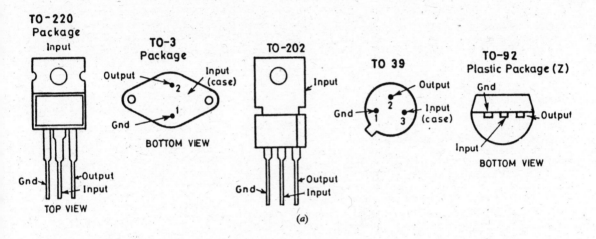

(a)

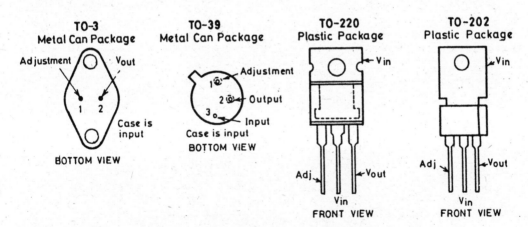

Fig. 1.62 (a): Lead identification: LM79XX, LM79LXX, series,
LM120-XX/LM320-XX series

(b): Lead identification : LM137/237/337,
LM137HV/237HV/337HV

53

LM120-XX/LM320-XX SERIES

LM120-XX/LM320-XX series regulators are again fixed output negative regulators available in a variety of voltage and current ratings. These regulators too have internal current limiting and thermal overload protection. These regulators have excellent ripple rejection and operate with Input-Output differential down to 1V.

LM137/LM237/LM337

These are adjustable 3-terminal negative regulators and are available in the current ratings of 0.1A, 0.5A, 1.5A. The output voltage is adjustable from −1.2 V to −37V. In the high voltage version of this series of regulators, LM137HV/LM237HV/LM337HV, the output voltage is adjustable from −1.2V to −47V. LM137, LM237, LM337 are identical in all respects except for their operational temperatue ranges. LM137 series features internal current limiting and thermal overload protection.

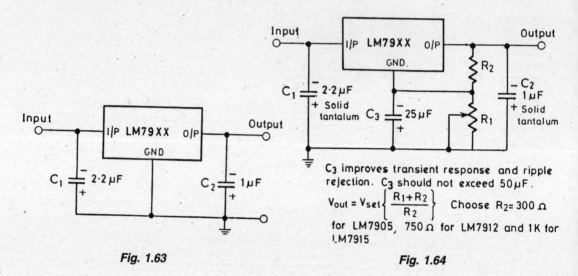

Fig. 1.63

C_3 improves transient response and ripple rejection. C_3 should not exceed $50 \mu F$.

$$V_{out} = V_{set} \left\{ \frac{R_1 + R_2}{R_2} \right\}$$

Choose $R_2 = 300 \, \Omega$ for LM7905, $750 \, \Omega$ for LM7912 and 1K for LM7915

Fig. 1.64

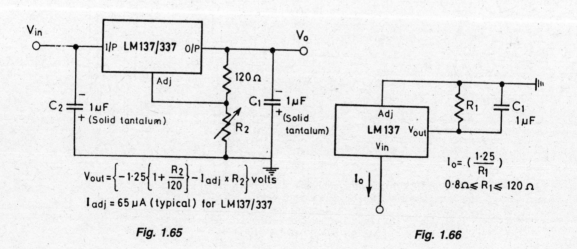

$$V_{out} = \left\{ -1 \cdot 25 \left\{ 1 + \frac{R_2}{120} \right\} - I_{adj} \times R_2 \right\} \text{volts}$$

$I_{adj} = 65 \, \mu A$ (typical) for LM137/337

Fig. 1.65

$$I_o = \left(\frac{1 \cdot 25}{R_1} \right)$$

$$0 \cdot 8 \Omega \leqslant R_1 \leqslant 120 \, \Omega$$

Fig. 1.66

APPLICATION GUIDELINES

Although 3-terminal negative regulators of the LM79XX series and LM120-XX/LM320-XX series have been designed primarily as fixed voltage regulators, these devices can be used with external components to obtain adjustable voltages and currents. Fig.1.63 shows the normal operational mode of the fixed output voltage regulators. Capacitor C_1 is required only if the regulator is away from the power supply filter for more than three inches or so. For the values given, the capacitors C_1 and C_2 should preferably be solid tantalums. 25µF aluminium electrolytics can be used instead. Fig.1.64 shows the use of fixed voltage regulators as adjustable output regulators. Fig.1.65 shows the application of LM137/LM337 to obtain adjustable negative voltage. C_1 is 1µF solid tantalum or a 10µF aluminium electrolytics. C_2 is required only if the regulator is located at a distance of more than say three or four inches from the power supply filter. It is typically 1µF solid tantalum. Fig.1.66 depicts use of LM137 as a current regulator.

DIGITAL INTEGRATED CIRCUITS

LOGIC GATES

Fig. 1.67(a) shows the logic symbol and the functional table (also known as the TRUTH TABLE) of a 2-input OR-gate expressed by the Boolean expression $y = A + B$ and read as y equals A OR B. In general, the output of an OR-gate is a logic '0' only when all its inputs are logic '0'. For all other possible input combinations, the output is logic '1'.

Fig. 1.67(b) shows the logic symbol and the functional table of a 2-input AND-gate expressed by $y = A.B$ and read as y equals A AND B. In general, the output of an AND-gate is logic '1' only when all its inputs are logic '1'. For all other input combinations, the output is logic '0'.

The third important logic circuit (not exactly a logic gate) is the NOT-circuit also known as an INVERTER circuit. It complements the input *i.e.* a logic '0' at the input yields a logic '1' at the output and vice versa. Fig. 1.67(c) shows its circuit symbol and the functional table.

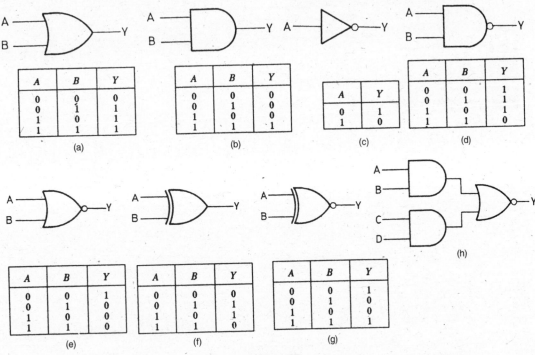

Fig. 1.67

Fig. 1.67(d) shows the circuit symbol and the functional table of a NAND-gate expressed by, y = $\overline{AB}$. In general, the output of a NAND-gate is logic '0' only when all its inputs are logic '1'. For all other input combinations, the output is a logic '1'. Complementing the output of an AND-gate yields a NAND-gate. The reverse is also true.

Fig. 1.67(e) shows the circuit symbol and the functional table of NOR-gate expressed by y = $\overline{A+B}$. In general, the output of a NOR-gate is logic '1' only when all its inputs are logic '0'. For all other possible input combinations, the output is a logic '0'. Complementing the output of a NOR-gate yields an OR-gate. The reverse is also true.

Shorting all the inputs of a NAND or a NOR to get a one input-one output circuit yields an inverter.

Fig. 1.67(f) shows the circuit symbol and functional table of an EX-OR gate expressed by y = $\overline{A}.B$ + A.$\overline{B}$. In general, the output of an EX-NOR gate is a logic '1' whenever the number of 1's in the input combination is odd and a logic '0' whenever the number of 1's in the input combination is even.

Fig. 1.67(g) shows the circuit symbol and functional table of an EX-NOR gate expressed by y = A.B + $\overline{A}$.$\overline{B}$. In general, the output of an EX-NOR gate is a logic '1' when the number of 1's, in the input combination is even and a logic '0', when the number of 1's in the input combination is odd. Complementing the output of EX-OR gate yields EX-NOR gate. The reverse is also true.

Fig. 1.67(h) shows the circuit symbol of an AND-OR-INVERT gate expressed by y = $\overline{(AB+CD)}$.

It is also called a 2-wide, 2-input AND-OR-INVERT gate. It is 2-wide as there are two AND-gates at the input. It is 2-input as each AND-gate has 2 inputs. Other varieties of these gates such as 2-wide, 4-input AND-OR-INVERT and 4-wide, 2-input AND-OR-INVERT gates are also available in IC form.

NAND and NOR gates can be used individually to get all other logic gate functions. Figs. 1.68(a) to 1.68(f) depict the use of NAND-gates

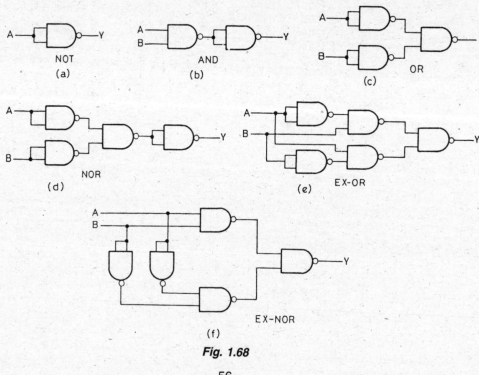

NOT
(a)

AND
(b)

OR
(c)

NOR
(d)

EX-OR
(e)

EX-NOR
(f)

Fig. 1.68

56

to make an inverter, an AND-gate, an OR-gate, a NOR-gate, an EX-OR gate and an EX-NOR gate respectively. Use of NOR gates to simulate gates other than NOR is depicted in Fig. 1.69(a) to 1.69(f). Due to this reason, NAND and NOR gates are also known as UNIVERSAL GATES.

The logic gates that we have discussed so far have a single input threshold voltage level. The input threshold voltage is the same for both Low to High as well as High to Low output transitions. There are some logic gate varieties like inverters and NAND-gates that are also available with a built-in schmitt action. These have two different input threshold voltage levels, one for LOW to HIGH output transition and the other for HIGH to LOW output transition. Figs. 1.70(a) and (b) show the circuit symbols of schmitt NAND and a schmitt inverter. Fig. 1.70(c) shows the typical transfer characteristics for such a logic circuit. The characteristics shown have been taken from the data sheet of 74LS132 which is nothing but a Quad 2-input schmitt trigger NAND gate with the two thresholds as 1.6V (for H to L transition) and 0.8V (for L to H transition). The difference between the two thresholds is known as the HYSTERISIS.

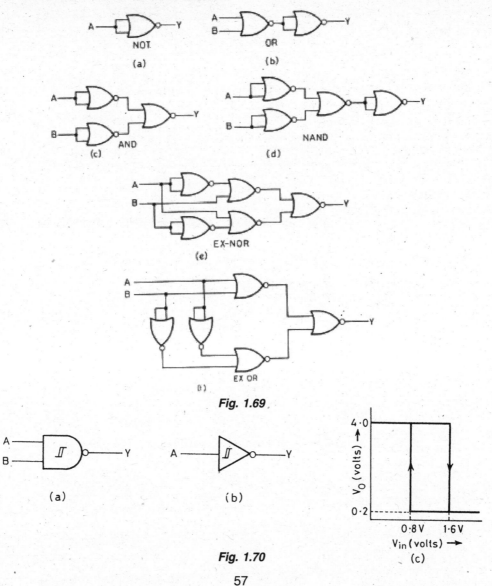

Fig. 1.69

Fig. 1.70

57

BUFFERS AND TRANSCEIVERS

The logic gates discussed in the last section have a limited load driving capability. A BUFFER (it could be an inverting or a non-inverting buffer with a single input and single output, a NAND-buffer, a NOR-buffer, an OR-buffer or an AND-buffer) has a larger load drive capability than a logic gate, DRIVER is another name for a buffer. A driver is sometimes used to designate a circuit that has a larger drive capability than a buffer. Buffers are usally tristate devices to facilitate their use in bus oriented systems. Fig.1.71 shows the symbols and functional tables of inverting and non-inverting buffers of the tristate type.

A TRANSCEIVER is a bi-directional buffer with additional direction control and enable inputs. It allows flow of data in both the directions depending upon logic status of control inputs. Transceiver ICs are are usually tristate devices to make them compatible with bus-oriented systems. Fig.1.72 shows symbols of an inverting and a non-inverting transceiver.

Fig.1.73 shows a typical logic circuit arrangement of tristate non-inverting transceiver alongwith its functional table.

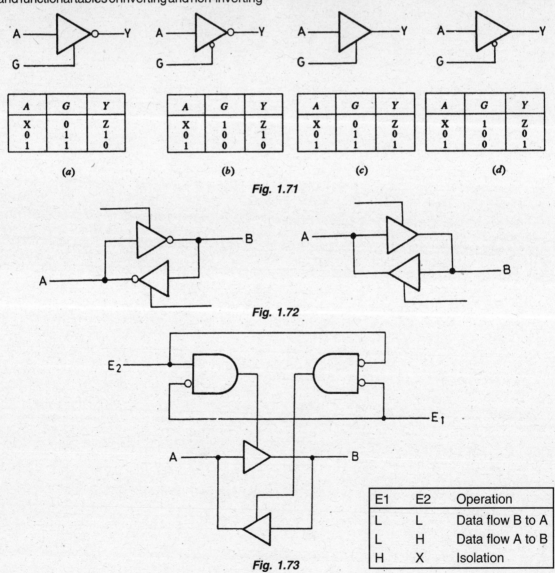

A	G	Y
X	0	Z
0	1	1
1	1	0

(a)

A	G	Y
X	1	Z
0	0	1
1	0	0

(b)

A	G	Y
X	0	Z
0	1	0
1	1	1

(c)

A	G	Y
X	1	Z
0	0	0
1	0	1

(d)

Fig. 1.71

Fig. 1.72

Fig. 1.73

E1	E2	Operation
L	L	Data flow B to A
L	H	Data flow A to B
H	X	Isolation

58

FLIP-FLOPS AND LATCHES

While a logic gate is the basic building block of combinational logic, flip flops and latches (latch is a form of flip flop) are the basis of sequential logic. Bistable multivibrator is another name for a flip flop. Different types of flip flops include the R-S flip flop, J-K flip flop, Toggle flip flop and D-type flip flop. But the flip flops that are usually available in the IC form are the J-K flip flop and D-type flip flop as all other flip flop functions can be implemented using these flip flops.

D-TYPE FLIP FLOP

In a D-type flip flop, the data bit present on the D-input is transferred to the Q-output everytime it is clocked. Fig.1.74(a) shows the symbol and functional table of the basic D-type flip flop. The D-type flip flops usually available in the IC form have four inputs and two outputs. The inputs are D, clock (CLK), PR (Preset) and CLR (Clear).

Q and $\overline{Q}$ (Complement of Q) are the two outputs.

The PR and CLR are the asynchronous inputs as they override information on all other inputs. Whenever PR (Preset) is active (The D flip flop of Fig.1.74(b) is active when LOW), the Q-output is always a logic '1' irrespective of logic status of D-input and the clock input. Whenever CLR (Clear) input is active (it is active when LOW is this case), the Q-output is always a logic '0'. Both PR and CLR are not allowed to be active at the same time during normal operation.

When both PR and CLR are inactive, a clock transition (a LOW to HIGH transition in this case) transfers the information on D-input to the Q-output. The Q-output retains the data bit till there is another genuine clock transition. There are D-type flip flops that are negative edge triggered i.e. they respond to HIGH to LOW transition of the clock signal. Fig.1.74(c) shows the symbol. SET-UP and HOLD TIME specifications are very important while using flip flops (both D-type as well as J-K flip flops).

Set-up time is the time interval immediately preceding the active transition of the timing pulse, usually the clock pulse, or preceding the transition of a control input to its latching level, during which the data to be recognised must be maintained at the input to ensure its recognition. A negative set-up time indicates that the correct logic level may be initiated sometime after the active transition of the timing pulse and still be recognised. Hold time is the time interval immediately following the active transition of the timing pulse, usually the clock pulse, or following the transition of the control input to its latching level, during which the data to be recognised must be maintained at the input to ensure its continued recognition. A negative hold time indicates that the correct logic level may be released prior to the active transition of the timing pulse and still be recognised.

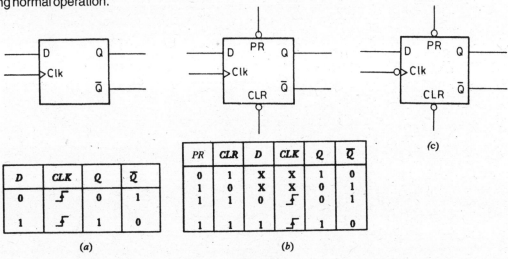

D	CLK	Q	$\overline{Q}$
0	⌐⌐	0	1
1	⌐⌐	1	0

(a)

PR	CLR	D	CLK	Q	$\overline{Q}$
0	1	X	X	1	0
1	0	X	X	0	1
1	1	0	⌐⌐	0	1
1	1	1	⌐⌐	1	0

(b)

(c)

Fig. 1.74

59

D-TYPE LATCH

The D-type latch usually has two inputs namely the D-input and an Enable input. The outputs are Q and $\overline{Q}$. It is used for temporary storage of binary information between the processing units and the Input/Output or Display units. Fig.1.75 shows the logic symbol and the functional table. When the Enable input is HIGH, the information present on the D-input is transferred to the Q-output. The Q-output follows change in binary information present on D-input as long as Enable is HIGH. If the Enable goes LOW, Q-output holds the information it had just prior to Enable going to LOW level until Enable goes HIGH again. D-type latch with active LOW enable input is also available.

J-K FLIP FLOP

A J-K flip flop with Present and Clear facilities has five inputs namely J, K, Clk, Pr (Preset) and Clr (Clear) and two outputs namely Q and $\overline{Q}$. Fig.1.76(a) shows the logic symbol of such a flip flop with active LOW Pr and Clr inputs and a negative edge triggered (High to Low) clock input. The functional table of such a flip flop is shown in Fig.1.76(b). Presettable and Clearable J-K flip flops that are positive edge triggered are also available. Fig.1.76(c) shows the logic symbol. The function table will be identical to the one shown in Fig.1.76(b) except that the flip flop responds to Low to High clock transitions.

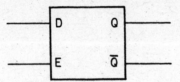

D	C/K	Q	$\overline{Q}$
0	1	0	1
1	1	1	0
X	0	Q_0	$\overline{Q}_0$

Fig. 1.75

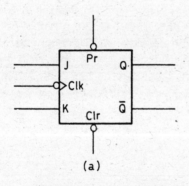

(a)

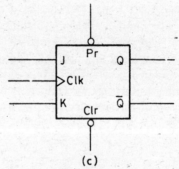

(c)

INPUTS					OUTPUTS	
Pr	Clr	Clk	J	K	Q	$\overline{Q}$
0	1	X	X	X	1	0
1	0	X	X	X	0	1
0	0	X	X	X	Indeterminate	
1	1	⌐L	0	0	Q_0	$\overline{Q}_0$
1	1	⌐L	1	0	1	0
1	1	⌐L	0	1	0	1
1	1	⌐L	1	1	Toggle	
1	1	1	X	X	Q_0	$\overline{Q}_0$

(b)

Fig. 1.76

60

The Preset and Clear inputs function in the same way as explained earlier in case of a D-flip flop. A logic '0' at the Preset input presets the Q-output to a logic '1' state whereas a logic '0' at the clear input clears the Q-oput to a logic '0' state. The output state for various J and K input combinations with both Pr and Clr in the High state are listed in the function table. The output is indeterminate when both Pr and Clr inputs are in LOW state as this is not allowed.

Again J and K inputs should be stable for a period equal to alteast the setup time prior to the clock transition and hold time after the same.

MASTER-SLAVE J-K FLIP FLOP

The M/S (Master/Slave) J-K flip flop has the same function table as that of a J-K flip flop just described with the difference that M/S units are pulse triggered ones rather than edge triggered. A M/S J-K flip flop internally is basically two J-K flip flops in cascade (Fig. 1.77(a). The J and K inputs of the Master flip flop are the J-K inputs of the M/S J-K flip flop unit. The Q and $\overline{Q}$ outputs of the Slave portion are the Q and Q output of the M/S J-K flip flop. Also, the Master is positive edge triggered while the Slave is negative edge triggered. The data present on J and K inputs of the Master is passed on to the master output on the LOW to HIGH transition of the clock inputs and from there onto the slave outputs on HIGH to LOW transition. Thus we need a complete clock pulse for the flip flop to function. The M/S J-K flip flop eliminates what is known as the RACE PROBLEM which is the problem of an indeterminate output state when the inputs are changing state. Fig. 1.77 (b) shows the functional table of a M/S J-K flip flop unit.

MONOSHOTS

The flip flops discussed just prior to this are basically bistable multivibrators. Another popular multivibrator circuit that is available in the IC form is the monostable multivibrator circuit (popularly known as a monoshot). Fig.1.78(a) shows the logic representation of a monoshot in the IC form alongwith the external components that mainly decide the pulse width once the monoshot is triggered. The Q-output is normally LOW. When it is triggered, the output goes to the HIGH state for a time period given by

$$t_p = KR_x C_x \quad (K \text{ is typically } 0.45).$$

The monoshot of this kind can be triggered again only after the output comes back to the initial state. A trigger during the period when the output is in the quasi-stable state has no effect on the output.

There are RETRIGGERABLE MONOSHOTS too (74122 is an example). When the retriggerable monoshot is triggered as the output is still in the

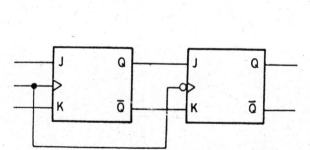

	INPUTS		OUTPUTS	
Clk	J	K	Q	$\overline{Q}$
⊓	0	0	Q_o	$\overline{Q}_o$
⊓	1	0	1	0
⊓	0	1	0	1
⊓	1	1	Toggle	

Fig. 1.77

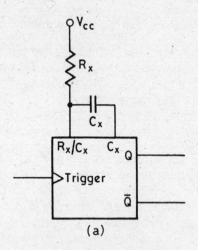 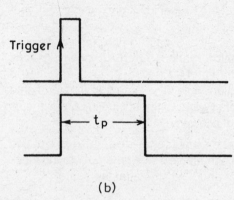

(a)   (b)

Fig. 1.78

quasi-stable state, the pulse width is increased and is given by t_p (original pulse width) + time period between two triggers pulses. Refer to Fig. 1.79. In general, everytime a retriggerable monoshot is retriggered when the output is still in the quasi-stable state, the pulse width gets extended by the time period equal to (T) where (T) is the time period between the occurence of the last trigger pulse and the one immediately preceding it.

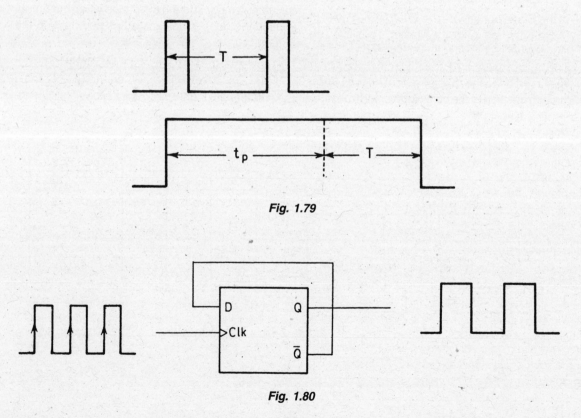

Fig. 1.79

Fig. 1.80

62

COUNTERS

A counter is another very important sequential logic circuit. Fig. 1.80 shows how a D-flip flop can be used as a one bit binary counter. The Q-output is a square waveform whose frequency is one half of the clock frequency. Infact, the D-flip flop has been wired as a toggle flip flop with the Q-output changing state on every LOW to HIGH transition of the clock input. A J-K flip flop could also be wired as a toggle flip flop to perform the same function. The flip flops can be cascaded to do larger bit operations. Counters are broadly

Shift registers are available in a variety of configurations with serial or parallel in, Serial or Parallel out, Right Shift or Left/Right Shift. A universal shift register has serial and parallel inputs, parallel outputs and is bi-directional.

DEMULTIPLEXERS/DECODERS

A DEMULTIPLEXER in general has a single data input, usually more than one control inputs and more than one outputs (Fig. 1.82). In the generalised demultiplexer symbol of Fig.1.82 (m) is the number of control inputs and (n) is the

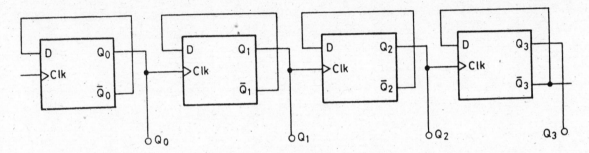

Fig. 1.81

classified as RIPPLE COUNTERS and SYNCHRONOUS counters. In the ripple counters, each flip flop in the cascade arrangement is clocked from the Q-output of the flip flop immediately preceding it *i.e.* the input clock signal is used to clock the LSB flip flop, the LSB flip flop Q-output clocks the flip flop representing the next higher bit (third MSB in case of 4-bit binary ripple counter of Fig. 1.81 and so on. Obviously, the counter is slow due to the very nature of clocking of different flip flops.

SHIFT REGISTERS

A register is used for temporary storage of binary information. The number of flip flops in the register equals the number of bits in the binary number to be stored. A register in addition to being used for temporary storage of data is an important building block for building shift counters and performing some of the arithmetic circuit functions like complementation, multiplication, division etc.

number of outputs. (m) and (n) are related as

$$2^m = n$$

The data information present on the control inputs can be used to steer the output signal to any of the output lines. In a typical case of 1- to -16 demultiplexer, with control inputs (Fig.1.83), sixteen different date bit combinations on the four control inputs (0000 to 1111) can be used to stear the data input to different output lines.

A DECODER is a special case of a demultiplexer block without data input and having only the control inputs and outputs. In the 1-to-16 demultiplexer discussed in the preceding paragraph, if we eliminate the date input, we get a 4-to-16 decoder that can be used to decode all the possible 4-bit combinations on the control inputs. Fig.1.84 (*a*) shows the logic symbol and Fig.1.84 (*b*) the functional table of such a circuit.

The (G) input shown in Fig.1.84 (*a*) is just an active LOW enable input. Other popular decoder

ICs are BCD-to-decimal decoder and BCD-to-seven segment decoder. The logic symbols and the functional tables for the two types are respectively shown in Figs.1.85 and 1.86.

The functional table shown in Fig. 1.86 (b) for a BCD-to-seven segment decoder is that of a decoder to be used with common-anode type seven-segment displays. For a decoder meant for

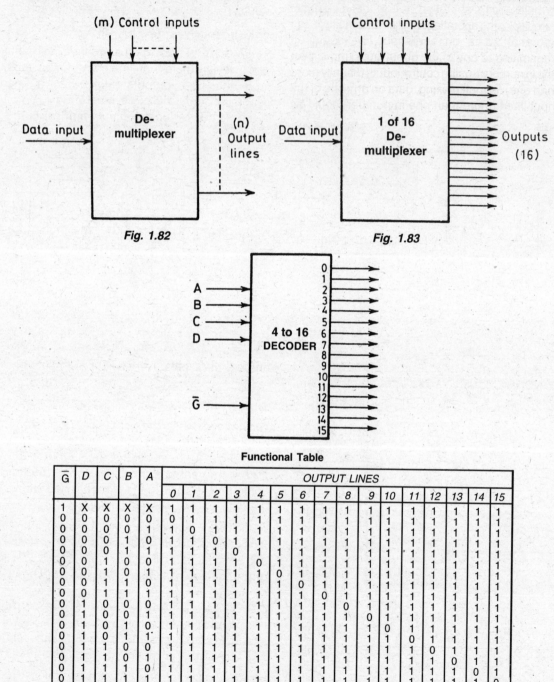

Fig. 1.82

Fig. 1.83

Fig. 1.84

Functional Table

$\overline{G}$	D	C	B	A	OUTPUT LINES															
					0	1	2	3	4	5	6	7	8	9	10	11	12	13	14	15
1	X	X	X	X	1	1	1	1	1	1	1	1	1	1	1	1	1	1	1	1
0	0	0	0	0	0	1	1	1	1	1	1	1	1	1	1	1	1	1	1	1
0	0	0	0	1	1	0	1	1	1	1	1	1	1	1	1	1	1	1	1	1
0	0	0	1	0	1	1	0	1	1	1	1	1	1	1	1	1	1	1	1	1
0	0	0	1	1	1	1	1	0	1	1	1	1	1	1	1	1	1	1	1	1
0	0	1	0	0	1	1	1	1	0	1	1	1	1	1	1	1	1	1	1	1
0	0	1	0	1	1	1	1	1	1	0	1	1	1	1	1	1	1	1	1	1
0	0	1	1	0	1	1	1	1	1	1	0	1	1	1	1	1	1	1	1	1
0	0	1	1	1	1	1	1	1	1	1	1	0	1	1	1	1	1	1	1	1
0	1	0	0	0	1	1	1	1	1	1	1	1	0	1	1	1	1	1	1	1
0	1	0	0	1	1	1	1	1	1	1	1	1	1	0	1	1	1	1	1	1
0	1	0	1	0	1	1	1	1	1	1	1	1	1	1	0	1	1	1	1	1
0	1	0	1	1	1	1	1	1	1	1	1	1	1	1	1	0	1	1	1	1
0	1	1	0	0	1	1	1	1	1	1	1	1	1	1	1	1	0	1	1	1
0	1	1	0	1	1	1	1	1	1	1	1	1	1	1	1	1	1	0	1	1
0	1	1	1	0	1	1	1	1	1	1	1	1	1	1	1	1	1	1	0	1
0	1	1	1	1	1	1	1	1	1	1	1	1	1	1	1	1	1	1	1	0

Fig. 1.84

common-cathode displays, the output entries should be complemented.

MULTIPLEXERS/ENCODERS/DATA SELECTORS

A multiplexing operation is just the reverse of demultiplexing operation. While in a demultiplexing operation, data on one input line could be transmitted to any of the ouput lines (more than one in number), using control inputs (usually more than one); in multiplexing, data on any one of the input lines (more than one in number) could be transmitted to the output line depending on the information on the control inputs (usually more than one in number). Fig. 1.87 shows the generalised logic symbol of a multiplexer (or Data Selector). The multiplexer has (n) data inputs, (m) control inputs and one output.

Here $2^m = n$

From the hardware viewpoint, an ENCODER is again nothing but a multiplexer without the single output line. Fig.1.88 shows the logic symbol.

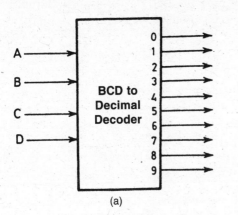

(a)

Functional Table

D	C	B	A	0	1	2	3	4	5	6	7	8	9
0	0	0	0	0	1	1	1	1	1	1	1	1	1
0	0	0	1	1	0	1	1	1	1	1	1	1	1
0	0	1	0	1	1	0	1	1	1	1	1	1	1
0	0	1	1	1	1	1	0	1	1	1	1	1	1
0	1	0	0	1	1	1	1	0	1	1	1	1	1
0	1	0	1	1	1	1	1	1	0	1	1	1	1
0	1	1	0	1	1	1	1	1	1	0	1	1	1
0	1	1	1	1	1	1	1	1	1	1	0	1	1
1	0	0	0	1	1	1	1	1	1	1	1	0	1
1	0	0	1	1	1	1	1	1	1	1	1	1	0

(b)

Fig. 1.85

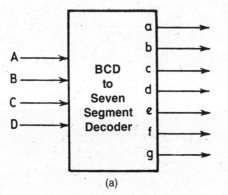

(a)

Functional Table

D	C	B	A	a	b	c	d	e	f	g
0	0	0	0	0	0	0	0	0	0	1
0	0	0	1	1	0	0	1	1	1	1
0	0	1	0	0	0	1	0	0	1	0
0	0	1	1	0	0	0	0	1	1	0
0	1	0	0	1	0	0	1	1	0	0
0	1	0	1	0	1	0	0	1	0	0
0	1	1	0	0	1	0	0	0	0	0
0	1	1	1	0	0	0	1	1	1	1
1	0	0	0	0	0	0	0	0	0	0
1	0	0	1	0	0	0	1	0	0	0

(b)

Fig. 1.86

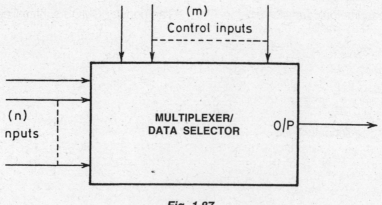

Fig. 1.87

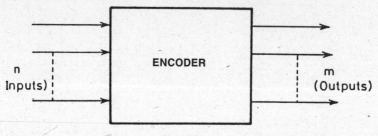

Fig. 1.88

LOGIC FAMILIES

There are a variety of circuit configurations or more appropriately various approaches on which different digital integrated circuits available today are based. Each such fundamental approach is called a LOGIC FAMILY. The idea is that different logic functions when fabricated in the form of an IC with the same approach or in other words belonging to the same logic family shall have identical electrical characteristics. These characteristics include supply voltage range, speed of response, power dissipation, input and output logic levels etc. In other words, the set of digital ICs belonging to the same logic family are electrically compatible with each other. A digital system in general comprises of digital ICs performing different logic functions and choosing these ICs for the same logic family guarantees that different ICs are compatible with respect to each other and that the system a whole performs the intended logic function. In case, output of an IC belonging to a certain family feeds the inputs of another IC belonging to a different family, established interface techniques should be used to ensure compatibility.

POPULAR LOGIC FAMILIES

The entire range of digital ICs is fabricated using either the BIPOLAR DEVICES or the MOS DEVICES. Different logic families falling in the first category are called BIPOLAR FAMILIES and some of these are the Resistance Transistor Logic (RTL), the Diode Transistor Logic (DTL), Transistor Transistor Logic (TTL), Emitter Coupled Logic (ECL) also known as Current Mode Logic (CML), Integrated Injection Logic ($I^2 L$) and High Threshold Logic (HTL). The logic families that use MOS devices as their basis are known as MOS familiers and the families belonging to this category are the PMOS-family (using P-channel MOSFETs), NMOS-family (using N-channel MOSFETs) and CMOS-family (Using both N and P channel devices).

The two most popular logic families are the TTL logic family and the CMOS logic family. The TTL logic family has several subfamilies namely:

(i) Standard TTL

(ii) Low power TTL

(iii) High power TTL

(iv) Low power Schottky TTL

(v) Schottky TTL

(vi) Advanced low power schottky TTL

(vii) Advanced schottky TTL.

The ICs belonging to TTL family are designated as 74 or 54 (for standard TTL), 74L or 54L (for low power TTL), 74H or 54H (for high power TTL), 74LS or 54LS (for low power schottky TTL), 74S or 54S (for schottky TTL), 54ALS or 74ALS (for advanced low power schottky TTL) and 74AS or 54AS (for advanced schottky TTL). An alphabetic code preceding this indicates the name of the manufacturer (DM for National Semiconductors, SN for Texas Instruments and so on). A two, three or four digit numerical code tells the logic function performed by the IC. It may be mentioned that 74-series devices and 54-series devices are identical except for their operational temperature range. 54-series are MIL-qualified (operational temperature range of –55°C to +125°C) versions of corresponding 74-series ICs (operational temperature range of 0°C to +70°C). For example, 7400 and 5400 are both Quad 2-input NAND gates.

The popular CMOS subfamilies include

(i) 4000 A CMOS family

(ii) 4000 B CMOS family

(iii) 4000 UB CMOS family

(iv) 54/74C family

(v) 54/74HC family

(vi) 54/74HCT family

(vii) 54/74AC family

(viii) 54/74ACT family.

TTL LOGIC FAMILY

TTL as outlined above stands for TRANSISTOR-TRANSISTOR LOGIC. It is a logic family implemented with bipolar process technology that combines or integrates NPN transistors, PN junction diodes and diffused resistors in a single monolithic structure to get the desired logic function. NAND-gate is the basic building block of this logic family. Table 1.7 gives a comparison of the major performance specifications of the TTL logic subfamilies. Different terms and definitions used in Table 1.7 have been described in Table 1.8.

CMOS LOGIC FAMILY

The basic difference between different CMOS logic subfamilies such as 4000A series, 4000B series, 4000UB series, 74C series etc. is in the fabrication process used and not in the design of the circuits used to implement the intended logic

Table: 1.7

Logic Family	Supply Voltage		Min. V_{IH} (V)	Max. V_{IL} (V)	Min. V_{OH} (V)	Max. V_{OL} (V)	Max. I_{IH} (μA)	Max. I_{IL} (mA)	Max. I_{OH} (mA)	Max. I_{OL} (mA)	Prop. Delay (ns)
	Min. (V)	Max. (V)									
74	4.75	5.25	2.0	0.8	2.4	0.4	40	1.6	0.4	16	22
74L	4.75	5.25	2.0	0.7	2.4	0.4	10	0.18	0.2	3.6	60
74H	4.75	5.25	2.0	0.8	2.4	0.4	50	2.0	20	20	10
74LS	4.75	5.25	2.0	0.8	2.7	0.5	20	0.4	0.4	8	15
74S	4.75	5.25	2.0	0.8	2.7	0.5	50	2.0	1.0	20	5
74ALS	4.5	5.5	2.0	0.8	2.5	0.5	20	0.1	0.4	8	11
74AS	4.5	5.5	2.0	0.8	2.5	0.5	20	0.5	2.0	20	4.5

Table: 1.8

Parameter	Notation	Description
Maximum high level input current	I_i	When the input is applied the maximum voltage as specified by the concerned logic family, the current flowing into the inputs is then the maximum high level input current.
High level input current	I_{IH}	It is the current flowing into an input when it is applied a high level input voltage equal to the minimum high level output voltage specified for the family.
Low level input current	I_{IL}	When the voltage applied at the input is equal to the maximum low level output voltage specified for the family, the current flowing out of the logic input is the low level input current (I_{IL}).
High level output current	I_{OH}	The current flowing out of an output when the input conditions are such that the output is in logic HIGH state. It tells about the current sourcing capability of the output.
Low level output current	i_{OL}	The current flowing out of an output when the input conditions establish a logic LOW at the output. It tells about the current sinking capability of the output.
High level input voltage	V_{IH}	It is the minimum positive voltage level applied at the input to be recognised as a legal HIGH level for the specified family.
Low level input voltage	V_{IL}	It is the maximum positive voltage level applied at the input to be recognised as a legal LOW level for the specified family.
High level output voltage	V_{OH}	It is the output voltage when the input conditions establish a logic HIGH at the output for the specified family.
Low level output voltage	V_{OL}	It is the output voltage when the input conditions establish a logic LOW at the output for the specified family.
Supply Current	I_{CC}	The supply current when the output is HIGH, LOW and in high impedance state is respectively designated as I_{CCH}, I_{CCL} and I_{CCZ}.
Rise Time	t_r	It is the time that elapses between 10% and 90% of the final signal level when signal is making a transition from a logic LOW to a logic HIGH.
Fall Time	t_F	It is the time delay that elapse between 90% and 10% of the signal level when the signal is making a HIGH to LOW transition.

Parameter	Notation	Description
Propagation Delay (Low to High)	t_pLH	It is the time between the specified voltage points on the input and output waveforms with the output changing from LOW to HIGH.
Propagation Delay (High to Low)	t_pHL	It is the time delay between the specified voltage points on the input and output waveforms with the output changing from HIGH to LOW.
Maximum Clock frequency	f_{max}	It is the maximum clock frequency that can be used with a logic circuit without causing any false change of logic states both at input and output.
Speed-Power Product		The speed of a logic circuit can be increased (*i.e.* propagation delay can be reduced) at the expense of power dissipation. The Speed-Power dissipation product (usually measured in pico-joules) is a useful figure-of-merit for evaluating different logic families. It is the product of power dissipated per gate in milliwatts and the propagation delay measured in nano-seconds to give the product in pico-joules. Smaller the value of this product, better the logic family is.

function. Figs.1.89 to 1.91 show the circuit schematics of the basis CMOS inverter, NAND-gate and NOR-gate respectively.

4000A-series CMOS ICs were the first to arrive at the scene from the CMOS logic family. 4000A CMOS subfamily is obsolete now and has been replaced by 4000B and 4000UB subfamilies. 4000B series is a high voltage version of 4000A series and also all the outputs in this series are buffered. 4000UB series is also a high voltage version of 4000A series but the outputs are not buffered. 74C CMOS subfamily offers pin to pin replacements of 74 series TTL logic functions. For instance, if 7400 is a Quad 2-input NAND in standard TTL, then 74C00 is a Quad 2-input NAND with same pin connections in CMOS.

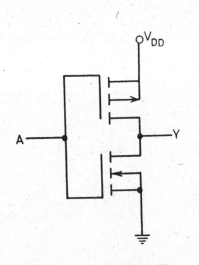

Fig. 1.89

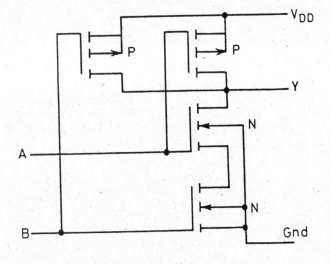

Fig. 1.90

74HC series is the high speed CMOS version of the 74 series logic functions. This is achieved using silicon gate CMOS technology rather than metal gate CMOS technology used in earlier CMOS subfamilies. 74HCT series is only a process variation of 74HC series. The parameters like V_{IH}, V_{IL}, V_{OH} and V_{OL} in 74HCT series are compatible with those in bipolar TTL Logic families. 74AC is presently the fastest CMOS logic family. This logic family has the best combination of high speed, low power consumption and high output drive capability. Again 74ACT is only a process variation of 74AC. The input thresholds (V_{IH}, V_{IL}) and output voltage levels (V_{OH}, V_{OL}) in 74ACT are compatible with bipolar TTL families. Table 1.9 gives a comparison different CMOS logic subfamilies.

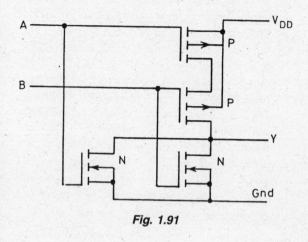

Fig. 1.91

Table : 1.9

Logic Family	Supply Voltage		Min. V_{IH} (V)	Max. V_{IL} (V)	Min. V_{OH} (V)	Max. V_{OL} (V)	Max. I_{IH} (μA)	Max. I_{IL} (μA)	Max. I_{OH} (mA)	Max. I_{OL} (mA)	Prop. Delay (nS)
	Min. (V)	Max. (V)									
4000A	3	12	3.5	1.5	4.95	0.05	1	1	0.24	0.24	120
4000B	3	18	3.5	1.5	4.95	0.05	1	1	0.42	0.42	250
4000UB	3	18	4	1	4.95	0.05	1	1	0.42	0.42	120
74C	3	15	3.5	1.5	4.5	0.5	1	1	0.01	0.01	90
74HC	2	6	3.15	0.9	3.84	0.33	1	1	4	4	23
74HCT	4.5	5.5	2	0.8	3.84	0.33	1	1	4	4	25
74AC	2	6	3.15	1.35	3.76	0.37	1	1	24	24	8.5
74ACT	2	6	2	0.8	3.76	0.37	1	1	24	24	12.5

GUIDELINES TO USING TTL ICS

1. **Compatibility while using different TTL Subfamilies:** Replacing a TTL IC of one TTL subfamily with another belonging to another subfamily (the type numbers remaining the same) should not be done blindly. The designer should ensure that the replacement device is compatible with the existing circuit with respect to parameters like output drive capability, input loading, speed and so on. As an illustration, let us assume that you are using 74S00 (Quad 2-input NAND) whose output drives twenty different NAND inputs

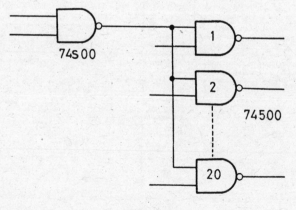

Fig. 1.92

implemented using 74S00 again (Fig. 1.92). This circuit works well as the schottky TTL family has a fan out of 20 with an output HIGH drive capability of 1 mA and input HIGH current requirement of 50 μA. If you try replacing 74S00 that is driving others with a 74LS00, the circuit fails to work as 74LS00 NAND has an output HIGH drive capability of 0.4 mA only. It cannot feed 20 NAND input loads implemented using 74S00.

2. None of the inputs and outputs of TTL ICs should be driven by more than 0.5 V below ground reference.

3. Proper grounding techniques should be used while designing the PCB layout. If the grounding is improper, the ground loop currents give rise to voltage drops with the result that different ICs will not be at the same reference. This effectively reduces the noise immunity.

4. The power supply rail must always be properly decoupled with appropriate capacitors so that there is no drop in (V_{cc}) rail as the inputs and outputs make logic transitions. Usually, two capacitors are used at the (V_{cc}) point of each IC. A 0.1 μF ceramic disc should be used to take care of high frequency noise while typically a 100 μF electrolytic is good enough to eliminate any low frequency variations resulting from variations in (I_{cc}), current drawn from (V_{cc}), depending upon logic states of inputs and outputs. The decoupling capacitors to be effective should be wired as close as feasible to the (V_{cc}) pin of the IC.

5. The unused inputs should not be left floating. All unused inputs should be tied to a solid logic level preferably to (V_{cc}) through a 1 K to 5 K resistor.

6. While using open collector devices, resistive pull-up should be used. The value of pull-up resistance should be determined from the following equations:

(i)
$$R_x = \frac{V_{CC(max)} - V_{OL}}{I_{OL} - N_{2(LOW)} \times 1.6 \text{ mA}}$$

(ii)
$$R_{(max)} = \frac{V_{cc(min)} - V_{OH}}{N_1 \times I_{OH} + N_{2(HIGH)} \times 40\mu A}$$

where R_x = External pull-up resistor

N_1 = Number of wired-OR outputs

N_2 = Number of unit input loads being driven

I_{OH} = Output HIGH leakage current

I_{OL} = Low level fan out current of driving element

V_{OL} = Low level output voltage

V_{OH} = High level output voltage.

Also one TTL unit load in HIGH state = 40 μA and one TTL unit load in LOW state = 1.6 mA.

GUIDELINES TO HANDLING AND USING COMS ICs

1. Proper handling of CMOS ICs before they are used and also after they have been mounted on the PC boards is very important as these ICs are highly prone to damage to electrostatic discharge. Although all CMOS ICs have inbuilt protection networks to guard them against electrostatic discharge, yet precautions should be taken to avoid such an eventuality. While handling unmounted chips, potential differences should be avoided. It is a good practice to cover the chips with a conductive foil. Once the chips have been mounted on the PC board, it is a good practice again to put conductive clips or conductive tape on the PC board terminals. Remember that PC board is nothing but an extension of the leads of the ICs mounted on it unless it is integrated with the overall system and proper voltages are present.

2. All unused inputs must always be connected to either (V_{ss}) or (V_{DD}) depending upon the logic involved. A floating input can result in a faulty logic operation. In case of high current types such as buffers, it can also lead to the maximum power dissipation of the chip being exceeded thus causing device damage. A resistor (typically 220K to 1M) should

preferably be connected between input and the (V_{SS}) or (V_{DD}) if there is a possibility of device terminals becoming temporarily unconnected or open.

3. The recommended operating supply voltage ranges are 3 to 12 V for A-series (3 to 15 V being the maximu rating) and 3 to 15 V for B-series and UB-series (3 to 18 V being the maximum). CMOS IC application circuits that operated in a linear mode over a portion of voltage range such as RC or crystal oscillators, a minimum (V_{DD}) of 4V is recommended.

4. Input signals should be maintained with the power supply voltage range $V_{SS} \leq V_i \leq V_{DD}$ (-0.5 V $\leq V_i \leq V_{DD} + 0.5$ V being the absolute maximum). If the input signal exceeds the recommended input signal range, the input current should be limited to ±100 µA.

5. CMOS ICs like active pull-up TTL ICs cannot be connected in WIRE-OR configuration. Paralleling of inputs and outputs of gates is also recommended for ICs in the same package only.

6. Majority of CMOS clocked devices has maximum rise and fall time ratings of normally 5 to 15 microseconds. The device may not function properly with larger rise and fall times. The restriction however does not apply to those CMOS ICs having in abuilt schmitt trigger shaping in the clock circuit.

7. Whenever two sequential CMOS ICs (flip flops for instance, are cascaded and clocked synchronously, the maximum rise time of the clock should be limited as per

Maximum $t_{r(clock)} = \dfrac{0.8\, V_{DD}}{1.25} \times t_p$ (ns) for A-series CMOS ICs.

$$= \dfrac{0.8\, V_{DD}}{1.15} \times t_p \text{(ns) for B-series}$$
CMOS ICs.

where $t_p = t_p$ HL or tpLH whichever is less of the first input device as per the device's data sheet at specified value of (V_{DD}) and loading conditions.

INTERFACING WITH DIFFERENT LOGIC FAMILIES

CMOS and TTL are the two most widely used logic families *i.e.* majority of digital ICs in use today belongs to either of these two families. Though ICs belonging to the same logic family have no special interface requirements, that is, output of one can directly feed the input of the other, same is not the case if we have to interconnect digital ICs belonging to different logic families. Incompatibility of ICs belonging to different families mainly arises from different voltage levels and current requirements associated with LOW and HIGH logic states at the inputs and outputs. In this section we shall discuss simple interface techniques that can be used for CMOS-to-TTL and TTL-to-CMOS interconnections.

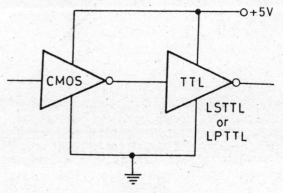

Fig. 1.93

CMOS-TO-TTL INTERFACE

First possible type of CMOS-to-TTL interface is the one where both ICs are operated from a common supply. We have read in the earlier sections that TTL family has a recommended supply voltage of 5 V whereas CMOS family devices can operate over a wide supply voltage range of 3 V to 18 V. In the present case, both ICs would operate from 5 V. As far as the voltage levels in the two logic states are concerned, the two have become compatible. CMOS output has a $V_{OH(min)}$ of $\approx$ 5 V (for $V_{CC} = 5$ V) and a $V_{OL(max)}$ 0V which is compatible which $V_{IH(min)}$ and $V_{IL(max)}$ requirements of approximately 2 V and 0.8 V respectively of TTL family devices. Infact, in a CMOS-to-TTL interface, with the two devices operating on the same (V_{cc}), the voltage level compatibility is always there. It is the current level compatibility that needs attention. That is, in the LOW state, the output current sinking capability of CMOS IC in question must at least equal the input current sinking requirement of the TTL IC being driven. Similarly, in the HIGH state, the HIGH output current drive capability of CMOS IC must equal or exceed the HIGH level input current requirement of TTL IC. For a proper interface, both the above conditions must be met with. As a thumb rule, a CMOS IC belonging to 4000 B family (the most widely used CMOS family) can feed one LS TTL or two low power TTL unit loads. When a CMOS IC needs to drive a standard TTL or a Schottky TTL device, a CMOS buffer (4049 B or 4050 B) is used. 4049 B and 4050 B are hex buffers of inverting and non-inverting types respectively with each buffer capable of driving two standard TTL loads. Fig. 1.93 shows CMOS-to-TTL interface with both devices operating from 5 V supply and the CMOS IC driving a low power TTL or a low power Schottky TTL device. Fig. 1.94 shows the CMOS-to-TTL interface where the TTL device in use is either a standard TTL or a Schottky TTL.

CMOS-to-TTL interface when the two are operating a different power supply voltages can be achieved in several ways. One such scheme is shown in Fig. 1.95 As can be seen from the arrangement, there is both voltage level as well as current level compatibility.

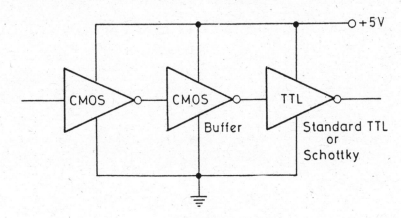

Fig. 1.94

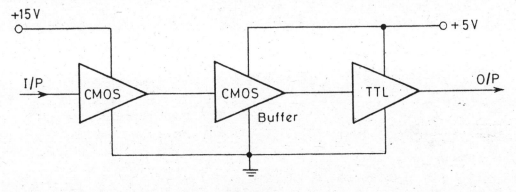

Fig. 1.95

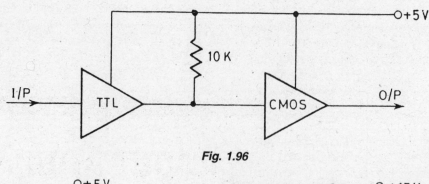

Fig. 1.96

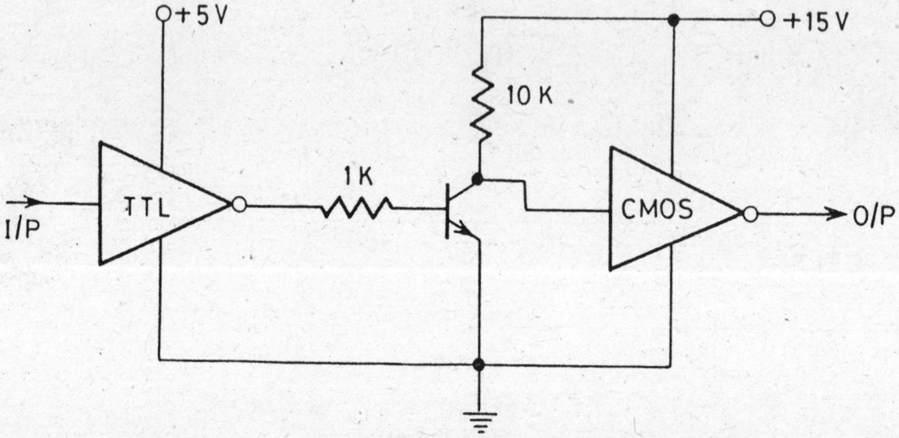

Fig. 1.97

TTL-TO-CMOS INTERFACE

In the TTL-to-CMOS interface, current compatibility is always there. The voltage level compatibility in the two states is a problem. When the two devices are operating on the same power supply voltage *i.e.* 5 V, a pull-up resistor of 10 K achieves compatibility (Fig. 1.96). When the two are operating on different power supplies, one of the simplest interface techniques is to use a transistor (as a switch) in between the two as shown in Fig. 1.97.

INTERPRETING DIGITAL IC NOMENCLATURE
IC CLASSIFICATION

We are all familiar with terms like SSI, MSI, LSI, VLSI being used with reference to digital integrated circuits. These terms refer to groups in which digital ICs have been divided based on the complexity of the circuitry that has been integrated on the chip. It is a common practice to consider the complexity of a logic gate as a reference for defining the complexities of the other digital IC functions. A broadly accepted definition of different groups of ICs mentioned above is as follows:

A VLSI (Very Large Scale Integration) chip contains circuitry equivalent in complexity to 1000 or more gates.

An LSI (Large Scale Integration) chip is the one that contains circuitry equivalent in complexity to 100 or more gates.

An MSI (Medium Scale Integration) chip is the one that contains circuitry equivalent in complexity to 10 or more gates.

An SSI (Small Scale Integration) chip has a circuit complexity less than that of an MSI chip.

Interpreting Manufacturer's Code

The manufacturer's name can usually be guessed from its logo that is printed on the IC. The alphabet

74

preceding the IC type number also indicate the manufacturer's code. Refer to the IC packages shown in Fig. 1.98 (*a*) and (*b*). While Fig. 1.98 (*a*) shows an IC with National Semiconductor's logo, the IC shown in Fig. 1.98 (*b*) is from Texas Instruments. Also alphabet DM and SN respectively indicate 'National Semiconductors' and 'Texas Instruments'.

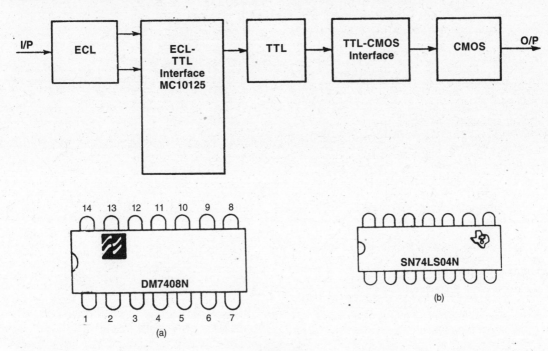

Fig. 1.98

Interpreting Package Style

The package style is usually indicated by the letter suffixing the IC type number. Information like package outline (Dual-in-line etc.) and package material (Plastic, Ceramic, etc.) are given in this part of the nomenclature. Suffix N or P stand for dual-in-line plastic package while suffix J or L stand for dual-in-line ceramic package. Suffix F or W stand for flat ceramic package. Some examples are shown in Fig. 1.99.

Interpreting IC Function

The middle portion *i.e.* the IC type number tells about the IC function and also the family which the particular IC belongs to. For instance, in the IC type number 74LS00, '74' stands for TTL family, 'LS' stands for 'Low power schottky' subfamily of the main TTL family and '00' tells us that it is quad 2-input NAND.

Fig. 1.99

75

CHAPTER-2

FABRICATION, TEST AND MEASUREMENT GUIDELINES

THE OBJECTIVE

In the first chapter, we have discussed the operational features and other application relevant aspects of a large variety of electronic components including passive components like Resistors, Capacitors, Transformers etc., active components like Diodes, Transistors, Thyristors, etc., general purpose linear integrated circuits like Opamps, Timers and general purpose digital integrated circuits like Logic gates, Flip-flops, Counters and so on. The objective in this chapter is to introduce to the readers, particularly our large group of electronics hobbyists, some useful guidelines relevant to some of the topics of practical interest.

There may not be anything absolutely new in this chapter for those who have been practicing electronics for sometime yet it would be worthwhile including an outline on these topics for the benefit of those who are out to make a beginning in this fascinating hobby of electronics experimentation.

The contents of the present chapter are a mixed lot. In this chapter, we shall on one hand talk about the guidelines for making PCBs, on the other, we shall also outline some useful tips to good soldering. Guidelines to using some basic test instruments like multimeters, oscilloscopes forms the concluding part of the chapter.

2.1 PRINTED CIRCUIT BOARDS

A PRINTED CIRCUIT BOARD popularly known as a PCB is the first thing you would require when you decide to build an electronics circuit. A proper PCB ensures that various circuit components are interconnected as per the circuit diagram once they have been placed on the PCB in their proper positions and subsequently soldered.

PCB design and fabrication techniques have undergone so much of development that it has become a subject in itself. Double sided PCBs, Multilayer PCBs, PCBs with PTH (Plated Through Holes), using CAD software packages for PCB layout designing, Flexible PCBs etc. are only some of the developments. An average hobbyist or experimenter however need not go into the details of these technologies nor is he supposed to learn the intricacies of the art of PCB layout designing. What he needs is a familiarisation with different steps involved in PCB fabrication particularly the etching process so that he can make his own PCB economically from an available PCB layout design. The projects or the construction articles given in various books on the subject and Electronics magazines are usually complete in relevant technical/fabrication information including the PCB layout, the components layout, components parts list and so on. What you need the most in such cases is only a familiarisation with the etching process. But in case you want to build a circuit for which a lay out is not available, you will have to design the layout too.

PCB FABRICATION

Different steps involved in the fabrication of a PCB are as follows :

1. **Components layout designing**
2. **PCB layout designing**
3. **Transferring the PCB layout design onto the PC board laminate.**
4. **Developing or Etching the PCB**
5. **Other operations like Drilling, Cutting, Tinning etc.**

COMPONENTS LAYOUT DESIGNING

Components layout designing is the exercise of placement of different components constituting the circuit and then showing their interconnections

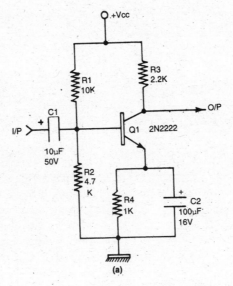

(a)

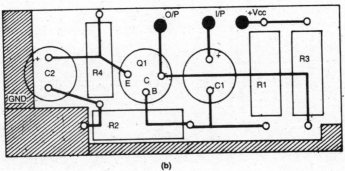

(b)

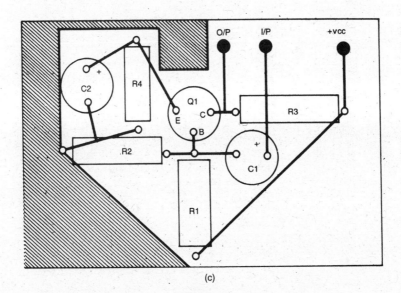

(c)

Fig. 2.1

77

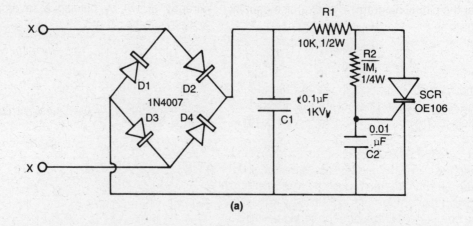

(a)

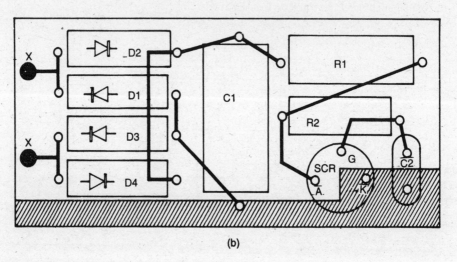

(b)

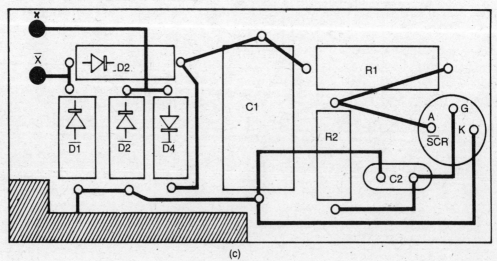

(c)

Fig. 2.2

78

as per the circuit diagram. This exercise usually begins with an estimate of the size of the PCB (length and breadth) needed to accommodate various circuit components. The estimated dimensions are marked on a graph paper and an attempt made to optimally place the components. It may be mentioned here that the relative position of different components will largely depend upon nature of interconnections and also on the circuit input, output, supply and ground points. Knowledge of dimensions of different components making up the circuit is another prerequisite to designing the components layout. Having placed all the components, the interconnections can be made by drawing lines (known as tracks). Ensure that the tracks are of optimum length and are not unnecessarily long. Infact, the components layout can be best drawn by carrying out the twin jobs of placement of the components and making the interconnections side by side. As an illustration, Fig. 2.1(b) shows the components layout for the circuit of Fig. 2.1(a) to give you an idea as to how an optimum components layout for the given circuit should look like. Fig. 2.1(c) shows an improperly done components layout design for the circuit of Fig. 2.1(a). The circuit considered here is a simple one and involves only a few components. The job becomes increasingly difficult with increase in component count and the number of input and output connections. But in perfecting the art of components layout designing or PCB layout designing, theoretical knowledge does not help as much as does the experience and constant practice. Some more examples of improper and optimum components layout designing for given circuits of little greater complexities are shown in Figs. 2.2 to Fig. 2.4. Figs. 2.2(b), 2.3(b) and 2.4(b) show the correct components' layouts while the improper layouts are shown in Figs. 2.2(c), 2.3(c) and 2.4(c).

PCB LAYOUT DESIGNING

The PCB layout design is nothing but the mirror image of components layout. The components layout is drawn looking from the components side whereas the PCB layout is drawn looking from the copper side. It can best be obtained by taking a carbon copy of the components layout

already drawn by placing a reversed carbon underneath the paper. All the construction projects covered in this book are accompanied by a PCB layout drawing. The hobbyist can take a photocopy of the layout onto the copper side of the PCB laminate.

TRANSFERRING PCB LAYOUT ONTO PCB LAMINATE

The first thing to be done here is to choose the type of PCB laminate. Two types of laminates are commercially available for the purpose. These are (i) Phenolic boards and (ii) Fiber glass epoxy boards. Phenolic boards are much cheaper and are good enough for most of the commercial applications.

The next step is to thoroughly clean the copper side of the laminate with petrol or acetone or alcoholic spirit to make it completely free from any contaminants. Some cleaning sprays are also commercially available for the purpose.

The PCB layout can now be transferred onto the copper side of the laminate by using a pointed tool (a ball point pen would also serve the purpose) and a carbon paper. Utmost care should be taken to mark the position of the holes so that you don't miss any. After carbon copying the PCB layout pattern, the same can be redrawn giving proper width to different tracks and leaving proper space for component terminals. All this can be done simply with the help of enamel paint and a fine brush. Some special marker pens are also available for the purpose. A large variety of commonly used terminal ends, pads (both for discrete components as well as ICs of different sizes), tracks of different widths ranging from 0.5mm to 5mm are available as dry transfers (Fig. 2.5). What you need to do is to only place the dry transfer at the desired place and rub it against copper. The pattern gets transferred onto the laminate. Adhesive tapes (Fig. 2.6)of different widths are also available for making the tracks. Use of dry transfers and tapes however turns out to be expensive if you have to make only one or two PCBs of a particular type. In such cases, the method of using enamel paint is not only economic, it yields very good results after a little bit of practice. After the pattern has been drawn

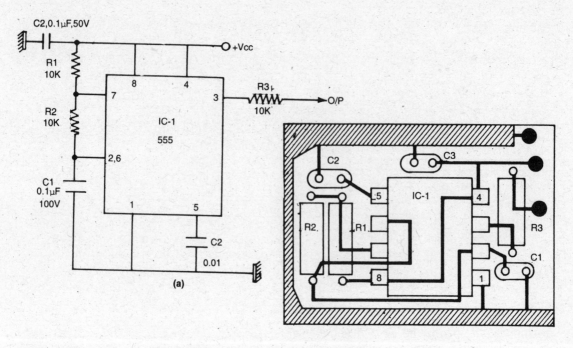

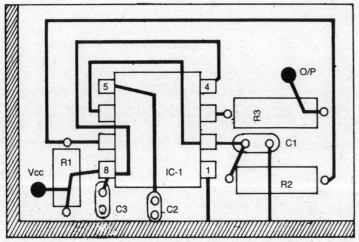

Fig. 2.3

with the paint, it should be allowed to fully dry up before it is etched.

ETCHING

In the etching process, all excess copper is removed leaving behind only the painted pattern. To do etching, the painted PCB board laminate is placed in a flat plastic tray usually seen at a photographer's shop with the copper side facing upwards. An aqueous solution of ferric chloride with the quantity depending upon the size of the

PCB to be etched is then poured in the tray. The PCB should be fully immersed in the ferric chloride solution. The solution is prepared by adding about 40 to 50 grams of ferric chloride to every 100 ml of water heated to about 75°C. The solution should be nicely stirred and a few drops of hydrochloric acid added if you want to speed up the etching process. The tray can be moved up and down slowly so as to allow the solution to repeatedly interact with the copper side of the

80

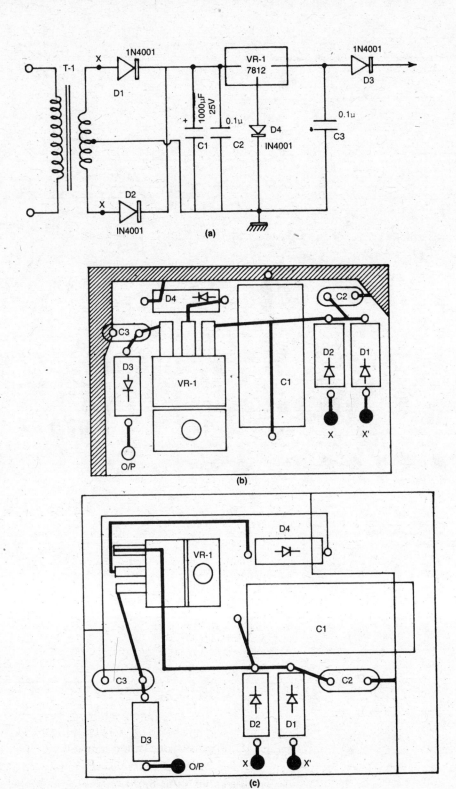

Fig. 2.4

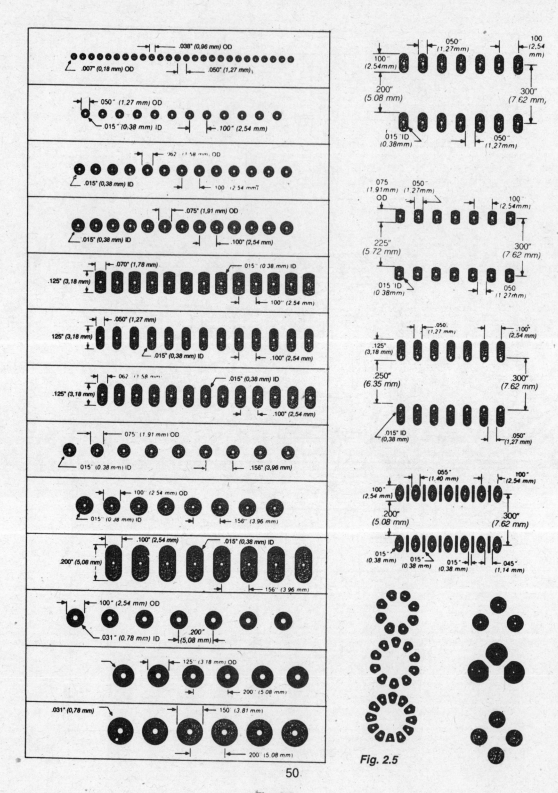

Fig. 2.5

50

Fig. 2.5

82

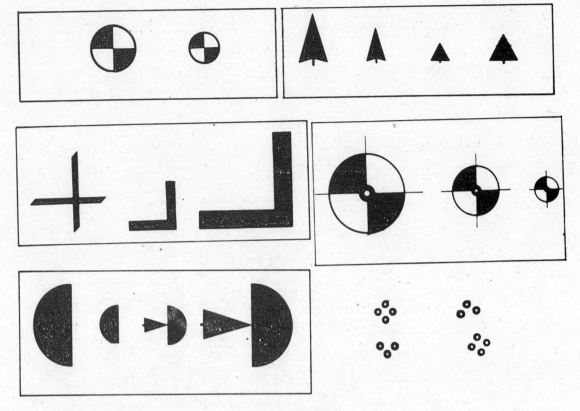

Fig. 2.5 (Contd.)

Fig. 2.6

laminate. The etching process may take about half an hour to one hour, the etching time again depending upon the size of PCB and the area to be etched. You must ensure that the PCB is neither under-etched nor over-etched. If the PCB is kept immersed in the solution after the etching is complete, the solution is likely to penetrate the copper portions that you wanted to preserve and cause some etching of the desired tracks too. Such a PCB after etching may look like what is shown in Fig. 2.7(a). Fig. 2.7(b) shows a correctly etched PCB. The ferric chloride solution should be preserved in a bottle or a container for future use and should not be considered as wasted. Solution once made could certainly last for about three to four etchings.

The laminate is thoroughly washed in water after etching is complete. The paint is then removed with alcohol or acetone.

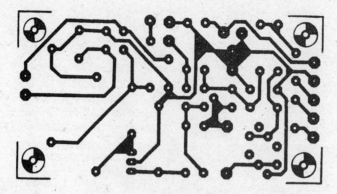

Fig. 2.7(a)

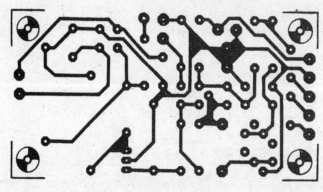

Fig. 2.7(b)

DRILLING-TINNING

The next major operation after etching is the drilling of holes. The diameter of holes varies from component to component. It is 1mm for IC pins, 1.25 mm for resistors and capacitors, 1.5mm for diodes and even larger for mounting presets and potentiometers. The size of holes for resistors would also vary depending upon resistor wattage.

The oxidation of copper portions can be prevented by either tinning that can be done by using a soldering iron or by giving it a coat of some insulating varnish.

2.2. SOLDERING TECHNIQUES

A hobbyist or an experimenter may not know enough about electronics components or circuitry but he cannot afford to lack in the art of good if not perfect soldering. For him, good soldering is a prerequisite to attempting to build any electronics circuit. A single loose or dry or a bad solder connection could become the cause of failure or malfunctioning of the entire circuit. An average soldering quality would make the circuit function but then it affects the overall reliability. So, the soldering that is usually considered to be something that anybody can do, should be taken very seriously and I would suggest perfect soldering to be the first thing to be mastered by any electronics hobbyist. Some useful tips to good soldering are listed below.

SOME USEFUL TIPS TO GOOD SOLDERING

1. The two surfaces to be soldered should be thoroughly cleaned and made free from any dust, grease or oil. Infact, thorough cleaning of the PCB before beginning the soldering operation and proper tinning of the component

leads at the time of soldering that component achieves good results.

2. A small quantity of flux may be applied on the surfaces to be soldered. It is the function of the soldering flux to keep away any oxide film during soldering operation and allow the two surfaces to make a metallic contact and alloy with each other. The flux residue should be removed after the soldering is done.

3. One of the most common problems in soldering is the application of insufficient heat. The alloying action in soldering cannot be achieved without a uniform distribution of heat between the solder and the metal being soldered. If hot solder is applied to a cold metal or a cold solder is applied to a hot metal, there can never be a proper soldering action. Soldering will be proper only when the solder alloy is hot enough to remain in a liquid state as soldering is being done. To achieve a proper wetted soldered joint, heat up the component terminal end slightly (Remember not to exceed the component lead temperature beyond the safe recommended temperature. Excessive temperature can often damage sensitive semiconductor devices) and apply solder alloy right onto the component lead end instead of applying it on the soldering iron tip. Now with the soldering iron tip, melt the solder so that it flows over the joint. Avoid putting excessive solder metal and ensure that it is in the liquid state till it has completely flowed over the joint. A perfect soldered joint would give a shiny bead like appearance.

SOLDERING TEMPERATURES FOR DIFFERENT COMPONENTS

Table 2.1 lists the typical values of recommended soldering temperatures for different electronic components and devices.

2.3 TEST INSTRUMENTS

There are a large number of general purpose test instruments used to perform a variety of test and measurement functions. These include Ohmmeters, Multimeters, Capacitance meters, LCR meters, Oscilloscopes etc. Except for a multimeter, most of other test equipment are

Table: 2.1

S.No.	Type of Electronic Component	Soldering Temperature	Soldering Time
1.	General Purpose fixed and variable Resistors	350°C	5 seconds
2.	Light Dependent Resistors, Varistors, Thermistors	250°C	-
3.	Electrolytic Capacitors	225°C	5 seconds
4.	Other Capacitor types	200°C	Less than 5 seconds
5.	Silicon Diodes	250°C	5 seconds
6.	Germanium Diodes	200°C	5 seconds
7.	Low Wattage Zener Diodes	200°C	10 seconds
8.	Light Emitting Diodes	150°C	10 seconds
9.	Power Transistors (in TO-3 and TO-66 package)	275°C to 300°C	5 seconds
10.	Transistors (TO-39, TO-5 package)	225°C	5 seconds
11.	Transistors (TO-220AB package)	250°C	5 seconds
12.	Small signal transistors (in TO-92 plastic, TO-72, TO-18, SOT-25 package), FETs, MOSFETs	150°C to 200°C	-
13.	General purpose linear ICs like Opamps, Timers, IC Voltage Regulators, PLLs etc.	250°C	5 seconds
14.	TTL ICs	175°C	10 seconds
15.	CMOS ICs	200°C to 240°C	5 seconds

usually beyond the purchasing capacity of an average hobbyist or experimenter. But there is nothing to worry about it as majority of the test and measurement needs of an average hobbyist can be met with a multimeter.

Oscilloscope is another instrument a hobbyist should be familiar with even if he cannot afford to have one. It is a very useful diagnostic tool when it comes to observing and analysing waveforms. A multimeter would be quite useless if you wanted to know the amount of ripple in a power supply output or the quality of IC timer output waveform.

ANALOG METERS

We shall begin with a general introduction to the basic meter movement being used in various types of analog meters (Ohmmeters, Voltmeters, Ammeters, etc.) and the basic operational principles of these different types of analog meters.

THE BASIC METER MOVEMENT

The basic meter movement used in almost all kinds of analog meters meant for measuring resistance, current and voltage is the PERMANENT MAGNET TYPE MOVING COIL movement. The deflection produced in such a meter is proportional to the average (or DC) value of the current flowing through the meter coil. How this meter is used to measure different electrical parameters mentioned above shall be explained a little later. First we shall see as to what this movement is made up of and also as to why does the meter pointer deflect linearly as per the current flowing through the meter coil.

Fig. 2.8 shows the basic constructional features of permanent magnet type moving coil meter movement. As shown in Fig. 2.8, it consists of a coil wound with many turns of enamelled copper wire on an aluminium former. The former with coil wound on it is placed in the magnetic field of a permanent magnet. As the former is pivoted on jewelled bearings, it is free to move in the field of the permanent magnet. The pointer (or the needle) is carried by the spindle attached to the former. Thus the movement of the former is the same as the movement of the pointer.

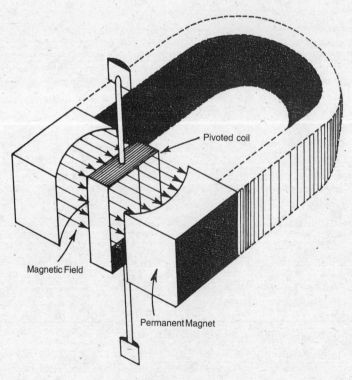

Magnetic Field

Pivoted coil

Permanent Magnet

Fig. 2.8

86

Now how does this basic meter function? The current to be measured is made to pass through the meter coil. The coil carrying current is thus surrounded by a magnetic field whose strength is proportional to the magnitude of current flowing through the coil. This magnetic field interacts with the magnetic field of the permanent magnet and thus produces a torque whose magnitude and direction are proportional to the magnitude and polarity of the current passing through the coil which is nothing but current under measurement. The scale of the meter is calibrated to directly read the current.

ACCURACY and SENSITIVITY are the two most important specifications of the basic current meter described above. ACCURACY is the plus or minus difference between the actual value of the current under measurement and the value read by the meter movement. It is expressed in terms of percentage of full scale deflection. The SENSITIVITY of the current meter is the current required to give full scale deflection. The moving coil movements available commercially typically have sensitivities ranging from 10μA to 20mA. Smaller the current required for full scale deflection, more sensitive the meter is. Accuracy specification has one very interesting practical implication. Let us take the case of a 100μA, ± 3% meter movement. Now an accuracy of ± 3% is the maximum error on the full scale deflection. In the present case, this error would be ± 3μA. If we had a 50μA meter with the same accuracy specification of ± 3%, this error would have been ± 1.5μA. Now what is interesting here is that when we are measuring a current that is less than the full scale deflection, then the percentage error in the measured value increases from what is specified for full scale deflection.

For instance, if you are measuring a current of 50μA with 100μA, ± 3% meter movement, the actual current may be anywhere between 47 and 53μA which means an error of ± 6%. And similarly, if you are measuring a current of 10μA with the same meter, the percentage error will shoot up to ± 30%, as the error in the measured current value is again ± 3μA. **Remember that you choose a**

meter or the meter range (in case of a multirange meter) that gives near full scale deflection for the current under measurement.

MEASURING LARGER CURRENTS — AMMETERS

The basic meter movement would give full scale deflection for a current that ranges from 10μA to about 20mA depending upon the meter. The current measuring capability of these meters can be enhanced by connecting a low value resistance across the meter coil. The current under measurement then is shared by the meter coil resistance and the shunt resistance as per the relative values of the two resistances. Naturally, if the shunt resistance value is much smaller than the meter coil resistance value, bulk of the current would be passing through the shunt resistance thus increasing the current measuring capability of the meter manifold. As an illustration, if you have a basic current meter with a full scale deflection current rating (or current sensitivity) of 10μA and the meter coil resistance of 10,000 ohms, the shunt resistance required to extend the range of this meter to say 1 Amp will be about 100 milli-ohms. In general (Refer to Fig. 2.9).

$$R_{sh} = I_{FS} \times R_M / (I - I_{FS})$$

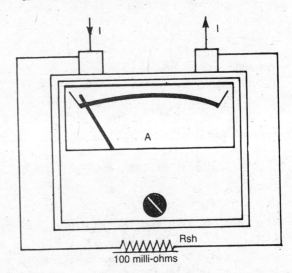

Fig. 2.9

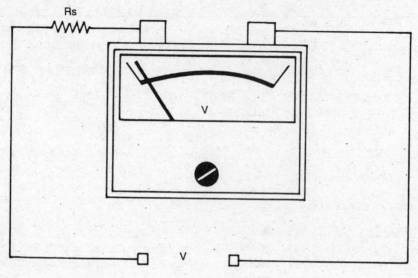

Fig. 2.10

MEASURING VOLTAGES — VOLTMETERS

The basic current meter having a current sensitivity of (I_{FS}) and a coil resistance of (R_M) ohms would give a full scale deflection for an applied DC voltage of ($I_{FS} \times R_M$) volts. This implies that the meter can not be used to measure DC voltages larger than that. As an illustration, the basic current meter with 10μA sensitivity and 10,000 ohms coil resistance can at the most measure a DC voltage of 100mV. In other words, this meter can sustain across it a maximum DC voltage of 100mV. The voltage measuring capability of this meter can be enhanced by connecting an appropriate resistance in series with the meter (Fig. 2.10) so as to drop across it a voltage equal to the maximum voltage to be measured minus the maximum voltage the meter coil can withstand. In general, the series resistance can be calculated from

$$R_S = (V/I_{FS}) - R_M$$

where (V) is the maximum voltage to be measured. The sensitivity of a voltmeter is expressed in terms of its OHMS PER VOLT rating which is nothing but the total resistance (meter coil resistance plus the series resistance) required to enable it measure a maximum voltage of 1 volt. It is given by reciprocal of current sensitivity of the basic current meter used. As an illustration, the

Ohms per volt ratings of 10μA and 1mA meter movements respectively would be 100000 ohms/volt and 1000 ohms/volt. Naturally, higher the ohms/volt rating, more sensitive the meter is.

Ammeters and Voltmeters are extensively used for measurement of currents (from microamperes to kiloamperes) and voltages (from milli-volts to kilovolts) in various types of electrical and electronic systems and also as indicators of voltages and currents in general purpose test equipment like Regulated power supplies, Insulation testers etc. These are available in different shapes, sizes and electrical specifications. Some of these types are shown in Fig. 2.11.

MEASURING RESISTANCE-OHMMETERS

The basic current meter can be used to measure resistance value by connecting it in the arrangement as shown in Fig. 2.12. Resistance (R) is so chosen as to give a full scale deflection for the reference voltage (V). This reference voltage is provided by a battery located inside the meter. The unknown resistance is inserted between X-X. When X-X are shorted (i.e. when the unknown resistance is zero), the meter shows maximum deflection and the current through the meter is given by $V/(R+R_M)$. Thus maximum deflection in this case indicates zero unknown

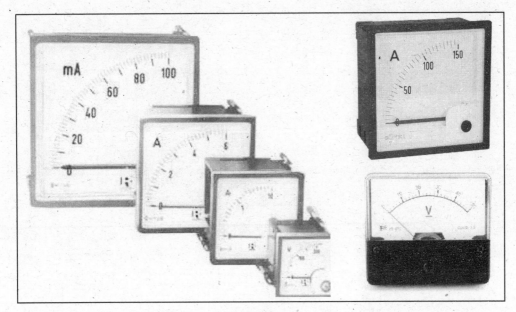

Fig. 2.11

resistance. When a certain resistance is inserted into the circuit between X-X, the deflection reduces due to a smaller current flowing through the meter. The current in this case is given by $V/(R+R_M+R_X)$. The deflection is thus inversely proportional to the value of unknown resistance. You would have noticed that the zero resistance is marked on the rightmost extreme and the infinite resistance is marked on the left most extreme of the scale in an ohmmeter. As the ohmmeter scale extends from zero to infinity, the error in the measured value in this case can not be expressed by a fixed number as was done in case of an ammeter or a voltmeter. It can be proved that the least error occurs when the meter gives half scale deflection for the resistance value under measurement. To ensure this, the ohmmeters also have different resistance ranges.

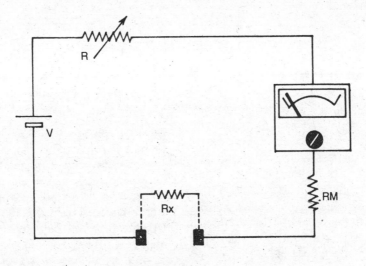

Fig. 2.12

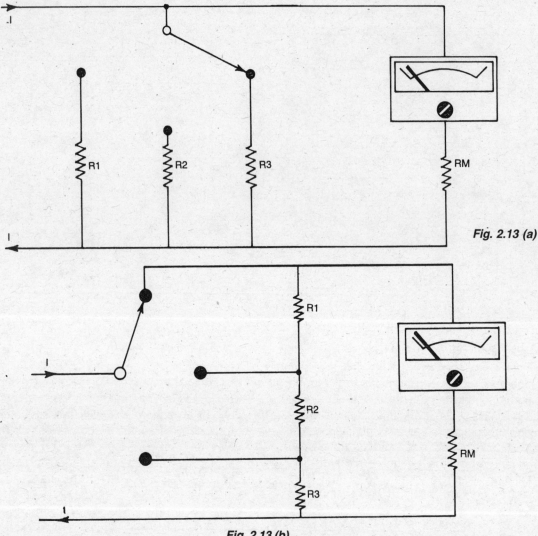

Fig. 2.13 (a)

Fig. 2.13 (b)

MULTI-RANGE AMMETERS AND VOLTMETERS

Multi-range ammeters can be constructed by having different shunt resistances connected across the meter for different current ranges. A rotary switch can be used to switch resistances. One such arrangement is shown in Fig. 2.13(a). This arrangement has the disadvantage that there is always a danger of excessive current flow through the meter while switching ranges if the switch contacts are of the usual Break-before-Make type. This problem does not exist if we use the arrangement of Fig. 2.13(b).

Multi-range voltmeters can be constructed by switching different series resistors as shown in Fig. 2.14.

AC VOLTMETERS

What we have been discussing so far with reference to voltage measurements is the DC voltmeters. AC voltage measurements are usually made with a moving coil type meter movement by first converting the AC voltage into a proportional DC voltage using a half wave rectifier (Fig. 2.15a) or a full wave rectifier (Fig. 2.15b). In Fig. 2.15c), diode D2 prevents any reverse current to flow through the meter during negative half cycles.

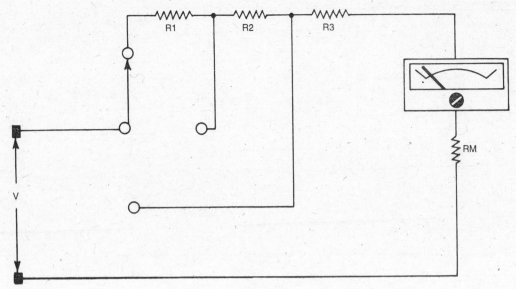

Fig. 2.14

MULTIMETERS

A MULTIMETER is a test instrument that combines in itself the functions of an OHMMETER (that measures resistance), an AMMETER (that measures current) and a VOLTMETER (that measures voltage). More precisely, it is a multi-range ohmmeter, multirange voltmeter and a multi-range ammeter - all in one. Basically a permanent magnet moving coil type movement (Mind you, we are presently talking about ANALOG MULTIMETERS) of the type described in earlier sections is the heart of the system. It is provided with a battery to make it an ohmmeter, with shunt resistors of different values for making it a multi-range ammeter and with series resistors of different values to make it a multi-range voltmeter.

For making AC measurements (Voltages and Currents), as outlined above, these are first rectified inside the meter and a proportional DC generated which is then applied to the meter movement.

PRECAUTIONS WHILE USING ANALOG MULTIMETERS

One must take the following precautions while making measurements with a multimeter.

1. The approximate value of voltage, current or resistance — as the case may be — must be known before making the measurement so that a proper range can be selected. For instance, if we try to measure a high voltage, say more than 100 volts, while keeping the multimeter in 10 volts range, we may damage the meter movement by letting excessive current flow through the meter movement.

2. Not only this, for least error, we must always choose a range so that we get near full scale deflection for voltage or current and about half-scale deflection in case of resistance measurement.

3. While making resistance measurements, the resistance under test must be isolated from other circuit components ; otherwise what you would read would be erroneous.

4. While making resistance measurements, the circuit must be de-energised i.e. all voltage or current sources must be removed otherwise there is every likelihood that the voltage is excessive and causes damage to the instrument. Such a situation is more likely during resistance measurements with electrical machines.

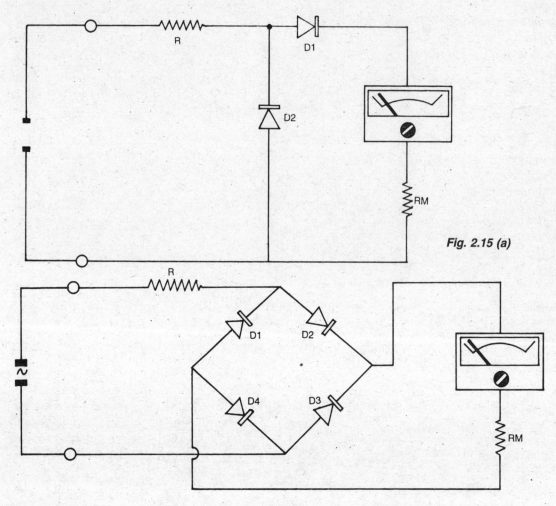

Fig. 2.15 (a)

Fig. 2.15 (b)

DIGITAL MULTIMETER

A digital multimeter does all that is done by its analog counterpart. It displays the measured voltage, current or resistance as discrete numerals instead of a needle deflection on a continuous scale as in an analog multimeter. Numerical readout is advantageous as it eliminates inaccuracies due to parallax, human errors and interpolation errors. Other advantages include better resolution (typically 0.1% in $3\frac{1}{2}$ digit multimeters against 1% in analog meters) and higher accuracy (typically ±0.1% in digital multimeters against ±3% in analog multimeters. Features like AUTORANGING, AUTOMATIC

POLARITY, DIODE AND TRANSISTOR TEST FACILITY etc. are commonly available in modern general purpose digital multimeters.

SIGNIFICANCE OF HALF DIGIT IN DIGITAL MULTIMETERS

A half digit is usually the one that can display either a '0' or a '1' while the usual full digits can display all digits from 0 through 9. Addition of a half digit in the MSB position of the display preserves the maximum resolution of the multimeter upto a higher range. For instance, a 3 digit multimeter has a resolution of 0.1V upto 99.9 volts and beyond that the resolution is 1 volt. A $3\frac{1}{2}$ digit multimeter with practically no additional circuit hardware would give you a resolution of 0.1 V upto 199.9 Volts. That is why, you would always come across digital multimeters with a display having this additional $1/_2$-digit ($3^1/_2$-digit, $4^1/_2$-digit, $5^1/_2$-digit, etc.).

COMMERCIALLY AVAILABLE MULTIMETERS

Both Analog and Digital multimeters are manufactured in a wide range of sizes, shapes and performance specifications. Prominent amongst analog multimeter brands are the MOTWANE, MECO, SANWA. Fig. 2.16 shows some general purpose analog multimeters. Similar models from other manufacturers also have similar specifications.

The multimeter shown can be used to measure both AC and DC voltages upto 1000 volts (max) and so do majority of their counterparts. It can be used to measure DC currents upto 10A and resistance upto a maximum of 20M. Detailed technical specifications of this multimeter which can be considered a representative of general purpose analog multimeters are listed ahead. Any specific precautions to be observed while using an analog multimeter of a given brand are usually given in the brochure that is supplied by the manufacturer along with the instrument.

TECHNICAL SPECIFICATIONS

1. DC Voltages: 0-2.5, 10, 25, 100, 250, 1000V

   Sensitivity = 20,000 ohms per volt

   Accuracy = ± 2% FSD (Full Scale Deflection)

2. AC Voltages: 0-2.5, 10, 25, 100, 250, 1000V

   Sensitivity = 9000 ohms per volt.

   Accuracy = ± 3% FSD at 50 Hz

3. DC Current: 0-100µA, 1, 10, 100, 1000 mA and 10A

   Accuracy = ± 2% FSD (± 4% FSD at 10A)

4. Resistance: 0-20K, 2M and 20M ranges

   Accuracy = ± 2% FSD

5. Frequency response: ± 3% from 50Hz to 3kHz

6. Battery: 9V

General purpose handheld $3^1/_2$-digit digital multimeters have become very popular with

Fig. 2.16

engineers and technicians as these are much more convenient to use and also because these are now available at a much lower price tag. In addition, majority of general purpose DMMs come with Diode test, Transistor test and Continuity test facilities. Fig. 2.17 shows a typical $3\frac{1}{2}$ digit LCD display digital multimeter. Major performance specifications of this multimeter and most of the other $3\frac{1}{2}$ digit DMMs are listed ahead. Some of the DMM types also have Auto ranging feature. This feature simplifies and speeds up the use of meter. With Auto ranging facility, you need not bother about what range to select thus avoiding long range changing delays.

TECHNICAL SPECIFICATIONS

1. DC Voltage: upto 1000 V (max) in the ranges of 320 mV (Resolution = 100μV), 3.2V (Resolution = 1 mV), 32V (Resolution = 10 mV), 320V (Resolution = 100 mV) and 1000V (Resolution = 1V)

2. AC Voltage: upto 1000 V (max) in the same ranges and resolutions as listed in case of DC Voltages.

3. Resistance: 32M (max) in the ranges of 320 ohms (0.1 ohm resolution), 3.2K (1 ohm resolution), 32K (10 ohms resolution), 320K (100 ohms resolution), 3.2M (1K resolution) and 32M (10K resolution)

4. DC and AC Current: 10A (max) in the ranges of 320 μA (0.1 μA resolution), 3200μA (1μA resolution), 32 mA (10 μA resolution), 320 mA (100 μA resolution) and 10 A (10 mA resolution).

5. Display type: $3\frac{1}{2}$ Digit LCD Display

6. Power Requirement: Single 9V battery

7. Has Auto ranging, Diode test and Continuity indication facilities.

OSCILLOSCOPES

After multimeters, an oscilloscope is the most commonly used electronic test instrument. Be it the electronics industry or a research laboratory, the oscilloscope is an indispensable test and measurement tool for an electronics engineer or a technician. However, very few of us are familiar with the use of multiciplicity of front panel controls of an oscilloscope. An understanding of functioning of these controls is key to the use of an oscilloscope for making a variety of measurements.

One of the most common applications of an oscilloscope is to get a display of a time varying signal. There is an electron-gun whose beam can be deflected both horizontally (by means of X-plates) and vertically (by means of Y-plates). The pairs of plates X-X and pair of plates Y-Y are mutually at right angles. By applying appropriate potentials, the beam spot can be shifted anywhere on screen.

Most of the oscilloscope applications require a time-base that produces linear motion of the beam along the horizontal axis. This is achieved by applying a sweep waveform (Sawtooth

Fig. 2.17

waveform) to the horizontal deflection plates. The trace period gives a bright horizontal line (if the frequency of sawtooth waveform is large enough) and the retrace is pretty fast and is blanked out (like in TV picture tube) to make it invisible.

Now how can we display a time-varying waveform on the oscilloscope screen. Simultaneous application of time varying voltage to the Y-input (either directly or through an amplifier within the oscilloscope) and a sweep voltage to horizontal deflection plates results in the signal being applied to vertical deflection plates getting displayed on oscilloscope screen. If the sweep frequency is a submultiple of the signal frequency being displayed, the spot will trace the same path on successive sweeps and the pattern will appear as stationary plot of waveform being analysed. If it is not so, the pattern moves back and forth on the screen. There is a provision of sweep frequency adjustments (both coarse as well as fine) on the front panel. In fact, there are a lot more controls that need to be handled while viewing unknown waveforms on oscilloscopes. These will be discussed a little later.

To keep the pattern locked at the set rate, a part of the vertical input signal is processed and applied to the input of the sweep generator to control its frequency so that the two remain in step. This is termed as Internal Synchronization.

Such a feature is specially helpful while aligning TV receivers with a sweep generator. In some oscilloscopes, there is a provision for "triggered-mode" sweep. This enables precise locking of the time base with any portion of the input waveform. Such a facility is helpful in studying one shot events or transients.

OSCILLOSCOPE PROBES
Oscilloscope probe is a shielded cable used to connect the signal to be displayed from the source to the vertical input of the oscilloscope. A shielded cable is used to prevent pick-up of interfering signals or Hum due to hand capacitance. The capacitance of such a cable together with the input capacitance of the oscilloscope is about 50 to 60 pF. Although the shunting affect of this capacitance might not alter the waveshape of audio range signals but will certainly affect the higher frequency components. So, a low capacitance probe might be needed for viewing these signals. Fig. 2-18(a) shows the equivalent circuit of an oscilloscope probe of the 10x type whereas Fig. 2-18(b) shows the photograph of a typical oscilloscope probe.

THE FRONT PANEL OPERATING CONTROLS.
Fig. 2.19 shows the picture of the front panel of a general purpose analog oscilloscope. It can be considered to be representative of all general purpose analog oscilloscopes. The relative positions of these controls may vary from scope

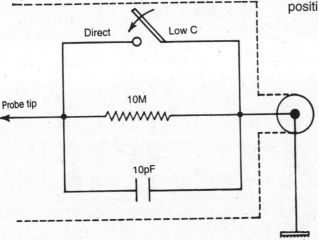

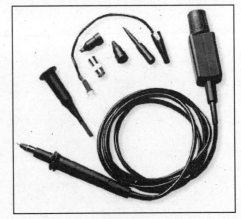

Fig. 2.18

to scope, but the nature of these controls remains the same.

The front panel operating controls (that are usually needed to be handled) of an oscilloscope are as follows:

The **INTENSITY** controls the brightness of the display. The display can be adjusted from very bright to total darkness. The setting of the intensity control may affect the correct focus of display. Slight readjustment of focus-control may be necessary when the intensity level is changed. The intensity of the display should never be kept higher than what is satisfactory (especially at low sweep rates).

FOCUS is used to properly focus the display. The focus control can be adjusted to get a very fine electron beam spot. In fact, **FOCUS** and **INTENSITY** controls should be used together to get a sharp, low intensity trace. The trace intensity should never be so bright that it burns a hole in the phosphor coating on the CRT screen.

SCALE ILLUMINATION controls scale illumination. It provides sharp reproduction of lines when photographs are taken from screen.

TRACE FINDER/BEAM FIND: It returns the display to screen, when pressed, by reducing horizontal and vertical deflection. It provides a means of locating a display that over scans the viewing area either horizontally or vertically.

VOLTS/DIV selects the vertical deflection factor. In majority of analog oscilloscopes, **VOLTS/DIV** or the Vertical Deflection factor can be selected from 5 mV/DIV to 5V/DIV in different steps.

HOR. POSITION controls the horizontal position of the display.

VERT. POSITION controls the vertical position of the display.

AC-GND-DC: It selects method of coupling input signal to the vertical input of the oscilloscope. In AC, the DC component of the input signal is blocked. In GND, the input circuit is grounded but the applied signal is not connected to a DC ground. In DC, all components of input signal (ac and dc) are passed to the vertical input amplifier of the oscilloscope.

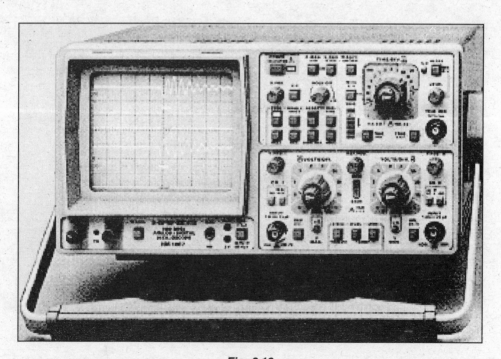

Fig. 2.19

MODE: Selects vertical mode of operation. This control is found on only those oscilloscopes having more than one modes of operation.

INPUT: It is the vertical input connector for the signal.

EXT. TRIG. INPUT: It is input connector for external triggering signal, Connector also serves as an external horizontal input when horizontal display switch is in Ext. Hor. position.

SOURCE: It selects the source of triggering signal. This control selects the type of signal used to synchronise the horizontal sweep oscillator. INT Provides internal trigger. In the INT. Position, the trigger signal is obtained from vertical system. In LINE position, a sample of power line frequency is connected to the trigger generator. Line triggering is useful when the input signal is time related to the line frequency. In EXT position, an external signal fed to the "EXT. TRIG. INPUT" connector can be used to trigger the sweep. The external signal must be time related to the displayed signal for stable display.

COUPLING: It determines the method of coupling triggering signal to trigger circuit. On some oscilloscopes, this function is combined with trigger source control. The AC position blocks the DC component of the trigger signal. The triggering point in AC position depends on the average level of the trigger signals. DC coupling can be use to provide stable triggering with low frequency signals that would be attenuated in AC position.

LEVEL: The level control can be adjusted to provide triggering at desired DC level on the waveform being displayed.

SLOPE: This determines whether the trigger circuit responds on the positive going or negative going portion of the trigger signals.

TIME/DIV: It selects calibrated horizontal sweep rates for the internal sweep generators.

CAL.: It is the calibration signal output connector. It typically provides a 1 kHz square-waveform.

SWEEP MODE: It determines sweep operating mode. It is also referred to as SWEEP SELECTOR. It provides three basic operating modes (i) Linear sawtooth sweep (Int.) (ii) External (iii) Line frequency sine wave (Int.)

CALIBRATION OF OSCILLOSCOPE AND ITS PROBE

It order to maintain an oscilloscope at its inherent accuracy, the oscilloscope and its probe must be calibrated before use for any critical measurement. The procedure for calibration is as follows:

Most scopes have available on the front panel a calibration voltage or a calibrator with a range of selectable voltages. The oscilloscope probe may be contacted to any of these calibration voltages. The calibration voltage should preferably be of the same order of magnitude as the voltage to be measured. If the oscilloscope is of "X10" variety i.e. if it attenuates the signal to be measured by a factor of 10, it must be compensated prior to calibration.

Fig. 2.20 shows the equivalent circuit of an oscilloscope probe of (X10) type along with the input of vertical amplifier of the oscilloscope. Note that oscilloscope input impedance consists of a 1 M resistor in parallel with a 20 pF capacitor. To attenuate the input signal to the oscilloscope, so that larger signals may be measured, a probe with 9M resistor as shown may be used which has the added advantage of increased input impedance of oscilloscope. However, this resistance in combination with input capacitance of oscilloscope causes the signal seen by oscilloscope to become distorted because of high frequency filtering effect of input capacitance. To compensate for this, oscilloscope manufacturers provide a variable capacitor in parallel with probe resistance as shown in Fig. 2.20. Fig. 2.21 illustrates the traces that result when the probe is under or overcompensated as the calibration voltage is viewed. The compensating capacitor is generally located on a probe-tip although sometimes it is integral with the connector to the oscilloscope. The procedure is simply to adjust the capacitor until the corners of the square wave trace are as square as possible.

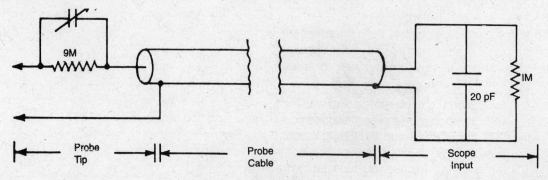

Probe
Tip

Probe
Cable

Scope
Input

9M

20 pF

IM

Fig. 2.20

Once this procedure has been completed, the sensitivity of the vertical amplifier labeled VERT. GAIN ADJUST is adjusted until proper deflection is obtained. For example, with deflection sensitivity of 2V/cm, and a 2V square wave from calibrator, the vertical sensitivity is adjusted until 1cm. deflection is achieved. The scope is now ready for use.

MAKING ROUTINE MEASUREMENTS WITH AN OSCILLOSCOPE

Measurement of VOLTAGE, FREQUENCY and ANALYSIS OF WAVEFORMS are the most frequently used oscilloscope functions. Carrying out these measurements becomes simple and a routine job once you are familiar with the operation and capabilities of the multiplicity of the controls found on the front panel of an oscilloscope.

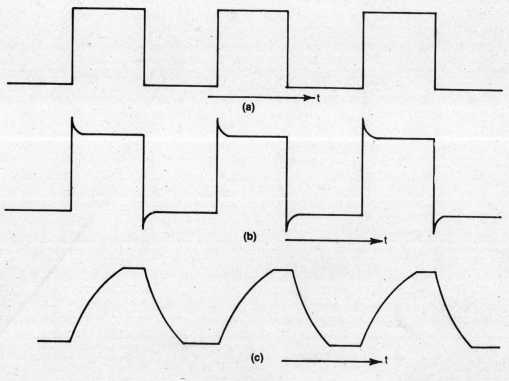

(a)

(b)

(c)

Fig. 2.21

The procedure for carrying out above measurements is identical. Following steps should be followed while trying to use an oscilloscope for measuring either voltage or frequency or analysing a signal waveform.

1. Switch on the oscilloscope and wait for the trace to appear on the oscilloscope screen. Use the FOCUS and INTENSITY controls jointly to get a clear, sharp and not-too-intense trace. In case you don't get the trace after you have switched on the scope, you can make use of HORIZONTAL and VERTICAL POSITION controls to get the same. And in case you fail to do so even with these controls, you can use scope's VIEW FIND facility provided on majority of oscilloscopes. By pressing the VIEW FIND push button, you will see a spot somewhere on the screen. You can now use position controls to bring this spot to the center (intersection point of X-axis and Y-axis). Release the VIEW FIND button and there you have the trace.

2. Connect a probe to the oscilloscope's vertical input and ensure that the scope is calibrated and also that the probe is properly compensated. Both these things can be ensured by viewing the CALIBRATION SIGNAL of the scope. The TIME/DIV and VOLTS/DIV controls should be set as per the available calibration signal amplitude and frequency.

3. Set the Vertical Deflection Factor (VOLTS/DIV) and Horizontal Time Base (TIME/DIV) controls as per the expected amplitude and frequency of the signal to be analysed so that the signal fills most of the screen in the vertical direction and you get a few cycles of the waveform in the horizontal direction. If you are using a 10X probe, don't forget to multiply the chosen Volts/Div setting by 10 to get the effective deflection factor. For instance, if you have set at 1V/Div and you are using a 10X probe, then the effective setting would be 10 V/Div.

4. Select appropriate VERTICAL INPUT COUPLING MODE (Usually DC), SWEEP MODE (Usually INTERNAL and AUTO) and VERTICAL DISPLAY MODE (This is important when you are using a Dual trace Oscilloscope). INTERNAL sweep mode means that a repetitive trace appears even in the absence of any vertical input signal as the sweep trigger in this case is provided by the sweep circuit and the moment a vertical input signal is applied, the sweep gets triggered by this signal as per TRIGGER SLOPE and TRIGGER LEVEL settings. AUTO SWEEP means that the sweep generating circuit is a free running oscillator. In the VERTICAL DISPLAY MODES, you have the CHOP MODE used for viewing signals upto a frequency of several tens of kilohertz and the ALTERNATE MODE used for viewing higher frequency signals.

5. Connect the probe tip to the circuit point where the desired signal is appearing with the probe ground connected to the circuit ground. The waveform is displayed on the screen. You might have to adjust the VOLTS/DIV and TIME/DIV controls once again to get a desired display. You will also be required to adjust the Trigger level and the Trigger Slope controls to get a stable display.

6. Measurement of voltage and Frequency from the oscilloscope display are obvious.

Some signal waveforms obtained while making such measurements are depicted in Figs. 2.22(a) to 2.22(d). if the probe used in the first two cases is the 1X type and a 10X probe is used for the waveforms shown in Figs. 2.22(c) and (d), then following observations can be made:

1. The pulse train of Fig. 2.22(a) has a peak amplitude of 5 volts, a duty cycle of 0.6 and a frequency of 10kHz.

2. The sinusoidal signal of Fig. 2.22(b) has a frequency of 100 kHz and a peak to peak amplitude of 30 volts.

3. The ramp waveform of Fig. 2.22(c) has a peak amplitude of 150 volts, a slope of 3.75 V/μS and a frequency of 25kHz.

4. The square waveform of Fig. 2.22(d) has overshoots of 50% on all leading edges and undershoots of 25% on all trailing edges.

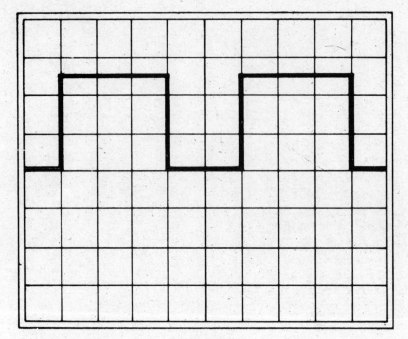

Fig. 2.22 (a)

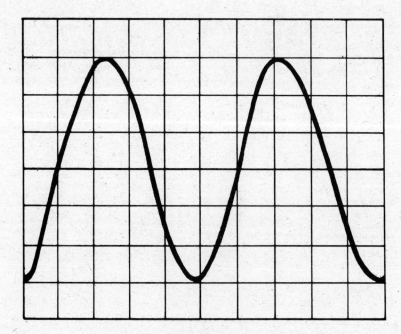

Fig. 2.22 (b)

100

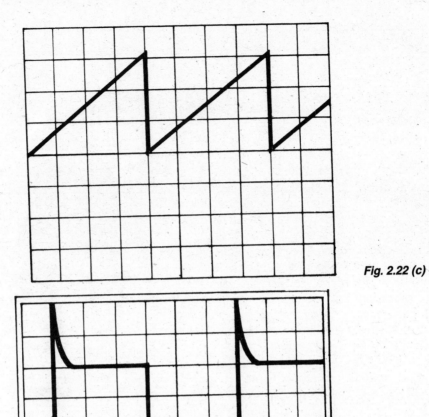

Fig. 2.22 (c)

Fig. 2.22 (d)

(a) Vertical Deflection factor knob setting = 2V/DIV

Time Base setting = 20μS/DIV

(b) Vertical Deflection factor knob setting = 5V/DIV
Time Base setting = 20μS/DIV

(c) Vertical Deflection factor knob setting = 5V/DIV
Time Base setting = 10μS/DIV

(d) Vertical Deflection factor knob setting = 5V/DIV
Time Base setting = 10μS/DIV

CHAPTER-3

APPLICATION INFORMATION ON LINEAR AND DIGITAL INTEGRATED CIRCUITS

We have already covered the operational basics of various electronic components, both passive including resistors, capacitors, inductors etc. and active including discrete semiconductor devices and integrated circuits. We all appreciate that linear and digital integrated circuits are increasingly used in electronics circuitry. Electronic gadgets and other similar circuits of interest to electronics hobbyist or enthusiast are no expception. Detailed application information in case of some of the very popular integrated circuits was presented in chapter-1. It would be beyond the scope of this book to give an equally detailed coverage on many more devices that would be of interest to practicing hobbyist. Nevertheless, it would be worthwhile presenting brief application oriented information on a wider choice of these devices, which is the objective of this chapter. In this chapter, we shall give listing of a wide range of integrated circuits, both linear and digital, along with their major specifications.

GLOSSARY OF COMMONLY USED LINEAR INTERGRATED CIRCUITS

The information given in this part falls under the following headings:

1. Operational Amplifiers

2. IC Timers

3. IC Voltage Regulators

1. OPERATIONAL AMPLIFIERS

Type	Brief Description	Major Specifications
LM741	General Purpose, Single	GBW = 1MHz, Slew Rate = 0.5V/μs
NE/SE5534	Low Noise, Single	GBW = 10MHz, Slew Rate = 13V/μs
LM748	General Purpose, Single	GBW = 1MHz, Slew Rate = 0.5V/μs
LF155 / 255/355	JFET-input, Single	GBW = 6 MHz, Slew Rate = 6V/μs
LF156 / 256/356	JFET-input, High SR, Single	GBW = 8 MHz, Slew Rate = 13V/μs
LF157/ 257/357	JFET-input, High SR, Single	GBW = 30 MHz, Slew Rate = 60V/μs
OP-07	Instrumentation opamp, Single	GBW = 0.8 MHz, Slew Rate = 0.3V/μs
OP-27	Low Noise, Single	GBW = 8MHz, Slew Rate = 2.8V/μs
OP-37	Low Noise, Single	GBW = 63 MHz, Slew Rate = 17V/μs
OP-47	Low Noise, High SR, Single	GBW = 70 MHz, Slew Rate = 50V/μs
OP-77	Precision, Single	GBW = 0.6 MHz, Slew Rate = 0.2V/μs
OP-111	General Purpose, Single	GBW = 6MHz, Slew Rate = 6V/μs
OP-177	General Purpose, Single	GBW = 6MHz, Slew Rate = 6V/μs
LM747	General Purpose, Dual	GBW = 1MHz, Slew Rate = 0.5V/μs
MC 1458	Genral Purpose, Dual	GBW = 1MHz, Slew Rate = 0.8V/μs
LM158 258/358	General Purpose, Dual	GBW = 1MHz, Slew Rate =
NE/SE5532	Low Noise, Dual	GBW = 10MHz, Slew Rate = 8V/μs
NE/SE5538	High SR, Dual	GBW = 6MHz, Slew Rate = 60V/μs

LM124/ 224/324	General Purpose, Quad	GBW = 1MHz, Slew Rate = 0.5V/µs
LM148/ 248/348	General Purpose, Quad	GBW = 1MHz, Slew Rate = 0.5V/µs
LM2900/3900	Notron Opamp, Quad	GBW = 2.5MHz (for Inverting input), Slew Rate = 0.5V/µs (Positive Output Swing), 20V/µs (Negative Output Swing)
LM111/ 211/311	Opamp Comparator, Single	Response time = 200ns, Open Collector Output
NE/SE527	Opamp Comparator, Single	Response time = 16ns, TTL Output
NE/SE529	Opamp Camparator, Single	Response time = 12ns, TTL Output
LM119/ 219/319	Opamp Comparator, Dual	Response time = 80ns, Open Collector Output
LM139/ 239/339	Opamp Comparator, Quad	Response time = 1300µs, Open Collector Output
NE/SE527	Opamp Comparator, Single	Response time = 16ns, TTL Output
NE/SE529	Opamp comaparator, Single	Response time = 12ns, TTL Ouput

2. IC TIMERS

Type	Brief Description	Salient Features
LM555	Single timer	Commonly used in Monostable and Astable configurations, Has RESET and CONTROL pins
LM556	Dual timer	Basically Dual 555 timer
LM558	Quad timer	Each of the four timers has features similar to those of 555 timer

3. THREE-TERMINAL IC VOLTAGE REGULATORS

Type	Brief Description	Salient Features
LM78LXX	Positive, Fixed Output Voltage	Drop-out Voltage = 1.7V, Current = 100mA
LM78MXX	Positive, Fixed Output Voltage	Drop-out Voltage = 2V, Current = 500mA
LM78XX	Positive, Fixed Output Voltage	Drop-out Voltage = 3V, Current = 1500mA
LM140-XX/ LM340-XX	Positive, Fixed Output Voltage	Drop-out Voltage = 3V, Current = 1500mA
LM79LXX	Nagative, Fixed Output Voltage	Drop-out Voltage = 1.7V, Current = 100mA
LM78MXX	Negative, Fixed Output Voltage	Drop-out Voltage = 2V, Current = 500mA
LM79XX	Negative, Fixed Output Voltage	Drop-out Voltage = 3V, Current = 1500mA
LM117L/ 217L/317L	Voltage (1.2V to 37V)	
LM117M/ 217/317	Positive, Adjustable Output Voltage (1.2V to 37V)	Drop-out Voltage = 3V, Current = 500mA
LM120-XX/ LM320-XX	Negative, Fixed Output Voltage	Drop-out Voltage = 2.5 to 3V Current = 200mA, 500mA, 1000mA and 1500mA output current versions
LM137L/ 237L/337L	Positive, Ajustable Output Voltage (-1.2V to -37V)	Drop-out Voltage = 3V, Current = 100mA
LM137M/ 237M/337M	Positive, Adjustable Output Voltage (-1.2V to -37V)	Drop-out Voltage = 3V, Current = 500mA
LM137/ 237/337	Negative, Adjustable Output Voltage (-1.2V to -37V)	Drop-out Voltage = 3V, Current = 1500mA

GLOSSARY OF DIGITAL INTERGRATED CIRCUITS

There information given in this part of the book falls under the following headins:

1. CMOS IC Numerical Index
2. CMOS IC Functional Index
3. TTL IC Numerical Index
4. TTL IC Functional Index

1. CMOS IC NUMERICAL INDEX

Device No.	Description
4001B	Quad 2-Input NOR Gate
4002B	Dual 4-Input NOR Gate
4006B	18-Stage Static Shift Register
4007UB	Dual Complementary Pair Plus Inverter
4008B	4-Bit Binary Full Adder
4011B	Quad 2-Input NAND Gate
4012B	Dual 4-Input NAND Gate
4013B	Dual D Flip-Flop
4014B	8-Bit Shift Register
4015B	Dual 4-Bit Static Shift Register
4016B	Quad Bilateral Switches
4017B	5-Stage Johnson Counter
4018B	Presettable Divide-by-N Counter (Obsolete-For Ref. Only)
4019B	Quad 2-input Multiplexer
4020B	14-Stage Binary Counter
4021B	8-Bit Shift Register
4022B	4-Stage Divide-by-8 Johnson Counter
4023B	Triple 3-Input NAND Gate
4024B	7-Stage Binary Counter
4025B	Triple 3-Input NOR Gate
4027B	Dual JK Flip-Flop
4028B	1-of-10 Decoder
4029B	Synchronous Up/Down Counter
4030B	Quad Exclusive-OR Gate
4031B	64-Stage Static Shift Register
4034B	8-Bit Universal Bus Register
4035B	4-Bit Universal Shift Register
4040B	12-Stage Binary Counter
4041B	Quad True/Complement Buffer (Obsolete—For Ref. Only)
4042B	Quad D Latch
4043B	Quad R/S Latch with 3-State Ouput (Obsolete—For Ref. Only)
4044B	Quad R/S Latch with 3-State Output
4045B	21-Stage Binary Counter
4046B	Micropower Phase-Locked Loop
4047B	Monostable/Astable Multivibrator
4049B	Hex Inverting Buffer
4050B	Hex Non-Inverting Buffer
4051B	8-Channel Analog Multiplexer/Demiultiplexer
4052B	Dual 4-Channel Analog Multiplexer/Demultiplexer
4053B	Triple 2-Channel Analog Multiplexer/Demultiplexer
4066B	Quad-Bilateral Switches
4067B	16-Channel Analog Multiplexer/Demultiplexer
4068B	8-Input NAND Gate (Obsolete—For Ref. Only)
4069UB	Hex Inverter

4070B	Quad Exclusive-OR Gate
4071B	Quad 2-Input OR Gate
4073B	Triple 3-Input AND Gate (Obsolete—For Ref. Only)
4075B	Triple 3-Input OR Gate (Obsolete—For Ref. Only)
4076B	Quad D Flip Flop with 3-State Output
4077B	Quad Exclusive-NOR Gate (Obsolete—For Ref. Only)
4078B	8-Input NOR Gate (Obsolete—For Ref. Only)
4081B	Quad 2-Input AND Gate
4085B	Dual 2-Wide, 2-Input AND-OR-INVERT Gate
4086B	4-Wide, 2-Input AND-OR-INVERT Gate
4093B	Quad 2-Input NAND Schmitt Trigger
40014B	Hex Schmitt Trigger
40085B	4-Bit Magnitude Comparator
40097B	3-State Hex Non-Inverting Buffer
40098B	3-State Hex Inverting Buffer
40161B	4-Bit Synchronous Counter
40163B	4-Bit Sunchronous Counter
40174B	Hex D Flkp-Flop
40175B	Quad D Flkp-Flop
40193B	4-Bit Up//Down Binary Counter
40194B	4-Bit Bi-directional Unversal Shift Register (Obsolete—For Ref. Only)
40195B	4-Bit Universal Shift Register (Obsolete—For Ref. Only)
4104B	Quad Low Voltage to High Voltage Translator with 3-State Outputs
4510B	Up/Down Decade Counter
4511B	BCD to 7-Segment Latch/Decoder/Driver
4512B	8-Input Multiplexer with 3-State Output
4514B	1-of-16 Decoder/Demultiplexer with Input Latch
4515B	1-of-16 Decoder/Demultiplexer with Input Latch
4516B	Up/Down Counter
4518B	Dual 4-Bit Decade Counter
4520B	Dual 4-Bit Binary Counter
4521B	24-Stage Binary Counter
4522B	4-Bit BCD Programmable Down Counter
4526B	4-Bit Binary Programmable Down Counter
4527B	BCD Rate Multiplier
4528B	Dual Retriggerable Resettable Monostable Multivibrator
4531B	13-Input Parity Checker/Generator (Obsolete—For Ref. Only)
4532B	8-Input Priority Encoder (Obsolete—For Ref. Only)
4539B	Dual 4-Input Multiplexer
4543B	BCD to 7-Segment Latch/Decoder/Driver for Liquid Crystals
4555B	Dual 1-of-4 Decoder Demultiplexer
4556B	Dual 1-of-4 Decoder Demultiplexer
4557B	1-to-64 Bit Variable Length Shift Register
4582B	Carry Look Ahead Generator (Obsolete—For Ref. Only)
4702B	Programmable Bit Rate Generator
4703B	FIFO Buffer Memory
4710B	Register Stack 16 × 4-Bit RAM with 3-State Output Register
4720B	256-Bit RAM with 3-State Output
4722B	Programmable Timer/Counter
4723B	Dual 4-Bit Addressable Latch
4724B	8-Bit Addressable Latch
4725B	64-Bit RAM with 3-State Output
4727B	7-Stage Counter
4731B	Quad 64-Bit Static Shift Register
4741B	4 × 4 Cross Point Switch
6508B	1024-Bit (1024 × 1) CMOS RAM with 3-State Output

2. CMOS IC FUNCTIONAL INDEX

Function	Description
Counters	
4017B	5-Stage Johnson Counter
4020B	14-Stage Binary Counter
4022B	4-Stage Divide-by-8 Johnson Counter
4024B	7-Stage Binary Counter
4029B	Synchronous Up/Down Counter
4040B	12-Stage Binary Counter
4045B	21-Stage Binary Counter
4510B	Up/Down Decade Counter
4516B	Up/Down Binary Counter
4518B	Dual 4-Bit Decade Counter
4520B	Dual 4-Bit Binary Counter
4521B	24-Stage Binary Counter
4522B	4-Bit BCD Programmable Down Counter
4526B	4-Bit Binary Programmable Down Counter
4722B	Programmable Timer/Counter
4727B	7-Stage Counter
40161B	4-Bit Synchronous Counter
40163B	4-Bit Synchronous Counter
40193B	4-Bit Up/Down Binary Counter
Registers	
4006B	18-Stage Static Shift Register
4014B	8-Bit Shift Register
4015B	Dual 4-Bit Static Shift Register
4021B	8-Bit Shift Register
4031B	64-Stage Static Shift Register
4034B	8-Bit Universal Bus Register
4035B	4-Bit Univeral Shift Register
4557B	1-to-64 Variable Length Shift Register
4731B	Quad 64-Bit Static Shift Register
Decoders and Demultiplexers	
4028B	1-of-10 Decoder
4511B	BCD to 7-Segment Latch/Decoder/Driver
4514B	1-of-16 Decoder/Demultiplexer with Input Latch
4515B	1-to-16 Decoder/Demultiplexer with Input Latch
4543B	BCD to 7-Segment Latch/Decoder/Driver for Liquid Crystals
4555B	Dual 1-of-4 Decoder Demultiplexers
4556B	Dual 1-of-4 Decoder Demultiplexers
4723B	Dual 4-Bit Addressable Latch
4724B	8-Bit Addressable Latch
Digital Multiplexers	
4019B	Quad 2-Input Multiplexer
4512B	8-Input Multiplexer with 3-State Output
4539B	Dual 4-Input Multiplexer
Analog Switches and Multiplexers/Demultiplexers	
4016B	Quad Bilateral Switch
4051B	8-Channel Analog Multiplexer/Demultiplexer
4052B	Dual 4-Channel Analog Multiplexer/Demultiplexer

4053B	Triple 2-Channel Analog Multiplexer/Demultiplexer
4066B	Quad Bilateral Switch
4067B	16-Channel Analog Multiplexer/Demultiplexer
4741B	4 × 4 Cross Point Switch

Latches

4042B	Quad D Latch
4044B	Quad R/S Latch with 3-State Output
4511B	BCD to 7-Segment Latch/Decoder/Driver
4543B	BCD to 7-Segment Latch/Decoder/Driver for Liquid crystals
4723B	Dual 4-Bit Addressable Latch
4724B	8-Bit Addressable Latch
40174B	Hex D Flip-Flop
40175B	Quad D Flip-Flop

Trnaslslators

| 4104B | Quad Low Voltage to High Voltage Translator with 3-State Output |

Artihmetic Operators

4008B	4-Bit Binary Full Adder
4527B	BCD Rate Multiplier
40085B	4-Bit Magnitude Comparator

NAND Gates

4011B	Quad 2-Input NAND Gate
4012B	Dual 4-Input NAND Gate
4023B	Triple 3-Input NAND Gate
4093B	Quad 2-Input NAND Schmitt Trigger

AND Gates

| 4081B | Quad 2-Input AND Gate |

NOR Gates

4001B	Quad 2-Input NOR Gate
4002B	Dual 4-Input NOR Gate
4025B	Triple 3-Input NOR Gate

OR Gates

| 4071B | Quad 2-Input OR Gate |

Inverters and Buffers

4049B	Hex Inverting Buffer
4050B	Hex Non-Inverting Buffer
4069UB	Hex Inverter
40097B	3-State Hex Non-Inverting Buffer
40098B	3-State Hex Inverting Buffer

Complex Gates

4007UB	Dual Complementary Pair Plus Inverter
4030B	Quad Exclusive-OR Gate
4070B	Quad Exclusive-OR Gate
4086B	4-Wide, 2-Input AND-OR-INVERT Gate
4093B	Quad 2-Input NAND Schmitt Trigger
40014B	Hex Schmitt Trigger

Flip Flops

4013B	Dual D Flip-Flop
4027B	Dual JK Flip-Flop
4076B	Quad D Flip-Flop with 3-State Output
40174B	Hex D Flip-Flop
40175B	Quad D Flip-Flop

Memories

4703B	FIFO Buffer Memory
4710B	Register Stack 16 × 4 Bit RAM with 3-State Output Register
4720B	256-Bit RAM with 3-State Output
4725B	64-Bit RAM with 3-State Output
6508B	1024-Bit (1024 × 1) CMOS RAM with 3-State Ouput

Frequency Generator

4702B	Programmable Bit Rate Generator

Multivibrators, Phase-Locked Loops, Timers

4046B	Micropower Phase-Locked Loop
4047B	Low-Power Monostable/Astable Multivibrator
4528B	Dual Retriggerable Resettable Monostable Multivibrator
4722B	ProgrammableTimer/Counter

3. TTL IC NUMERICAL INDEX

Type Number	Function
54/7400	Quad 2-Input NAND Gate
54/7401	Quad 2-Input NAND Gate (Open Collector)
54/7402	Quad 2-Input NOR Gate
54/7403	Quad 2-Input NAND Gate (Open Collector)
54/7404	Hex Inverter
54/7405	Hex Inverter (Open Collector)
54/7408	Quad 2-Input AND Gate
54/7409	Quad 2-Input AND Gate(Open Collector)
54/7410	Triple 3-Input NAND Gate
54/7411	Triple 3-Input AND Gate
54/7412	Triple 3-Input NAND Gate (Open Collector)
54/7413	Dual 4-Input NAND Schmitt Trigger
54/7414	Hex Schmitt Trigger Inverter
54/7415	Triple 3-Input AND Gate (Open Collector)
54/7418	Dual 4-Input NAND Schmitt Trigger
54/7419	Hex Schmitt Trigger Inverter
54/7420	Dual 4-Input NAND Gate
54/7421	Dual 4-Input AND Gate
54/7422	Dual 4-Input NAND Gate (Open Collector)
54/7424	Quad 2-Input NAND Schmitt Trigger
54/7426	Quad 2-Input NAND Buffer (Open Collector)
54/7427	Trimple 3-Input NOR Gate
54/7428	Quad 2-Input NOR Buffer
54/7430	8-Input NAND Gate
54/7432	Quad 2-Input OR Gate
54/7433	Quad 2-Input NOR Buffer (Open Collector)
54/7437	Quad 2-Input NAND Buffer
54/7438	Quad 2-Input NAND Buffer (Open Collector)
54/7440	Dual 4-Input NAND Buffer
54/7442	1-of-10 Decoder
54/7451	Dual 2-Wide 2-Input/3-Input AND-OR-INVERT Gate
54/7454	2-3-3-2-Input AND-OR-INVERT Gate

54/7455	2-Wide 4-Input AND-OR-INVERT Gate
54/7473A	Dual JK Negative Edge-Triggered Flip Flop
54/7474A	Dual D-Type Positive Edge-Triggered Flip-Flop
54/7475	4-Bit D Latch
54/7476A	Dual JK Flip-Flop with Set and Clear
54/7478A	Dual JK Flip-Flop with Preset
54/7483A	4-Bit Full Adder with Fast Carry
54/7485	4-Bit Magnitude Comparator
54/7486	Quad 2-Input Exclusive OR Gate
54/7490	Decade Counter
54/7491	8-Bit Shift Register Serial-In Serial-Out
54/7492	Divide-by-12 Counter
54/7493	4-Bit Binary Counter
54/7495	4-Bit Shift Register
54/7496	5-Bit Shift Register
54/74107A	Dual JK Flip-Flop with Clear
54/74109	Dual JK Positive Edge-Triggered Flip-Flop
54/74109A	Dual JK Positive Edge-Triggered Flip-Flop
54/74112A	Dual JK Negative Edge-Triggered Flip-Flop
54/74113	Dual JK Negative Edge-Triggered Flip-Flop
54/74113A	Dual JK Negative Edge-Triggered Flip-Flop
54/74114	Dual JK Negative Edge-Triggered Flip-Flop
54/74114A	Dual JK Negative Edge-Triggered Flip-Flop
54/74122	Retriggerable Monostable Multivibrators
54/74123	Dual Retriggerable Monostable Multivibrators
54/74125	Quad 3-State Buffer (LOW Enable)
54/74125A	Quad 3-State Buffer (LOW Enable)
54/74126	Quad 3-State Buffer (HIGH Enable)
54/74126A	Quad 3-State Buffer (HIGH Enable)
54/74132	Quad 3-Input Schmitt Trigger NAND Gate
54/74133	13-Input NAND Gate
54/74136	Quad 2-Input Exclusive OR Gate (Open Collector)
54/74138	1-of-8 Decoder/Demultiplexer
54/74139	Dual 1-of-4 Decoder/Demultiplexer
54/74145	1-of-10 Decoder/Driver (Open Collector)
54/74147	10-Line to 4-Line Priority Encoder
54/74148	8-Input to 3-Line Priority Encoder
54/74151	8-Input to 3-Line Priority Encoder
54/74152	8-Input Multiplexer
54/74153	Dual 4-Input Multiplexer
54/74154	4-Line-to-16-Line Decoders/Demultiplexers
54/74155	Dual 1-of-4 Decoder/Demultiplexer
54/74156	Dual 1-of-4 Decoder/Demultiplexer (Open Collector)
54/74157	Quad 2-Input Multiplexer (Non Inverting)
54/74158	Quad 2-Input Multiplexer (inverting)
54/74160	BCD Decade Counter, Asynchronous Reset
54/74160A	BCD Decade Counter, Asynchronous Reset
54/74161	4-Bit Binary Counter, Asynchronous Reset
54/74161A	4-Bit Binary Counter, Asynchronous Reset
54/74162	BCD Decade Counter, Synchronous Reset
54/74162A	BCD Decade Counter, Synchronous Reset
54/74163	4-Bit Binary Counter, Synchronous Reset
54/74163A	4-Bit Binary Counter, Synchronous Reset
54/74164	8-Bit Shift Register (Serial-In Parallel-Out)
54/74166	8-Bit Shift Register (Parallel-In Serial-Out)
54/74168	Up/Down Decade Counter
54/74169	Up/Down Binary Counter
54/74170	4 × 4 Register File (Open Collector)

Contd...

Type Number	Function
54/74173A	4-Bit D-Type Register (3-State)
54/74174	Hex D-Type Flip-Flop with Clear
54/74175	Quad D-Type Flip-Flop with Clear
54/74181	4-Bit ALU
54/74183	Dual Carry-Save Full Adder
54/74190	Presettable BCD/Decade Up/Down Counter
54/74191	Presettable 4-Bit Binary Up/Down Counter
54/74192	Presettable BCD/Decade Up/Down Counter
54/74193	Presettable 4-Bit Binary Up/Down Counter
54/74194A	4-Bit Binary Up/Down Counter
54/74195A	4-Bit Shift Register
54/74196	Decade Counter
54/74197	4-Bit Binary Counter
54/74221	Dual Monostable Multivibrator
54/74240	Octal Inverting Bus/Line Driver (3-State)
54/74241	Octal Bus Line Driver (3-State)
54/74242	Quad Inverging Bus Transceiver (3-State)
54/74243	Quad Non Inverting Bus Transceiver (3-State)
54/74244	Octal Non Inverting Driver (3-State)
54/74245	Octal Non Inverting Bus Transceiver (3-State)
54/74247	BCD to 7-Segment Decoder/Driver (Open Collector)
54/74248	BCD to 7-Segment Decoder/Driver with pull Ups
54/74251	8-Input Multiplexer (3-State)
54/74253	Dual 4-Input Multiplexer (3-State)
54/74256	Dual 4-Input Addressable Latch
54/74257	Dual 2-Input Multiplexer (3-State)
54/74257A	Dual 2-Input Multiplexer (3-State)
54/74258	Dual 2-Input Multiplexer (3-State)
54/74258A	Dual 2-Input Multiplexer (3-State)
54/74259	8-Bit Addressable Latch
54/74260	Dual 5-Input NOR Gate
54/74266	Quad 2-Input Exclusive NOR Gate (Open Collector)
54/74273	OctalD-Type Flip-Flop with Master Reset
54/74279	Quad set-Reset Latch
54/74280	9-Bit Odd/Even Parity Generator/Checker
54/74283	4-Bit Binary Full Adder
54/74290	Decade Counter
54/74293	4-Bit Binary Counter
54/74295A	4-Bit Shift Register (3-State)
54/74298	Quad 2-Input Multiplexer with Output Latches
54/74299	8-Bit Shift/Storage Register (3-State)
54/74322A	8-Bit Shift Register with sign extended (3-State)
54/74323	8-Bit Shift/Storage Register (3-State)
54/74348	8-Input to 3 Line Priority Encoder (3-State)
54/74352	Dual 4-Input Multiplexer
54/74353	Dual 4-Input Multiplexer
54/74365A	Hex Buffer with Common Enable (3-State)
54/74366A	Hex Inverter Buffer with Common Enable (3-State)
54/74367A	Hex Buffer, 4-Bit and 2-Bit (3-State)
54/74368A	Hex Inverter, Buffer 4-Bit and 2-Bit (3-State)
54/74373	Octal Transparent Latch (3-State)
54/74374	Octal D-Type Flip-Flop (3-State)
54/74377	Octal D-Type Flip-Flop with Common Enable
54/74378	Hex D-Type Flip-Flop with Enable
54/74379	4-Bit D-Type Flip-Flop with Enable

54/74386	Quad 2-Input Exclusive OR Gate
54/74390	Dual Decade Counter
54/74393	Dual 4-Bit Binary Counter
54/74395	4-Bit Shift Register (3-State)
54/74395A	4-Bit Shift Register (3-State)
54/74398	Quad 2-Input Multiplexer with Output Register
54/74399	Quad 2-Input Multiplexer with Output Register
54/74465	Octal Buffer Gated Enable-inverted (3-State)
54/74490	Dual Decade Counter
54/74533	Octal Transparent Latch (3-State)
54/74534	Octal D-Type Flip-Flop (3-State)
54/74540	Octal Inverting Buffer/Line Driver (3-State)
54/74541	Octal Buffer/Line Driver (3-State)
54/74568	Decade Up/Down Counter (3-State)
54/74569	Binary Up/Down Counter (3-State)
54/74573	Octal D-Type Latch (3-State)
54/74574	Octal D-Type Flip-Flop (3-State)
54/74640	Octal Bus Transceiver (3-State)
54/74641	Octal Non Inverting Bus Transceiver (3-State)
54/74645	Octal Non Inverting Bus Transceiver (3-State)
54/74670	4 × 4 Register File (3-State)
54/74682	8-Bit Magnitude Comparator (3-State)
7641	512 × 8 PROM
7643	1K × 4 PROM
7681	1K × 8 PROM
7685	2K × 4 PROM
7689	2K × 4 PROM
76161	2K × 8 PROM
93415	1K × 4 Static RAM
76422	256 × 4 Static RAM
76425	1K × 4 Static RAM
76478	256 × 9 Static RAM
76479	256 × 9 Static RAM

4. TTL IC FUNCTIONAL INDEX

Function	Device
AND Gates	
Quad 2-Input AND Gate	54/7408
Quad 2-Input AND Gate (Open Collector)	54/7409
Triple 3-Input AND Gate	54/7411
Triple 3-Input AND Gate (Open Collector)	54/7415
Dual 4-Input AND Gate	54/7421
OR Gate	
Quad 2-Input OR Gate	54/7432
NAND Gates	
Quad 2-Input NAND Gate	54/7400
Quad 2-Input NAND Gate (Open Collector)	54/7401
Quad 2-Input NAND Gate (Open Collector)	54/7403
Triple 3-Input NAND Gate	54/7410
Triple 3-Input NAND Gate (Open Collector)	54/7412
Dual 4-Input NAND Schmitt Trigger	54/7413
Dual 4-Input NAND Schmitt Trigger	54/7418
Dual 4-Input NAND Gate	54/7420
Dual 4-Input NAND Gate (Open Collector)	54/7422

Contd...

Function	Device
Quad 2-Input NANd Schmitt Trigger	54/7424
Quad 2-Input NANd Buffer (Open Collector)	54/7424
8-Input NAND Gate	54/7430
Quad 2-Input NAND Buffer	54/7437
Quad 2-Input NAND Buffer (Open Collector)	54/7438
Dual 4-Input NAND Buffer	54/7440
Quad 2-Input Schmitt Trigger NAND Gate	54/74132
13-Input NAND Gate	54/74133

NOR Gate

Quad 2-Input NOR Gate	54/7402
Triple 3-Input NOR Gate	54/7427
Quad 2-Input NOR Buffer	54/7428
Quad 2-Input NOR Buffer (Open Collector)	54/7433
Dual 5-Input NOR Gate	54/74260

EX OR

Quad 2-Input Exclusive OR Gate	54/7486
Quad 2-Input Exclusive OR Gate (Open Collector)	54/74136
Quad 2-Input Exclusive OR Gate	54/7386

EX NOR

Quad 2-Input Exclusive NOR Gate (Open Collector)	54/74266

NOT

Hex Inverter	54/7404
Hex Inverter (Open Collector)	54/7405
Hex Schmitt Trigger Inverter	54/7414
Hex Schmitt Trigger Inverter	54/7419

AND-OR-INVERT

Dual 2-Wide 2-Input/3-Input AND-OR-INVERT Gate	54/7451
2-3-3-2-Input AND-OR-INVERT	54/7454
2-Wide 4-Input AND-OR-INVERT Gate	54/7455

Buffers

Quad 3-State Buffer (LOW Enable)	54/74125
Quad 3-State Buffer (LOW Enable)	54/74125A
Quad 3-State Buffer (HIGH Enable)	54/74126
Quad 3-State Buffer (HIGH Enable)	54/74126A
Octal Inverting Bus/Line Driver (3-State)	54/74240
Octal Bus Line Driver (3-State)	54/74241
Quad Inverting Bus Transceiver (3-State)	54/74242
Quad Non Inverting Bus Transceiver (3-State)	54/74243
Octal Non Inverting Driver (3-State)	54/74244
Octal Non Inverting Bus Transceiver (3-State)	54/74245
Hex Buffers with Common Enable (3-State)	54/74365A
Hex Inverter with Common Enable (3-State)	54/74366A
Hex Buffer, 4-Bit and 2-Bit (3-State)	54/74367A
Hex Inverting Buffer, 4-Bit and 2-Bit (3-State)	54/74368A
Octal Buffer Gated Enable-Inverted (3-State)	54/74465
Octal Inverting Buffer/Line Driver (3-State)	54/74540
Octal Buffer/Line Driver (3-State)	54/74541
Octal Bus Transceiver (3-State)	54/74640
Octal Non Inverting Bus Transceiver (3-State)	54/74641
Octal Non Inverting Bus Transceiver (3-State)	54/74645

Flip-Flops

Dual JK Negative Edge-Triggered Flip-Flop	54/7473A
Dual D-type Positive Edge-Triggered Flip-Flop	54/7474A
Dual JK Flip-Flop with Set and Clear	54/7476A
Dual JK Flip-Flop with Reset	54/7478A
Dual JK Flip-Flop with Clear	54/74107A
Dual JK Positive Edge-Triggered Flip-Flop	54/74109
Dual JK Positive Edge-Triggered Flip-Flop	54/74109A
Dual JK Negative Edge-Triggered Flip-Flop	54/74112A
Dual JK Negative Edge-Triggered Flip-Flop	54/74113
Dual JK Negative Edge-Triggered Flip-Flop	54/74114
Dual JK Negative Edge-Triggered Flip-Flop	54/74114A

Arithmetic Operators

4-Bit Full Adder with Fast Carry	54/7483A
4-Bit ALU	54/74181
Dual Carry-Save Full Adder	54/74183
4-Bit Binary Adder	54/74283

Counters

Decade Counter	54/7490
Divide-by-12 Counter	54/7492
4-Bit Binary Counter	54/7493
BCD Decade Counter, Asynchronous Reset	54/74160
BCD Decade Counter, Asynchronous Reset	54/74160A
4-Bit Binary Counter, Asynchronous Reset	54/74161
4-Bit Binary Counter, Asynchronous Reset	54/74161A
BCD Decade Counter, Synchronous Reset	54/74162
BCD Decade Counter, Synchronous Reset	54/74162A
4-Bit Binary Counter, Synchronous Reset	54/74163
4-Bit Binary Counter, Synchronous Reset	54/74163A
Up/Down Decade Counter	54/74168
Up/Down Binary Counter	54/74169
Presettable BCD/Decade Up/Down Counter	54/74190
Presettable 4-Bit Binary Up/Down Counter	54/74191
Presettable BCD/Decade Up/Down Counter	54/74192
Presettable 4-Bit Binary Up/Down Counter	54/74193
Decade Counter	54/74196
4-Bit Binary Counter	54/74197
Decade Counter	54/74290
4-Bit Counter	54/74293
Dual Decade Counter	54/74390
Dual 4-Bit Binary Counter	54/74393
Dual Decade Counter	54/74490
Decade/Up/Down Counter (3-State)	54/74568
Binary/Up/Down Counter (3-State)	54/74569

Decoders/Demultiplexers

1-of-10 Decoder	54/7442
1-of-8 Decoder/Demultiplexer	54/74138
Dual 1-of-4 Decoder/Demultiplexer	54/74139
1-of-10 Decoder/Driver (Open Collector)	54/74145
4 Line-to-16-Line Decoder/Demultiplexer	54/74154
Dual 1-of-4 Decoder/Demultiplexer	54/74155
Dual 1-of-4 Decoder/Demultiplexer (Open Collector)	54/74156
Dual 4-Bit Addressable Latch	54/74256
8-Bit Addressable Latch	54/74259

Contd...

Function	Device
Multiplexers	
8-Input Multiplexer	54/74151
8-Input Multiplexer	54/74152
Dual 4-Input Multiplexer	54/74153
Quad 2-Input Multiplexer (Non Inverting)	54/74157
Quad 2-Input Multiplexer (inverting)	54/74158
8-Input Multiplexer (3-State)	54/74251
Dual 4-Input Multiplexer (3-State)	54/74253
Quad 2-Input Multiplexer (3-State)	54/74257
Quad 2-Input Multiplexer (3-State)	54/74257A
Quad 2-Input Multiplexer (3-State)	54/74258
Quad 2-Input Multiplexer (3-State)	54/74258A
Dual 2-Input Multiplexer with Output Latches	54/74298
Dual 4-Input Multiplexer	54/7435
Dual 4-Input Multiplexer	54/74353
Quad 2-Input Multiplexer with Output Register	54/74398
Quad 2-Input Multiplexer with Output Register	54/74399
Latches and Flip-Flops	
4-Bit D-type Latch	54/7475
4 × 4 Register File (Open Collector)	54/74170
Hex D-Type Flip-Flop with Clear	54/74174
Quad D-Type Flip-Flop with Clear	54/74175
4-Bit Binary Counter	54/74197
Daul 4-Bit Addressable Latch	54/74256
8-Bit Addressable Latch	54/74259
Octal D-Type Flip-Flop with Master Reset	54/74273
Quad Set-Reset Latch	54/74279
Octal Transparent Latch (3-State)	54/74373
Octal D-Type Flip-Flop (3-State)	54/74374
Octal D-Type Flip-Flop with Common Enable	54/74377
Hex D-Type Flip-flop with Enable	54/74378
4-Bit D-Type Flip-Flop with Enable	54/74379
Octal Transparent Latch (3-State)	54/74533
Octal D-Type Flip-Flop (3-State)	54/74534
Octal D-Type Flip-Flop (3-State)	54/74573
Octal D-Type Flip-Flop (3-State)	54/74574
4 × 4 Register File (3-State)	54/74670
Registers	
8-Bit Shift Register Serial-In Serial-Out	54/7491
4-Bit Shift Register	54/7495B
5-Bit Shift Register	54/7496
8-Bit Shift Register Serial-In Parallel Out	54/74164
8-Bit Shift Register Parallel-In Serial Out	54/749166
4 × 4 Register File (Open Collector)	54/749170
4-Bit Right/Left Shift Register	54/74194A
4-Bit Shift Register	54/74195A
4-Bit Shift Register (3-State)	54/74295A
8-Bit Shift/Storage Register (3-State)	54/74299
8-Bit Shift Register with Sign Extend (3-State)	54/74322A
8-Bit Shift/Storage Register (3-State)	54/74323
4-Bit Shift Register (3-State)	54/74395
4-Bit Shift Register (3-State)	54/74395A
4 × 4 Register File (3-State)	54/74670

Comparators
4-Bit Magnitude Comparator	54/7485
8-Bit Magnitude Comparator (3-State)	54/74682

Multivibrators
Retriggerable Monostable Multivibrator	54/74122
Dual Retriggerable Monostable Multivibrator	54/74123
Dual Monostable Multivibrator	54/74221

Priority Encoders
10-Line to 4-Line Priority Encoder	54/74147
8-Input to 3-Line Priority Encoder	54/74148
8-Input to 3-Line Priority Encoder (3-State)	54/74348

Display Decoder/Drivers (BCD to Seven Segment)
BCD to 7-Segment Decoder/Driver (Open Collector)	54/74247
BCD to 7-Segment Decoder/Driver with Pull-Ups	54/74248

Parity Generator Checkers
9-Bit Odd/Even Parity Generator/Checker	54/74280

Memories
256 × 4 Static RAM	93422, 93L422
256 × 9 Static RAM	93478, 93479
1K × 4 Static RAM	93415, 93425
512 × 8 PROM	7641
1K × 4 PROM	7643
1K × 8 PROM	7681
2K × 4 PROM	7685, 7689
2K × 8 PROM	76161

Pin Connection Diagrams And Functional Tables Of Popular Type Numbers

TTL-Series Devices

Quad 2-Input NAND

nA, nB = Data Inputs
nY = Data Outputs

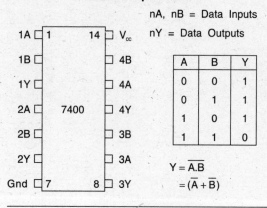

A	B	Y
0	0	1
0	1	1
1	0	1
1	1	0

$$Y = \overline{A.B}$$
$$= (\overline{A} + \overline{B})$$

Quad 2-Input NAND (Open Collector)

nA, nB = Data Inputs
nY = Data Outputs

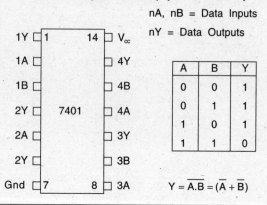

A	B	Y
0	0	1
0	1	1
1	0	1
1	1	0

$$Y = \overline{A.B} = (\overline{A} + \overline{B})$$

Quad 2-Input NOR

nA, nB = Data Inputs
nY = Data Outputs

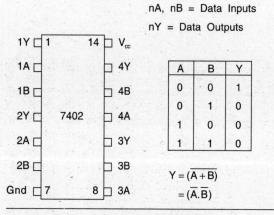

A	B	Y
0	0	1
0	1	0
1	0	0
1	1	0

$$Y = \overline{(A + B)}$$
$$= (\overline{A}.\overline{B})$$

Hex Inverter

nA = Data Inputs
nY = Data Outputs

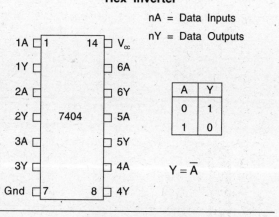

A	Y
0	1
1	0

$$Y = \overline{A}$$

Quad 2-Input AND

nA, nB = Data Inputs
nY = Data Outputs

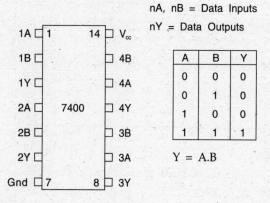

A	B	Y
0	0	0
0	1	0
1	0	0
1	1	1

$$Y = A.B$$

Triple 3-Input NAND

nA, nB, nC = Data Inputs
nY = Data Outputs

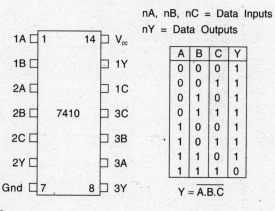

A	B	C	Y
0	0	0	1
0	0	1	1
0	1	0	1
0	1	1	1
1	0	0	1
1	0	1	1
1	1	0	1
1	1	1	0

$$Y = \overline{A.B.C}$$

116

Quad 2-NOR Buffer

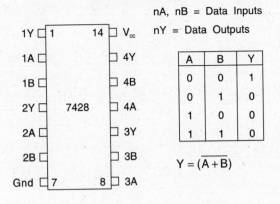

nA, nB = Data Inputs
nY = Data Outputs

A	B	Y
0	0	1
0	1	0
1	0	0
1	1	0

$Y = \overline{(A+B)}$

Quad 2-Input OR

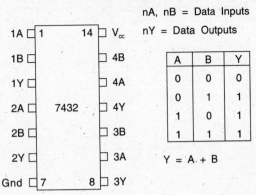

nA, nB = Data Inputs
nY = Data Outputs

A	B	Y
0	0	0
0	1	1
1	0	1
1	1	1

$Y = A + B$

BCD-to-Decimal Decoder (Open Collector Outputs)

A through D : Data Inputs (A is LSB)
0 though 9 : Decoded Outputs (Active LOW)

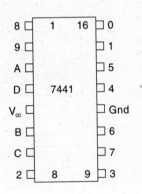

D	C	B	A	0	1	2	3	4	5	6	7	8	9
0	0	0	0	0	1	1	1	1	1	1	1	1	1
0	0	0	1	1	0	1	1	1	1	1	1	1	1
0	0	1	0	1	1	0	1	1	1	1	1	1	1
0	0	1	1	1	1	1	0	1	1	1	1	1	1
0	1	0	0	1	1	1	1	0	1	1	1	1	1
0	1	0	1	1	1	1	1	1	0	1	1	1	1
0	1	1	0	1	1	1	1	1	1	0	1	1	1
0	1	1	1	1	1	1	1	1	1	1	0	1	1
1	0	0	0	1	1	1	1	1	1	1	1	0	1
1	0	0	1	1	1	1	1	1	1	1	1	1	0
Over range													
1	0	1	0	0	1	1	1	1	1	1	1	1	1
1	0	1	1	1	0	1	1	1	1	1	1	1	1
1	1	0	0	1	1	0	1	1	1	1	1	1	1
1	1	0	1	1	1	1	0	1	1	1	1	1	1
1	1	1	0	1	1	1	1	0	1	1	1	1	1
1	1	1	1	1	1	1	1	1	0	1	1	1	1

BCD-to-Decimal Decoder

A through D : Data Inputs (A is LSB)
0 through 9 : Decoded Outputs (Active LOW)

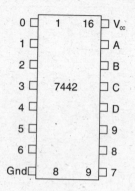

D	C	B	A	0	1	2	3	4	5	6	7	8	9
0	0	0	0	0	1	1	1	1	1	1	1	1	1
0	0	0	1	1	0	1	1	1	1	1	1	1	1
0	0	1	0	1	1	0	1	1	1	1	1	1	1
0	0	1	1	1	1	1	0	1	1	1	1	1	1
0	1	0	0	1	1	1	1	0	1	1	1	1	1
0	1	0	1	1	1	1	1	1	0	1	1	1	1
0	1	1	0	1	1	1	1	1	1	0	1	1	1
0	1	1	1	1	1	1	1	1	1	1	0	1	1
1	0	0	0	1	1	1	1	1	1	1	1	0	1
1	0	0	1	1	1	1	1	1	1	1	1	1	0
							Invalid						
1	0	1	0	1	1	1	1	1	1	1	1	1	1
1	0	1	1	1	1	1	1	1	1	1	1	1	1
1	1	0	0	1	1	1	1	1	1	1	1	1	1
1	1	0	1	1	1	1	1	1	1	1	1	1	1
1	1	1	0	1	1	1	1	1	1	1	1	1	1
1	1	1	1	1	1	1	1	1	1	1	1	1	1

BCD-to-7 Segment Decoder (Active LOW Open Collector Outputs)

A through D : Data Inputs (A is LSB)
a through g : Decoded Outputs (Active LOW)
LT : Lamp Test Input
RBI : Ripple Blanking Input
BI/RBO : Blanking Input/Ripple Blanking Output

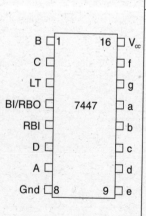

Function	LT	RBI	D	C	B	A	BI/RBO	a	b	c	d	e	f	g
0	1	1	0	0	0	0	1	0	0	0	0	0	0	1
1	1	X	0	0	0	1	1	1	0	0	1	1	1	1
2	1	X	0	0	1	0	1	0	0	1	0	0	1	0
3	1	X	0	0	1	1	1	0	0	0	0	1	1	0
4	1	X	0	1	0	0	1	1	0	0	1	1	0	0
5	1	X	0	1	0	1	1	0	1	0	0	1	0	0
6	1	X	0	1	1	0	1	1	1	0	0	0	0	0
7	1	X	0	1	1	1	1	0	0	0	1	1	1	1
8	1	X	1	0	0	0	1	0	0	0	0	0	0	0
9	1	X	1	0	0	1	1	0	0	0	1	1	0	0
10	1	X	1	0	1	0	1	1	1	1	0	0	1	0
11	1	X	1	0	1	1	1	1	1	0	0	1	1	0
12	1	X	1	1	0	0	1	1	0	1	1	0	0	0
13	1	X	1	1	0	1	1	0	1	1	0	1	0	0
14	1	X	1	1	1	0	1	1	1	1	0	0	0	0
15	1	X	1	1	1	1	1	1	1	1	1	1	1	1
Blank	X	X	X	X	X	X	0	1	1	1	1	1	1	1
Ripple Blank	1	0	0	0	0	0	0	1	1	1	1	1	1	1
Lamp Test	0	X	X	X	X	X	1	0	0	0	0	0	0	0

Dual J-K Flip-Flop

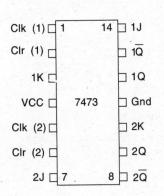

Clk (1)	1		14	1J
Clr (1)				$\overline{1Q}$
1K				1Q
VCC		7473		Gnd
Clk (2)				2K
Clr (2)				2Q
2J	7		8	$\overline{2Q}$

J : J-Input
K : K-Input
Clk : Clock Input
Clr : clear Input (Active LOW)
Q, $\overline{Q}$: Outputs
Q0 : Q-Output prior to the occurence of clock's negative going edge
7473 is available in two triggering schemes
(i) Negative Egde Triggered
(ii) Master Slave Type

Clr	Clk	J	K	Q	$\overline{Q}$
0	X	X	X	0	1
1	↓	0	0	Q_0	$\overline{Q_0}$
1	↓	1	0	1	0
1	↓	0	1	0	1
1	↓	1	1	Toggle	
1	1	X	X	Q_0	$\overline{Q_0}$

M/S					
Clr	Clk	J	K	Q	$\overline{Q}$
0	X	X	X	0	1
1	⊓	0	0	Q_0	$\overline{Q_0}$
1	⊓	1	0	1	0
1	⊓	0	1	0	1
1	⊓	1	1	Toggle	

Dual J-K Flip-Flop

1Clr	1		14	V_{cc}
1D				2Clr
1Clk				2D
1PR		7474		2Clk
1Q				2PR
$\overline{1Q}$				$\overline{2Q}$
Gnd	7		8	2Q

nD : Data Input
nClk : Clock Input
nPR : Preset Input
nClr : Clear Input
Q, $\overline{Q}$: Outputs

PR	Clr	Clk	D	Q	$\overline{Q}$
0	1	X	X	1	0
1	0	X	X	0	1
0	0	X	X	unstable	
1	1	↑	1	1	0
1	1	↑	0	0	1
1	1	0	X	Q_0	$\overline{Q_0}$

Q0 = State of Q prior to occurence of clock

Dual 2-Bit D-Type Latch

$\overline{1Q_0}$	1		16	$1Q_0$
1D0				1Q1
1D1				$\overline{1Q_1}$
1G		7475		2G
V_{cc}				Gnd
2D0				$2\overline{Q_0}$
2D1				$2Q_0$
$2\overline{Q1}$	8		9	2Q1

nD0, nD1 : Data Inputs
nG : Latch Enable Inputs
nQ_0, nQ1, $\overline{nQ_0}$, $n\overline{Q1}$: Outputs

D	G	Q	$\overline{Q}$
0	1	0	1
1	1	1	0
X	0	Q_0	$\overline{Q_0}$

Q_0 = Status of prior to occurence of negative going edge at G-input

4-Bit Full Adder

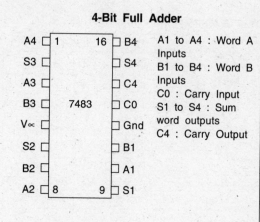

A1 to A4 : Word A Inputs
B1 to B4 : Word B Inputs
C0 : Carry Input
S1 to S4 : Sum word outputs
C4 : Carry Output

4-Bit Magnitude Comparator

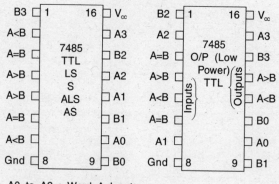

A0 to A3 : Word A Inputs
B0 to B3 : WOrd B Inputs

Quad 2-input EX-OR

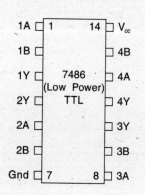

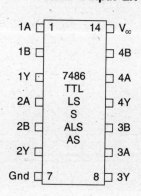

A	B	Y
0	0	0
0	1	1
1	0	1
1	1	0

$\overline{A}.B + A.\overline{B}$

BCD Counter (Decade)

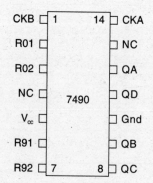

R01	R02	R91	R92	QD	QC	QB	QA
1	1	0	X	0	0	0	0
1	1	X	0	0	0	0	0
X	X	1	1	1	0	0	1
X	0	X	0	Count			
0	X	0	X	Count			
0	X	X	X	Count			
X	0	0	0	Count			

CKA : Clock for section A
CKB : Clock for section B, C and D
Q_A through Q_D : Outputs
R_{01}, R_{02} : Reset to '0' inputs
R_{91}, R_{92} : Reset to '9' inputs

Monostable Multivibrator (Positive and Negative Edge Triggered)

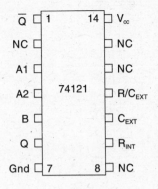

A1, A2 : Negative going trigger input
B : Positive going trigger input
R_{INT} : Connection to internal timing resistor
C_{EXT} : Connection for external timing capacitor
R/C_{ECT} : Connection for common point between external timing capacitor and reistor
Q, $\overline{Q}$: Outputs

A1	A2	B	Q	$\overline{Q}$
0	X	1	0	1
X	0	1	0	1
X	X	0	0	1
1	1	X	0	1
1	↓	1	⊓	⊔
↓	1	1	⊓	⊔
↓	↓	1	⊓	⊔
0	X	↓	⊓	⊔
X	0	↓	⊓	⊔

Retriggerable Monostable Multivibrator (Positive and Negative Triggered)

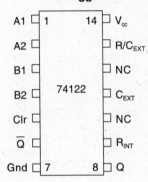

A1, A2 : Negative going trigger input
B : Positive going trigger input
R_{INT} : Connection to internal timing resistor
C_{EXT} : Connection for external timing capacitor
R/C_{EXT} : Connection for common point, between external timing capacitor and resistor
Q, $\overline{Q}$: Outputs

Clr	A1	A2	B1	B2	Q	$\overline{Q}$
0	X	X	X	X	0	1
X	1	1	X	X	0	1
X	X	X	0	X	0	1
X	X	X	X	0	0	1
1	0	X	↑	1	⊓	⊔
1	0	X	1	↑	⊓	⊔
1	X	0	↑	1	⊓	⊔
1	X	0	1	↑	⊓	⊔
1	1	↓	1	1	⊓	⊔
1	↓	↓	1	1	⊓	⊔
1	↓	1	1	1	⊓	⊔
↑	0	X	1	1	⊓	⊔
↑	X	0	1	1	⊓	⊔

Dual Retriggerable Monostable Multivibrator Multivibrator (Positive and Negative Triggered)

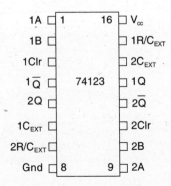

nA : Negative going trigger inputs
nB : Positive going trigger inputs
nC_{EXT} : Connection for external timing capacitor
nR/C_{EXT} : Connection for common point between external timing resistor and capacitor
nQ, $n\overline{Q}$: Outputs

1 : 16 Multiplexer

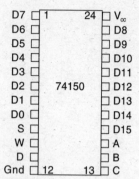

D0 through D15 : Data Inputs
W : Data Output (Active LOW)
A, B, C, D : Select Inputs
S : Strobe

D	C	B	A	S	W
X	X	X	X	1	1
0	0	0	0	0	$\overline{D0}$
0	0	0	1	0	$\overline{D_1}$
0	0	1	0	0	$\underline{D2}$
0	0	1	1	0	$\underline{D3}$
0	1	0	0	0	$\underline{D4}$
0	1	0	1	0	$\underline{D5}$
0	1	1	0	0	$\underline{D6}$
0	1	1	1	0	$\underline{D7}$
1	0	0	0	0	$\underline{D8}$
1	0	0	1	0	$\underline{D9}$
1	0	1	0	0	$\underline{D10}$
1	0	1	1	0	$\underline{D11}$
1	1	0	0	0	$\underline{D12}$
1	1	0	1	0	$\underline{D13}$
1	1	1	0	0	$\underline{D14}$
1	1	1	1	0	D15

8 : 1 Multiplexer (with strobe input)

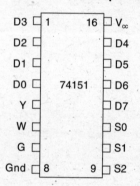

D0 through D7 : Data Inputs
Y : Data Output (Active HIGH)
W : Data Output (Active LOW)
S2, S1, S0 : Select Inputs
G : Strobe Input

G	S2	S1	S0	Y	W
1	X	X	X	0	$\underline{1}$
0	0	0	0	D0	$\underline{D0}$
0	0	0	1	D1	$\underline{D1}$
0	0	1	0	D2	$\underline{D2}$
0	0	1	1	D3	$\underline{D3}$
0	1	0	0	D4	$\underline{D4}$
0	1	0	1	D5	$\underline{D5}$
0	1	1	0	D6	$\underline{D6}$
0	1	1	1	D7	D7

4 : 16 Line Decoder

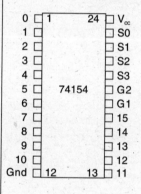

S0 through S3 : Select Inputs

0 through 15 : Data Outputs

G1, G2 : Strobe Inputs

BCD Decade Up-Counter

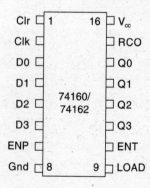

D0 through D3 : Preset Data Inputs
Q0 through Q3 : Data Outputs
RCO : Ripple Carry Output
Clk : Clock Input (Positive Edge Triggered)
LOAD : Preset Control (Synchronous, Active LOW)
Clr : Clear Input (Asynchronous, Active LOW) for 74160 and synchronous, Active LOW for 74162
ENP : Count Enable Parallel
ENT : Count Enable Trickle

74160

Clk	Clr	ENP	ENT	LOAD	Function
X	0	X	X	X	Clear
X	1	1	0	1	Count/RCO Disabled
X	1	0	1	1	Count Disabled
X	1	0	0	1	Count/RCO Disabled
-	1	X	X	0	LOAD
-	1	1	1	1	COUNT

74162

Clk	Clr	ENP	ENT	LOAD	Function
-	0	X	X	X	Clear
X	1	1	0	1	Count/RCO Disabled
X	1	0	1	1	Count Disabled
X	1	0	0	1	Count/RCO Disabled
-	1	X	X	0	LOAD
-	1	1	1	1	COUNT

4-Bit Binary Up-Counter

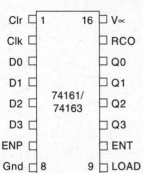

D0 through D3 : Preset Data Inputs
Q0 through Q3 : Data Outputs
RCO : Ripple Carry Output
Clk : Clock Input (Positive Edge Triggered)
LOAD : Preset Control (Synchronous, Active LOW)
Clr : Clear Input (Asynchronous, Active LOW for 74i61 an synchronous, Active LOW for 74163)
ENP : Count Enable Parallel
ENT : Count Enable Trickle

741614

Clk	Clr	ENP	ENP	LOAD	Function
X	0	X	X	X	Clear
X	1	1	0	1	Count/RCO Disabled
X	1	0	1	1	Count Disabled
↑	1	X	X	0	LOAD
↑	1	1	1	1	COUNT

74163

Clk	Clr	ENP	ENT	LOAD	Funtion
*	0	X	X	X	Clear
X	1	1	0	1	Count/RCO Disabled
X	1	0	1	1	Count Disabled
X	1	0	0	1	Count/RCO Disabled
↑	1	X	X	0	LOAD
↑	1	1	1	1	COUNT

4-Bit 3-State D-Type Flip-Flop

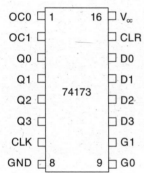

D0 through D3 : Data inputs
Q0 through Q3 : Data Outputs
CLK : Clock Input (Positive Edge Trigger)
CLR : Clear Input (Active HIGH)
G1, G0 : Latch Enables
OC1, OC0 : 3-State Output Control

OC0	OC1	G0	G1	CLR	CLK	D	Q
1	X	X	X	X	X	X	Z
0	1	X	X	X	X	X	Z
0	0	X	X	1	X	X	0
0	0	X	X	0	X	X	Q_0
0	0	1	X	0	↑	X	Q_0
0	0	X	1	0	↑	X	Q_0
0	0	0	0	0	↑	0	0
0	0	0	0	0	↑	1	1

6-Bit D-Type Flip-Flop

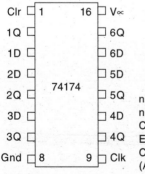

Clr	Clk	D	Q
0	X	X	0
1	↑	1	1
1	↑	0	0
1	0	X	Q_0

nD : Data Inputs
nD : Data Outputs
Clk : Clock (Positive Edge Trigger)
Clr : Clear Input (Active LOW)

4-Bits D-Type Flip-Flop
(Complementary Outputs)

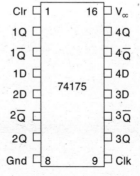

Clr	Clk	D	Q	Q
0	X	X	0	1
1	*	1	1	0
1	*	0	0	1
1	0	X	Q0	$\overline{Q_0}$

nD : Data Inputs
nQ, n$\overline{Q}$: Data Outputs
CLK : Clock (Positive Edge Trigger)
CLR : Clear Input (Active Low)

Up/Down Counter

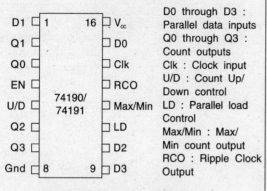

D0 through D3 : Parallel data inputs
Q0 through Q3 : Count outputs
Clk : Clock input
U/D : Count Up/Down control
LD : Parallel load Control
Max/Min : Max/Min count output
RCO : Ripple Clock Output

LD	EN	U/D	Clk	Function
1	0	0	↑	Count UP
1	0	1	↑	Count Down
0	X	X	X	Load
1	1	X	X	No Change

74190 : BCD
74191 : 4-Bit Binary

Up/Down Counter

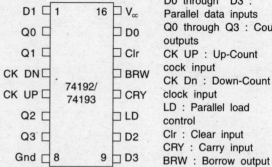

D0 through D3 : Parallel data inputs
Q0 through Q3 : Count outputs
CK UP : Up-Count cock input
CK Dn : Down-Count clock input
LD : Parallel load control
Clr : Clear input
CRY : Carry input
BRW : Borrow output

CKUP	CKDN	Clr	LD	Funtion
↑	1	0	1	Count UP
1	↑	0	1	Count DOWN
X	X	1	X	Clear
X	X	0	0	Load

74192 : BCD
74193 : 4-Bit Binary

BCD Counter (Divide-by-2/Divide-by-5)

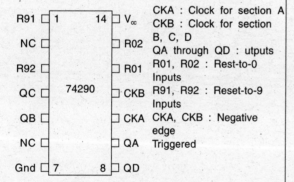

CKA : Clock for section A
CKB : Clock for section B, C, D
QA through QD : utputs
R01, R02 : Rest-to-0 Inputs
R91, R92 : Reset-to-9 Inputs
CKA, CKB : Negative edge Triggered

Q01	R02	R91	R92	QD	QC	QB	QA
1	1	0	X	0	0	0	0
1	1	X	0	0	0	0	0
X	X	1	1	1	0	0	1
X	0	X	0	COUNT			
0	X	0	X	COUNT			
0	X	X	0	COUNT			
X	0	0	X	COUNT			

4-Bit Binary Counter (Divide-2/Divide-by-8)

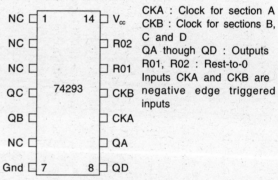

CKA : Clock for section A
CKB : Clock for sections B, C and D
QA though QD : Outputs
R01, R02 : Rest-to-0 Inputs CKA and CKB are negative edge triggered inputs

R01	R02	QD	QC	QB	QA
1	1	0	0	0	0
0	X	COUNT			
X	0	COUNT			

Dual BCD Ripple Counter

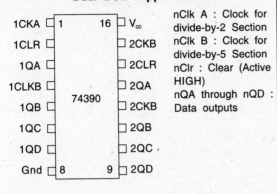

nClk A : Clock for divide-by-2 Section
nClk B : Clock for divide-by-5 Section
nClr : Clear (Active HIGH)
nQA through nQD : Data outputs

74390

1CKA	1	16 Vcc
1CLR		2CKB
1QA		2CLR
1CLKB		2QA
1QB		2CKB
1QC		2QB
1QD		2QC
Gnd	8	9 2QD

Dual 4-Bit Ripple Counter

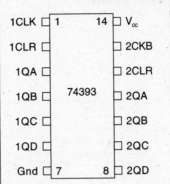

nCLK : clock inputs (negative dege trgger)
nCLK : Clear (Active HIGH)
nQA through nQD : Data outputs

74393

1CLK	1	14 Vcc
1CLR		2CKB
1QA		2CLR
1QB		2QA
1QC		2QB
1QD		2QC
Gnd	7	8 2QD

Octal D-Type Latch

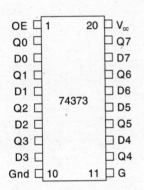

74373

OE	G	D	Q
0	1	1	1
0	1	0	0
0	0	X	Q_0
1	X	X	Z

D0 through D7 : Data inputs
Q0 through Q7 : Data outputs
G : Latch Enable (Active LOW)
OE : 3-State output enable (Active LOW)

8-Bit D-Type Flip Flop

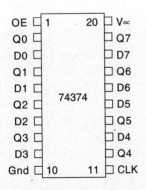

74374

OE	CLK	D	Q
0	↑	1	1
0	↑	0	0
0	0	X	Q_0
1	X	X	Z

D0 through D7 : Data inputs
Q0 through Q7 : Data outputs
CLK : Clock input (Positive Edge)
OE : 3-state output enable

125

CMOS-series ICs

NOR-Gate and Inverter

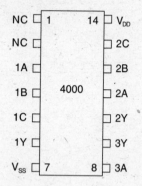

A	B	C	Y
0	0	0	1
0	0	1	0
0	1	0	0
0	1	1	0
1	0	0	0
1	0	1	0
1	1	0	0
1	1	1	0

1A, 1B, 1C : Data inputs for NOR Section-1
1Y : Data output for NOR Section-1
2A, 2B, 2C : Data inputs for NOR Section-2
2Y : Data Output for NOR Section-2
3A : Data input for inverter Section-3
3Y : Data output for inverter Section-3

A	Y
0	1
1	0

$$Y = \overline{A}$$

QUAD 2-input NOR

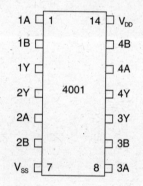

nA, nB : Data inputs
nY : Data outputs

A	B	Y
0	0	1
0	1	0
1	0	0
1	1	0

$$Y = \overline{(A + B)}$$

DUAL 4-input NOR

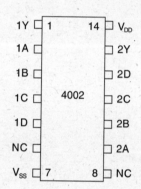

nA through nD : Data inputs
nY : Data outputs

D	C	B	A	Y
0	0	0	0	1
1	X	X	X	0
X	1	X	X	0
X	X	1	X	0
X	X	X	1	0

$$Y = \overline{(A + B + C + D)}$$

4-BIT ADDER

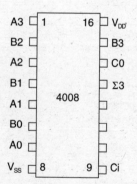

A0 through A3 : Word A input
B0 through B3 : Word B input
Σ0 through Σ3 : Sum output
Ci : Carry input
C0 : Carry output

Ci	B	A	C0	Σ
0	0	0	0	0
0	0	1	0	1
0	1	0	0	1
0	1	1	1	0
1	0	0	0	1
1	0	1	1	0
1	1	0	1	0
1	1	1	1	1

HEX INVERTING BUFFER

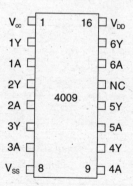

nA : Data inputs
nY : Data outputs

A	Y
0	1
1	0

$$Y = \overline{A}$$

NON INVERGING BUFFER

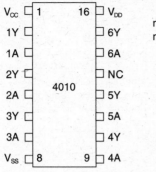

V_{CC}	1 16	V_{DD}
1Y		6Y
1A		6A
2Y	4010	NC
2A		5Y
3Y		5A
3A		4Y
V_{SS}	8 9	4A

nA : Data inputs
nY : Data outputs

A	Y
0	0
1	1

Y = A

QUAD 2-input NAND

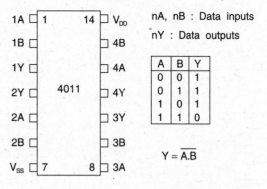

1A	1 14	V_{DD}
1B		4B
1Y		4A
2Y	4011	4Y
2A		3Y
2B		3B
V_{SS}	7 8	3A

nA, nB : Data inputs
nY : Data outputs

A	B	Y
0	0	1
0	1	1
1	0	1
1	1	0

$Y = \overline{A.B}$

DUAL 4-INPUT NAND

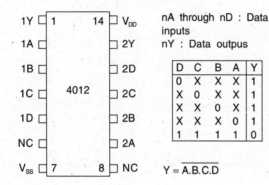

1Y	1 14	V_{DD}
1A		2Y
1B		2D
1C	4012	2C
1D		2B
NC		2A
V_{SS}	7 8	NC

nA through nD : Data inputs
nY : Data outpus

D	C	B	A	Y
0	X	X	X	1
X	0	X	X	1
X	X	0	X	1
X	X	X	0	1
1	1	1	1	0

$Y = \overline{A.B.C.D}$

DUAL D-TYPE FLIP FLOP

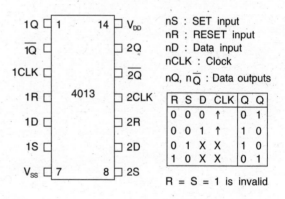

1Q	1 14	V_{DD}
$\overline{1Q}$		2Q
1CLK		$\overline{2Q}$
1R	4013	2CLK
1D		2R
1S		2D
V_{SS}	7 8	2S

nS : SET input
nR : RESET input
nD : Data input
nCLK : Clock
nQ, $n\overline{Q}$: Data outputs

R	S	D	CLK	Q	$\overline{Q}$
0	0	0	↑	0	1
0	0	1	↑	1	0
0	1	X	X	1	0
1	0	X	X	0	1

R = S = 1 is invalid

8-BIT SHIFT REGISTER

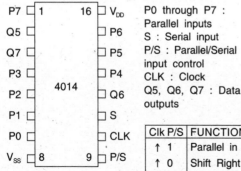

P7	1 16	V_{DD}
Q5		P6
Q7		P5
P3		P4
P2	4014	Q6
P1		S
P0		CLK
V_{SS}	8 9	P/S

P0 through P7 : Parallel inputs
S : Serial input
P/S : Parallel/Serial input control
CLK : Clock
Q5, Q6, Q7 : Data outputs

Clk	P/S	FUNCTION
↑	1	Parallel in
↑	0	Shift Right

8-BIT SHIFT REGISTER

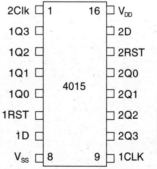

2Clk	1 16	V_{DD}
1Q3		2D
1Q2		2RST
1Q1		2Q0
1Q0	4015	2Q1
1RST		2Q2
1D		2Q3
V_{SS}	8 9	1CLK

nD : Serial Data input
nQ0 though nQ3 : Parallel Data outputs
nRST : RESET
nCLK : Clock

CLK	RST	FUNCTION
↑	0	Shift Right
X	1	Clear

DECADE COUNTER

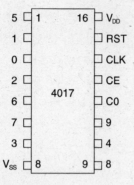

CLK : Clock
0 through 9 : Decimal outputs
RST : RESET
CE : Clock Enable
CO : Clock Output

Function Table

RST	CE	CLK	Function
1	X	X	Reset to '0'
0	0	↑	Count
0	1	↓	Count

Count Sequence Table

0	1	2	3	4	5	6	7	8	9	C0
1	0	0	0	0	0	0	0	0	0	1
0	1	0	0	0	0	0	0	0	0	1
0	0	1	0	0	0	0	0	0	0	1
0	0	0	1	0	0	0	0	0	0	1
0	0	0	0	1	0	0	0	0	0	1
0	0	0	0	0	1	0	0	0	0	0
0	0	0	0	0	0	1	0	0	0	0
0	0	0	0	0	0	0	1	0	0	0
0	0	0	0	0	0	0	0	1	0	0
0	0	0	0	0	0	0	0	0	1	0

14-STAGE BINARY COUNTER

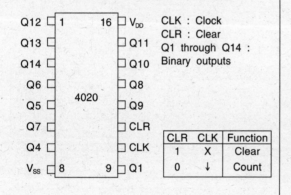

CLK : Clock
CLR : Clear
Q1 through Q14 : Binary outputs

CLR	CLK	Function
1	X	Clear
0	↓	Count

8-BIT SHIFT REGISTER

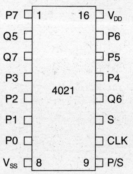

P0 through P7 : Parallel Data Inputs
S : Serial Data input
CLK : Clock
P/S : Parallel Serial Select
Q5, Q6, Q7 : Data outputs

Clk	P/S	Function
X	1	Parallel in
↑	0	Shift right

Dual J-K Flip-Flop

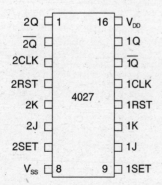

nJ, nK : J-K inputs
nSET : SET inputs
nRST : RESET inputs
nCLK : Clock
nQ, n$\overline{Q}$: Outputs

SET	RST	CLK	J	K	Q	$\overline{Q}$
1	0	X	X	X	1	0
0	1	X	X	X	0	1
1	1	X	X	X	Invalid	
0	1	↑	0	0	No change	
0	0	↑	0	1	0	1
0	0	↑	1	0	1	0
0	0	↑	1	1	Toggle	

128

Quad 2-input EX-OR

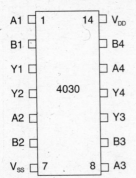

A1 — 1 — 14 — V_{DD}
B1 — B4
Y1 — A4
Y2 — 4030 — Y4
A2 — Y3
B2 — B3
V_{SS} — 7 — 8 — A3

nA, nB : Data inputs
nY : Data outputs

B	A	Y
0	0	0
0	1	1
1	0	1
1	1	0

$Y = A \oplus B$

Hex Inverting Buffer

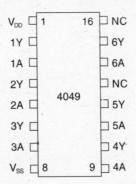

V_{DD} — 1 — 16 — NC
1Y — 6Y
1A — 6A
2Y — NC
2A — 4049 — 5Y
3Y — 5A
3A — 4Y
V_{SS} — 8 — 9 — 4A

nA : Data inputs
nY : Data outputs

A	Y
0	1
1	0

$Y = \overline{A}$

Hex Non-inverting Buffer

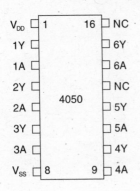

V_{DD} — 1 — 16 — NC
1Y — 6Y
1A — 6A
2Y — NC
2A — 4050 — 5Y
3Y — 5A
3A — 4Y
V_{SS} — 8 — 9 — 4A

nA : Data inputs
nY : Data outputs

A	Y
0	0
1	1

$Y = A$

HEX INVERTER

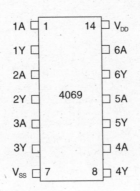

1A — 1 — 14 — V_{DD}
1Y — 6A
2A — 6Y
2Y — 4069 — 5A
3A — 5Y
3Y — 4A
V_{SS} — 7 — 8 — 4Y

nA, nB : Data inputs
nY : Data outputs

A	Y
0	1
1	0

$Y = \overline{A}$

Quad 2-input EX-OR

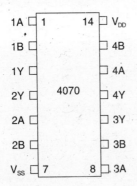

1A — 1 — 14 — V_{DD}
1B — 4B
1Y — 4A
2Y — 4070 — 4Y
2A — 3Y
2B — 3B
V_{SS} — 7 — 8 — 3A

nA, nB : Data inputs
nY : Data outputs

A	B	Y
0	0	0
0	1	1
1	0	1
1	1	0

$Y = A \oplus B$

Quad 2-input OR

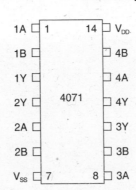

1A — 1 — 14 — V_{DD}
1B — 4B
1Y — 4A
2Y — 4071 — 4Y
2A — 3Y
2B — 3B
V_{SS} — 7 — 8 — 3A

nA, nB : Data inputs
nY : Data outputs

A	B	Y
0	0	0
0	1	1
1	0	1
1	1	1

$Y = A + B$

Quad 2-input AND

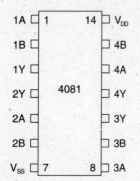

nA, nB : Data inputs
nY : Data outputs

A	B	Y
0	0	0
0	1	1
1	0	1
1	1	0

$$Y = A . B$$

Quad 2-input Schmitt NAND

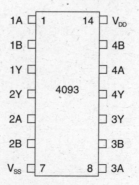

nA, nB : Data inputs
nY : Data outputs

A	B	Y
0	0	1
0	1	1
1	0	1
1	1	0

$$Y = \overline{A.B}$$

Dual Monostable Multivibrator

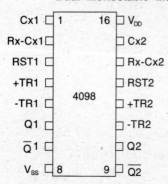

nCx : External Capacitor
nRx-Cx : Common point of external R and C
nRST : Reset (Active LOW)
(n) + TR : Positive edge trigger input
(n) - TR : Negative edge trigger input
nQ, n$\overline{Q}$: Output

Presettable UP/DOWN Counter

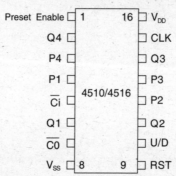

P1 through P4 : Preset inputs
Q1 through Q4 : outputs
RST : Reset input
CLK : Clock input
Ci : Carry IN
C0 : Carry OUT
U/D   NOTE : 4510 is a BCD-counter while 4516 is a 4-bit binary counter

BCD-to-7 Segment Latch Decoder Driver

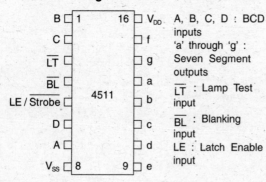

A, B, C, D : BCD inputs
'a' through 'g' : Seven Segment outputs
$\overline{LT}$: Lamp Test input
$\overline{BL}$: Blanking input
LE : Latch Enable input

Dual UP Counters

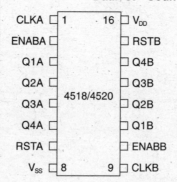

nRST : RESET (Active HIGH)
nCLK : Clock input (positive edge trigger)
nQ1 through nQ4 : outputs
nENAB : Enable input
4518 : Dual BCD Up-counter
4520 : Dual Binary UP-counter

130

Programmable Timer

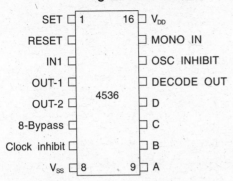

```
       ┌──────────┐
SET   ┤1       16├ V_DD
RESET ┤          ├ MONO IN
IN1   ┤          ├ OSC INHIBIT
OUT-1 ┤   4536   ├ DECODE OUT
OUT-2 ┤          ├ D
8-Bypass ┤       ├ C
Clock inhibit ┤  ├ B
V_SS  ┤8      9 ├ A
       └──────────┘
```

Dual Monostable Multivibrator

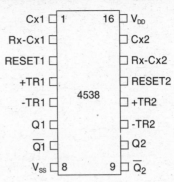

```
        ┌──────────┐
Cx1    ┤1      16├ V_DD
Rx-Cx1 ┤         ├ Cx2
RESET1 ┤         ├ Rx-Cx2
+TR1   ┤  4538   ├ RESET2
-TR1   ┤         ├ +TR2
Q1     ┤         ├ -TR2
Q̄1     ┤         ├ Q2
V_SS   ┤8     9 ├ Q̄2
        └──────────┘
```

Synchrounous Programmable 4-Bit Counters

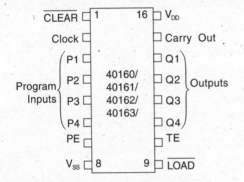

```
          ┌──────────┐
CLEAR    ┤1      16├ V_DD
Clock    ┤         ├ Carry Out
  ⎧ P1   ┤ 40160/  ├ Q1 ⎫
Program⎨ P2 ┤40161/  ├ Q2 ⎬ Outputs
Inputs⎩ P3 ┤40162/   ├ Q3 ⎪
   P4    ┤ 40163/  ├ Q4 ⎭
   PE    ┤         ├ TE
V_SS     ┤8     9 ├ LOAD
          └──────────┘
```

40160 : Decade with Asynchronous Clear
40161 : Binary with Asynchronous Clear
40162 : Decade with Synchronous Clear

HEX D-Type Flip Flop

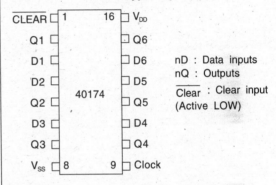

```
        ┌──────────┐
CLEAR  ┤1      16├ V_DD
Q1     ┤         ├ Q6
D1     ┤         ├ D6
D2     ┤  40174  ├ D5
Q2     ┤         ├ Q5
D3     ┤         ├ D4
Q3     ┤         ├ Q4
V_SS   ┤8     9 ├ Clock
        └──────────┘
```

nD : Data inputs
nQ : Outputs
Clear : Clear input
(Active LOW)

Quad D-Type Flip Flop

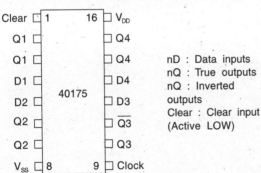

```
        ┌──────────┐
Clear  ┤1      16├ V_DD
Q1     ┤         ├ Q4
Q1     ┤         ├ Q4
D1     ┤  40175  ├ D4
D2     ┤         ├ D3
Q2     ┤         ├ Q̄3
Q2     ┤         ├ Q3
V_SS   ┤8     9 ├ Clock
        └──────────┘
```

nD : Data inputs
nQ : True outputs
nQ : Inverted outputs
Clear : Clear input
(Active LOW)

Presettable UP/DOWN Counter

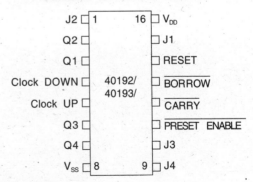

```
           ┌──────────┐
J2        ┤1      16├ V_DD
Q2        ┤         ├ J1
Q1        ┤         ├ RESET
Clock DOWN ┤ 40192/ ├ BORROW
Clock UP  ┤ 40193/  ├ CARRY
Q3        ┤         ├ PRESET ENABLE
Q4        ┤         ├ J3
V_SS      ┤8     9 ├ J4
           └──────────┘
```

40192 : BCD Counter
40193 : Binary Counter

4-Bit Bidirectional Universal Shift Register

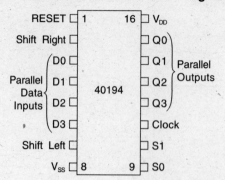

RESET — 1   16 — V_DD

V_{DD} appears at pin 16

RESET □ 1   16 □ V_{DD}

Shift Right □   □ Q0 ⎫
Parallel Data Inputs { D0 □   □ Q1 ⎬ Parallel Outputs
D1 □   40194   □ Q2
D2 □   □ Q3 ⎭
D3 □   □ Clock
Shift Left □   □ S1
V_{SS} □ 8   9 □ S0

UNDERSTANDING POWER SUPPLY BASICS

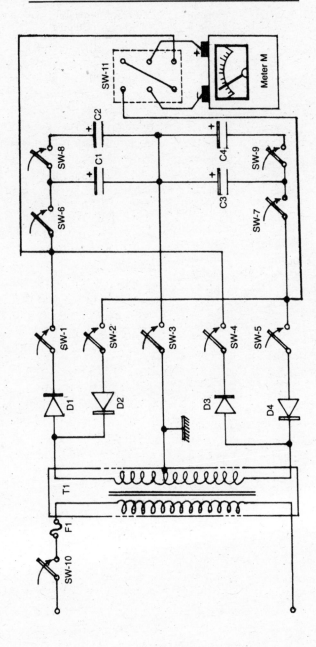

Fig. 1.1

OBJECTIVE

Majority of Electronics enthusiasts and hobbyists wants to build their own AC-DC power supplies to test the electronics circuits built by them. The objective of this easy to build and understand circuit is to familiarise the constructor or the hobbyist with the effect of changing the rectifier-filter configuration on the DC output voltage produced in a conventional mains operable AC/DC power supply.

By opening or closing an appropriate combination of switches (SW-1 to SW-9 in the circuit diagram), this circuit could be configured into any one of the popular power supply rectifier circuits like (i) Conventional Half Wave Rectifier with positive DC output voltage (ii) Conventional Half Wave Rectifier with negative DC output voltage (iii) Conventional Full Wave Rectifier with positive output DC voltage (iv) Conventional Full Wave Rectifier with negative DC output voltage (v) Full Wave Bridge Rectifier with positive or negative DC output voltage. The effect of adding the filter capacitor at the rectifier output on the DC voltage produced can also be seen. In addition, the effect of increasing the size of the filter capacitor (i.e. the value of filter capacitance) on the DC voltage produced can also be observed.

Undoubtedly, it will be a good starting point for a hobbyist who happens to be a beginner, but it would simply be excellent for a hobbyist studying at senior secondary level or in the first year of Diploma in Electronics to try to build this simple but informative circuit as a part of their project because Transformers, Rectifiers and Filters are a definite part of their curriculum too.

CIRCUIT DESCRIPTION

The input transformer steps down the AC mains voltage from 230V (nominal) to 12V (nominal) between the center tap and either of the two ends of the secondary winding. The transformer being used in the circuit has a capability to deliver a current of 250 mA. The 12VAC appearing across the secondary is the RMS value of the waveform and the peak value would be 12 x 1.414 = 16.8 volts. Diodes D1 to D4 rectify the AC waveform appearing across the secondary with the number

of diodes and the configuration depending upon the combination of switches chosen to be closed. Capacitors C1 to C4 provide filtering or the smoothing of the rectified waveform which although is a unidirectional one yet it is far from being a pure DC, more so in case of a half wave rectified waveform. Meter (M) with the help of DPDT switch (SW 11) has been used to monitor both positive as well as negative voltages thus eliminating the need to have separate meters. The fuse on the input is there to protect the circuit from inrush of heavy current in case there is any accidental short on the output side. Table 1.1 shows the position of various switches (OPEN or CLOSED) and the corresponding rectifier-filter configuration we get as a result of that.

CONSTRUCTION GUIDELINES

The PCB layout, as seen from components' side, and the components' layout are respectively depicted in Figs. 1.2 and 1.3. The project is so simple that it can very easily and conveniently be assembled on a general purpose PCB. In that case, different components need to be interconnected on the copper side of the PCB with the help of wires as per the circuit diagram.

PARTS LIST
Capacitors

C1, C2, C3, C4   : 220µF, 50V (Electrolytic) – Axial leads (Fig. 1.4)

Transformer

T1   : Mains Transformer, 230VAC input, 12-0-12 V output, 250mA (Fig.1.5.)

Switches

SW1, SW2, SW3 : ON-OFF type miniature
SW4, SW5,SW6,   toggle switches or a
SW7, SW8, SW9   DIP switch (Fig. 1.6).

SW10   : Power ON switch (Toggle switch rated for mains voltage) (Fig. 1.7)

SW11   : DPDT Switch (Fig.1.8)

Meter

M   : DC Voltmeter (0-15VDC) (Fig. 1.9)

Fuse

F1   : 500mA

Miscellaneous

Multistrand wires, solder metal

Table: 1.1

| Sl. No. | Position of Switches | | Configuration | Circuit |
| | OPEN | CLOSED | | |
	1	**2**	**3**	**4**
1.	SW-2, SW-4, SW-5, SW-6, SW-7, SW-8, SW-9	SW-1, SW-3	Conventional Half Wave with positive DC output Voltage.	
2.	SW-1, SW-2, SW-4, SW-6, SW-7, SW-8, SW-9	SW-3, SW-5	Conventional Half Wave with Negative DC output Voltage.	
3.	SW-2, SW-5, SW-6, SW-7, SW-8, SW-9	SW-1, SW-3, SW-4	Conventional Full Wave with Positive DC output Voltage.	
4.	SW-1, SW-4, SW-6, SW-7, SW-8, SW-9	SW-2, SW-3, SW-5	Conventional Full Wave with Negative DC output Voltage.	
5.	SW-3, SW-6, SW-7, SW-8, SW-9	SW-1, SW-2 SW-4, SW-5,	Full Wave Bridge. The polarity of the output here depends upon which output terminal is considered as common.	
6.	SW-2, SW-4, SW-5, SW-7, SW-8, SW-9	SW-1, SW-3, SW-6	Conventional Half Wave with filter capacitor C1 and positive DC output.	
7.	SW-1, SW-2, SW-4, SW-6, SW-8, SW-9	SW-3, SW-5, SW-7	Conventional Half Wave with filter capacitor C3 and negative DC output.	
8.	SW-2, SW-5, SW-7, SW-8, SW-9	SW-1, SW-3, SW-4, SW-6	Conventional Full Wave with filter capacitor C1 and positive DC output.	
9.	SW-1, SW-4, SW-6, SW-8, SW-9	SW-2, SW-3, SW-5, SW-7	Conventional Full Wave with filter capacitor C3 and negative DC output.	
10.	SW-3, SW-8, SW-9	SW-1, SW-2, SW-4, SW-5, SW-6, SW-7	Full Wave Bridge with filter capacitor. The filter capacitor in this case is a series combination of C1 and C3.	

NOTE: If SW-8 is also closed in cases listed at S. Nos. 6 and 8, the filter capacitor value would be a parallel combination of C1 and C2. Similarly, if SW-9 is closed in cases listed at S.Nos. 7 and 9, the filter capacitor would be a parallel combination of C3 and C4. If SW-8 and SW-9 are also closed for the case listed at S. No.10, the filter capacitor would be (C1-parallel-C2) in series with (C3-parallel-C4).

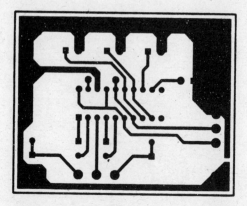

Fig. 1. 2

Testing Guidelines

A conventional half wave rectifier produces a DC output (on no load) that is 0.318 times the peak value of the voltage appearing across rectifier input (same as that appearing across the transformer secondary). This peak value would be 16.8 volts (nominal) for the transformer chosen for this project. Remember that this value would fluctuate with fluctuations in the mains input. The DC output (again on no load) for a full wave rectifier (conventional or bridge) is 0.636 times the peak value. The filter capacitor smooths the rectified waveform and has the effect of increasing the DC output. Larger the size of the filter capacitor, better is the quality of DC produced. All these effects can be observed by monitoring DC output.

NOTE: *The photograph of the meter shown in Fig.1.9 is only a representative photograph of a typical analog voltmeter to give an idea as to how the meter may look like.*

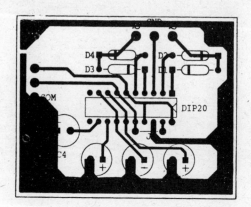
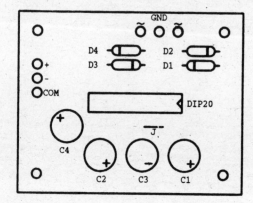

Fig. 1. 3

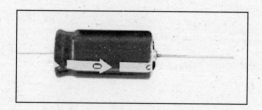

Fig. 1. 4

Fig. 1. 5

136

Fig. 1. 6

Fig. 1. 7

Fig. 1. 8

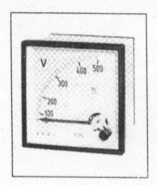

Fig. 1. 9

PROJECT : 2

Understanding Solid State (or Electronic) Switch Functions

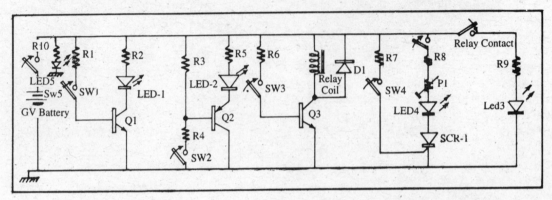

Fig. 2.1

OBJECTIVE

The objective of this simple exercise is to demonstrate the operation of solid state (or electronic) switches using electronic devices like TRANSISTORS or SCRs. There are many more electronic devices that can be used for the purpose. We have chosen these two as these are the most commonly used ones in this role, more so in the electronics circuits of hobbyists' interest. MOSFET (Metal Oxide Semiconductor Field Effect Transistor) is another commonly used switching device that has outclassed bipolar junction transistors in many switching applications. It is not covered here but is separately covered in the next project.

CIRCUIT DESCRIPTION

The first part of the circuit starting from extreme left and comprising of Resistors R1, R2, Switch SW1, LED-1 and Transistor Q1 illustrates the use of an NPN transistor as an ON/OFF type switch. **It can be demonstrated that the transistor can be made to behave as a simple SPST type switch between its Collector and Emitter terminals**. A transistor (NPN or PNP) shows an open circuit between its Collector and Emitter terminals when it is in the non-conducting or cut-off state. A transistor is non-conducting

when its Base-Emitter junction is forward biased less than 0.6 volt (Base positive with respect to Emitter in NPN and Emitter positive with respect to Base in PNP transistors). When the base-emitter junction's forward biased voltage is greater than 0.6V, the resulting base current drives the transistor ON and a collector current equal to the base current multiplied by the current gain of the transistor flows in the collector emitter lead. When talking about transistor as a switch, if the DC base current being fed is much less than the expected collector current that would flow when the transistor is driven to the ON state (equivalent to a closed switch) divided by the current gain of the transistor, then the transistor would stay in the non-conducting state. In this part of the circuit, when switch SW1 is open, base current is zero with the result that the transistor does not conduct as indicated by the non-glowing LED-1. When SW1 is closed, base current (depending upon the value of resistance R1) flows, the transistor conducts if the collector current (as decided by resistance R2) divided by the current gain is much less (about one tenth) than the actual base current being fed. Conduction of the transistor is indicated by a glowing LED-1.

The second part consisting of Resistor R3, R4,

R5, Switch SW2, LED-2 and transistor Q2 depicts the use of a PNP transistor as a switch. The concept is the same. Here also, the base current and hence the collector emitter (or more precisely the Emitter-Collector current in this case) current flows when the emitter-base junction is forward biased. And this would happen only when the switch SW2 is closed. You would notice a change in the location of the switch. This is to ensure that the emitter base voltage is less than the required forward bias of 0.6V (min) when the switch is open. Transistors are used extensively as a switch in various applications. One such application is in driving relay coils. When the transistor is switched ON, the relay coil is energised and its contacts changeover i.e. normally open contacts close and normally closed contacts open. In the circuit consisting of Resistor R6, Switch SW3, Diode D1, Relay RL-1 and the transistor Q3, the relay energised condition is indicated by a glowing LED-3. The reverse biased diode across the relay coil is to protect the transistor from any damage due to voltage spikes occuring due to sudden change in current when the transistor is switched from ON to OFF state.

SCR is another popular device used as a switch. However, it is a LATCHING device i.e. once triggered to the ON-state, it stays there even if the trigger is removed. Remember, in case of a transistor, you had to keep the switch SW1 or switch SW2 (as the case may be) closed in order to keep the transistor conducting and the LED glowing. In the SCR experiment shown, the moment you close the switch SW4, SCR conducts and the LED-4 glows. Now the LED-4 can be observed to continue to glow even if you open switch SW4. There is now only one method to bring the SCR back to the non-conducting state and that is to somehow bring its anode current below a certain minimum value which the SCR manufacturers refer to as the Holding Current. It is 10 mA for the chosen SCR. You could do that by disconnecting the anode supply (by opening switch SW5) or even by increasing the resistance in the anode lead till the SCR goes to the OFF state indicated by LED-4 getting extinguished. Since the minimum current required to drive an LED is typically 2 mA or so, a holding current of 10 mA for the chosen SCR ensures that the LED would extinguish because of the SCR going to the non-conducting state as the anode resistance is being increased.

A relay coil placed in the anode lead of the SCR makes the circuit as a latching type relay that needs just a pulse to get energised and stay energised. This part is not shown here as it would be similar to the one shown in case of NPN transistor.

CONSTRUCTION GUIDELINES
Parts List

Resistors	: All Resistors are carbon film or carbon composition type
R1, R3	: 22K,1/4W
R2, R4, R5, R6, R9 R 10	: 3.3K, 1/4W
R7	: 470 ohms, 1/4W
R8	: 470 ohms, 1/4W
Potentiometers	
P1	: 10K Preset
Transistors	
Q1, Q3	: 2N 2222
Q2	: 2N 2907
Diodes	
D1	: 1N4001
SCR	
SCR-1	: SN100 or any other 100 volts SCR.
LED-1 to LED-4	: Red LEDs (Other colour LEDs like green or yellow can also be used)
Relay	
RL-1	: 6VDC relay (Fig. 2.2)
Miscellaneous	
Battery	: 9VDC battery (Fig. 2.3)
Switches SW1 to SW5	: ON/OFF switches
Solder metal multistrand wires, etc.	

The PCB layout as seen from components' side and components' layout are shown in Figs. 2.4 and 2.5 respectively. The project circuit is so simple and the total number of components being used is so small that it can be conveniently assembled on a general purpose PCB if you may wish to do so.

Fig. 2.2

Fig. 2.3

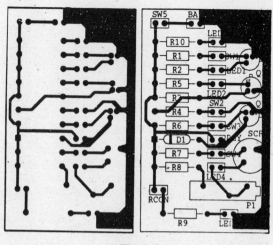

Fig. 2.4

TESTING GUIDELINES

There are four different experiments you can perform with this simple circuit. These are

(i) Use of NPN transistor as a switch

(ii) Use of PNP transistor as a switch

(iii) Use of a transistor switch to drive a relay and

(iv) Operation of an SCR as a latching switch.

After you have assembled the project, before the start of every experiment, switch ON SW5 to connect the battery voltage to the circuit. For the first experiment, switch on SW1 and see if LED-

1 glows. The LED should extinguish when you open SW1. Similarly, LED-2 would glow when SW2 is closed. Observe the energisation of the relay coil indicated by glowing LED-3 in the third experiment. In the fourth experiment, close switch SW4. LED-4 glows. Now open switch SW4, LED-4 continues to glow. Adjust the value of the potentiometer P1 towards increasing resistance. You would observe the LED-4 getting extinguished at a certain stage. You will notice that you have to once again close the switch SW4 and also adjust the present P1 towards reducing resistance to light the LED-4. Again, the LED-4 continues to glow when the switch SW4 is opened.

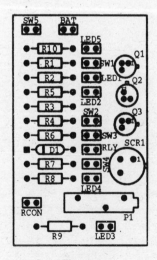

Fig. 2.5

140

PROJECT : 3

UNDERSTANDING MOSFET SWITCH FUNCTIONS

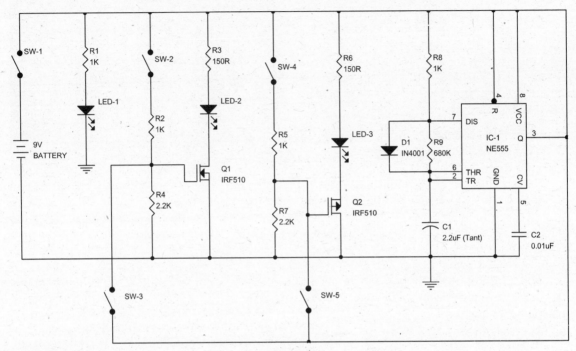

Fig. 3.1

OBJECTIVE

Under project-2, we have already seen how a bipolar transistor, NPN or PNP, can be used as a single pole. single throw switch. The transistor operating in saturation region with voltage across the switch being about 0.2 volt represents the ON-condition of the switch. The transistor operating in the cut-off region, where the only current that can flow through the switch is the collector-to-emitter leakage current represents the OFF-condition of the switch. We also demonstrated how an SCR can be used as a single pole single throw switch of the latching type. Another very important solid state device that can be usd as a switch in a way similar to the operation of a bipolar transistor is the Metal Oxide Semiconductor Field Effect Transistor (MOSFET) briefly mentioned in the last project.

In the present project activity, we shall experience the functioning of a MOSFET as a switch. Before we do that and go ahead with the description of the project circuit. It would be worthwhile mentioning a few important points about this device. First of all, we should remember that a MOSFET is a voltage-controlled device unlike the bipolar transistor, which is a current controlled device. Secondly, there are two categories of MOSFET namely the ENHANCEMENT type and the DEPLETION type. In case of the former, that is, the ENHANCEMENT type, the device conducts only when the gate-to-source voltage exceeds a certain minimum voltage called the threshold voltage (Vth). The device remains in cut-off region if the voltage is below that. On the other hand, a DEPLETION type device is usually conducting for a zero gate-to-source voltage and it can be switched to the conducting state by applying a gate-to-source voltage of a suitable magnitude. Thirdly, in each of the two categories, we have the N-channel and P-channel devices and ENHANCEMENT type MOSFETs are preferred for switching applications. Lastly, an N-channel ENHANCEMENT MOSFET can be switched ON by making gate terminal more positive than the source terminal by a voltage greater than the threshold voltage and a P-channel device can be switched ON by making gate terminal less positive than the source terminal by a voltage greater than the threshold voltage.

CIRCUIT DESCRIPTION

The first part of the circuit starting from left and comprising of R2. R4, R3, LED-2. MOSFET QI and switch SW-2 illustrates the use of an N-channel ENHANCEMENTtype MOSFET as a switch. It can be demonstrated that this device behaves like a single pole single throw switch between drain and source terminals. The second part of the circuit comprising of R5. R6, R7, LED-3. MOSFET Q2 and switch SW-4 can be used to demonstrate how a P-channel MOSFET can be used as a switch.

The third part of the circuit consists of an astable multivibrator circuit built around timer IC 555. The On-time of the output waveform appearing at pin-3 of the IC is given by $0.69R8C2$ and the OFF-time of the output waveform is given by $0.69R9C2$. The component values here have been so chosen as to produce ON and OFF times of 1 second each. The output waveform is applied to the gate terminals of the two MOSFETs through switches SW-3 and SW-5. SW-3 and SW-5 allow us to selectively apply the waveform to the two gates if desired.

The circuit operates on a 9-volt battery, which can be connected to the circuit through switch SW-1. A glowing LED-1 indicates the connection. Also. glowing LEDs LED-2 and LED-3 respectively indicate conduction of N-channel and P-channel MOSFETs.

The switching action of the two MOSFETs can be demonstrated through the use of switches SW-2 and SW-4. The repetitive switching action of the MOSFET can be demonstrated through the use of switches SW-3 and SW-5.

CONSTRUCTION GUIDELINES

The PCB layout and the components layout are respectively shown in Figs 3.2 and 3.3 respectively. The circuit can however be wired on a general purpose PCB without any problem.

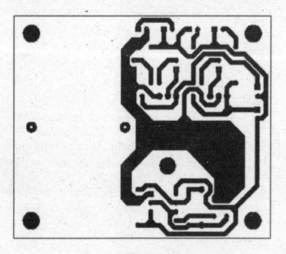

Fig. 3.2

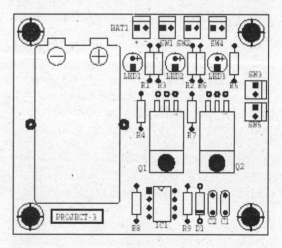

Fig. 3.3

PARTS LIST

Resistors

All Resistors are carbonfilm or carbon composition type

R1, R2, R5	: 1K, 1/4W
R3, R6	: 150 ohm, 1/4W
R4, R7	: 2.2K, 1/4W
R8, R9	: 680K, 1/4W

Capacitors

C1	: 0.01µF (ceramic disc)
C2	: 2.2µF (Tantalum)
C3	: 0.1µF (ceramic disc)

Semiconductors

D 1	: 1N4001
LED- 1 to	
LED-3	: Red colour LEDs (Other colour LEDs can also be used)
Q 1	: MOSFET type IRF510 or equivalent
Q2	: MOSFET type IRF9520 or equivalent
IC-1	: Timer 555

Miscellaneous

SW- 1	: Miniature toggle switch
SW-2 to SW-5	: Parts of a 4-pole DIP switch (Fig.3.4)

9V battery (Fig.3.5)

Multi-strand wires, General purpose PCB (If needed)

Solder metal

TESTING GUIDELINES

There are two different experiments that can be performed with this simple circuit. These includes:

1. Use of N-channel MOSFET as a switch
2. Use of P-channel MOSFFT as a switch

Use of N-channel MOSFFT as a switch

Initially keep all switches as open. Close SW-1 to connect the battery to the circuit. Glowing LED-1 indicates battery connection. Closing SW-2 now lights LED-2 indicating that MOSFET Q1 is conducting. LED-2 goes OFF if the switch SW-2 is opened. Opening SW-2 and closing SW-3 can test repetitive ON and OFF condition of the MOSFET. The timer output, which is HIGH and LOW for approximately one second each makes the LED-2 glow and extinguish alternately for one second.

Use of P-channel MOSFET as a switch

Initially keep all switches as open. Close SW-1 to connect the battery to the circuit. Glowing LED-1 indicates battery connection. Closing SW-4 now lights LED-3 indicating that MOSFET Q2 is conducting. LED-3 goes OFF if the switch SW-4 is opened. Opening SW-4 and closing, SW-5 can test repetitive ON and OFF condition of the MOSFET. The timer output, which is HIGH and LOW for approximately one second each, make the LED-3 glow and extinguish alternately for one second.

If SW-1. SW-3 and SW5 are only closed. LED-2 and LED-3 are observed to glow alternately for obvious reasons.

NOTE: *Remember that in case of N-channel MOSFET, the device conducts when the gate terminal is made HIGH and the source terminal is LOW. In case of P-channel MOSFET, the device conducts when the gate terminal is LOW and the source terminal is HIGH.*

Fig. 3.4

Fig. 3.5

THYRISTOR CONTROL OF AC POWER

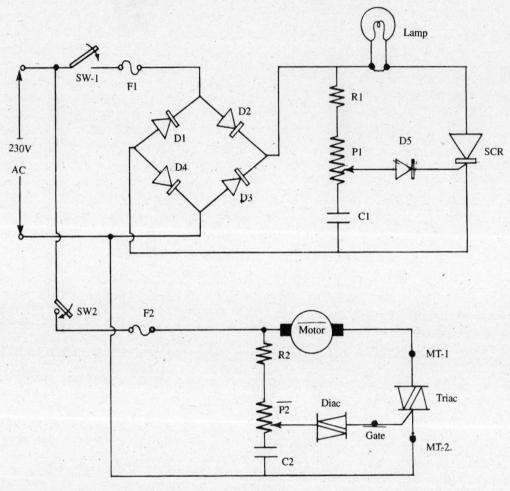

Fig. 4.1

OBJECTIVE

Thyristors (SCRs, Triacs) are very popular in AC power control applications where they are used to provide an active control of the AC power being fed to the load. **The load here could be anything that is operated from AC mains and whose parameter to be controlled happens to depend upon the amount of AC power. Speed of motors, Temperature of heating elements etc. are some of the examples.** Here, we would build a simple circuit to demonstrate separately the use of SCRs and Triacs to provide AC power control.

SCRs are used for those loads where it is immaterial whether the load current is unidirectional or bidirectional (though the AC input is always bidirectional). Heating element is one such load, an incandescent bulb is another. Remember that amount of heat is always

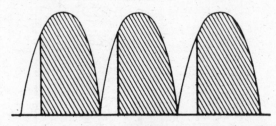

Fig. 4.2

proportional to square of current and square of both positive as well as negative quantities is always positive. Triacs are used to control AC power to the AC loads, AC motors for instance. **In the project under construction, SCR has been used to control power and thus vary the light output from an incandescent bulb while the triac has been used to control the speed of an AC motor**.

CIRCUIT DESCRIPTION

When the switch SW1 is closed and the switch SW2 is open, AC input is fed only to the SCR circuit. The bridge rectifier comprising of diodes D1 to D4 provides full wave rectification of the applied AC. Since the SCR is initially non-conducting, the full wave rectified waveform does not get applied to the load. The SCR fires (i.e. it switches to the conducting state) at some point on the rectified waveform depending upon the setting of potentiometer P1. After that, the rectified waveform gets applied to the load. As the rectified waveform is on the decline, the SCR turns OFF when the load current falls below the holding current value of the SCR used. It occurs very near to the zero voltage point. When the input is on the rise again, at the same point, the SCR fires again and the process repeats. Fig.4.2 shows the full wave rectified waveform and also the portion of the waveform that is fed to the load for a particular setting of the potentiometer P1. This portion can be altered by changing the setting of the potentiometer P1. The effect of changing input to the load can be clearly seen in the form of a changing light output from the bulb.

The triac circuit also behaves in the same fashion as the SCR circuit except that it is bidirectional. It can conduct in both positive as well as negative half cycles of the AC input (that is why there is no need for rectifying the input). The triac fires when the breakover voltage of the diac is reached. The shaded portion in the waveform of Fig.4.3 is the one that is actually applied across the load, an AC motor in this case. The effect of control can be clearly seen in the form of changing speed of the motor as the potentiometer P2 setting is changed.

CONSTRUCTION GUIDELINES

The PCB layout and the components layout are respectively shown in Figs.4.4 and 4.5.

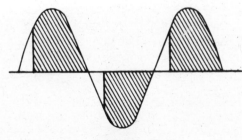

Fig. 4.3

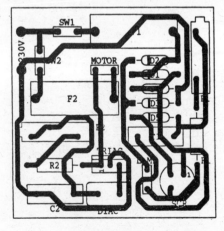

Fig. 4.4 (a)

145

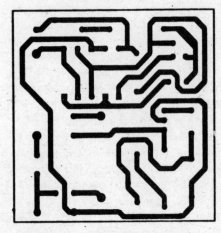

Fig. 4.4 (b)

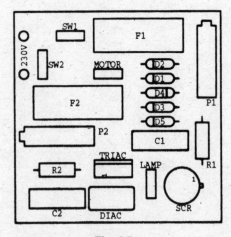

Fig. 4.5

PARTS LIST
Resistors and Potentiometers
R1   : 1K, 1/2 W
R2   : 1K, 1/2 W
P1   : 1M (LIN)
P2   : 1M (LIN)
Capacitors
C1   : 0.47 µF, 1000V (Polyester or ceramic)
C2   : 0.47 µF, 100V (Polyester or ceramic)
Semiconductor Devices
SCR   : OE 106/SN 106 or any 600 volts, 1 Ampere SCR
Diodes : BY 127/1N 4007
D1 to D4
Triac   : KT 206 (Any triac with breakdown voltage greater than 400V and current rating of 1A can be used)
Diac   : ±18V diac
Miscellaneous
Fuse, F1 : 1A rating
Fuse, F2 : 1A rating
Switch, SW1 and SW2 : Mains Power ON/OFF switches

An electric bulb (40 or 60 watts) and an AC motor as loads, solder metal, multistrand wires, etc.

TESTING GUIDELINES
1. Close switch SW1. The intensity of the light coming from the bulb can be varied with the help of potentiometer P1. The intensity is maximum when P1 introduces minimum resistance and it is minimum when it introduces maximum resistance. The average DC voltage can be observed to vary across the load as the potentiometer is adjusted. But it will be much more informative if you could make arrangement to see the waveform across the load on an oscilloscope. That way, you can clearly see a change in the firing point (or angle) as P1 is being adjusted.

2. Open switch SW1 and close SW2 instead. Adjustment of potentiometer P2 in this case can be used to vary the speed of the motor. Again observing the waveform across the load on an oscilloscope would tell you much more than what a multimeter would do. The gadget can be tested by connecting a household Juicer/Mixer or a fan and observe the variation in speed as P2 is adjusted.

IC TIMER TESTER

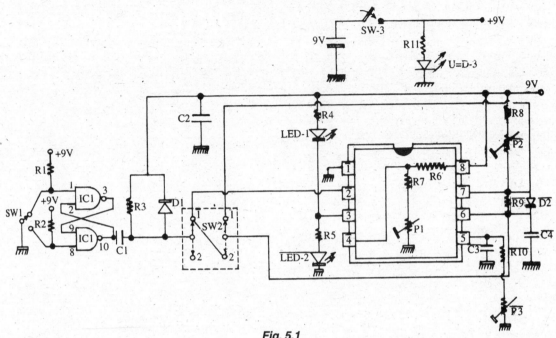

Fig. 5.1

OBJECTIVE

The objective of this construction project is to build simple and easy to use test gadget that can be used to identify good and bad IC TIMERS from a given lot. Like opamps, an IC timer is another widely used electronic device and it finds its place in almost every project of hobbyists' interest. This gadget not only enables you test the IC timer 555, it will also give you an opportunity to appreciate the tremendous functional potential of the various terminals of this truly versatile IC. Most of the circuits appearing in various magazines or books to test IC timers do the same by wiring the IC in one particular configuration only. **Testing the IC timer with the gadget being described here not only tests the IC in all basic configurations, it practically tests the functionality of each and every terminal of the timer with the result that a timer declared fit by this gadget is healthy in the true sense**

and is certainly going to stand by you in whatever mode or configuration you may try it. Also, if you clearly understand the capabilities of this gadget and theory responsible for these features, you will be in a position to think of many more different modes in which you can use an IC timer. **And moreover, it is going to be an excellent project for the students at diploma or an equivalent academic level.**

CIRCUIT DESCRIPTION

The two basic configurations in which the IC timer 555 can be used are the **(i) Astable mode** of operation and (ii) **Monostable mode** of operation. When the DPDT switch (SW2) is in position 1-1, the timer under test automatically gets wired as a monostable multivibrator. In this case, the monoshot can be triggered by the microswitch (SW1). The **Debouncing Circuit** constituted by the two NAND gates of IC-1 produces a clean rectangular pulse from the pulse produced by pressing the microswitch. Resistor R3, Capacitor C1 and the Diode D1 ensure that the trigger terminal of timer IC 555 (pin-2 is the trigger terminal) gets the desired Vcc-to-ground trigger pulse. This differentiator circuit also ensures that the width of the trigger pulse is less than the expected monoshot output pulse. The monoshot output pulse width here depends upon the resistance offered by series combination of R8 and potentiometer P2 and the capacitor C4. These values have been so chosen that even for the minimum output pulse width, the trigger pulse width (trigger pulse width depends upon the differentiator time constant) remains less than that. Remember! the trigger pulse width to be less than the expected monoshot output pulse width is an essential requirement of this mode of operation.

When the DPDT switch is in position 2-2, the timer gets connected in the astable mode of operation. The output is a pulse train with the HIGH time determined by the total resistance offered by the series combination of R8, R9, P2 and capacitor C4 whereas the LOW time is determined by resistor R9 and capacitor C4.

The RESET terminal of IC timer (pin-4) should be tied to Vcc in the normal circumstances. More precisely, voltage at pin-4 should be greater than 0.8V. A voltage of less than that resets the output. Whether you have connected the timer in the monoshot or astable mode of operation, the output goes LOW the moment you bring the RESET terminal below 0.8V.

The CONTROL TERMINAL (pin-5) can be used to change the HIGH-time or the ON-time of the output pulse train in the astable mode and the pulse width at the output in the monoshot mode by applying an external voltage. This external voltage basically changes the reference voltage levels of the comparators inside the IC. The levels are set by three identical resistors of usually 5K inside the IC connected from Vcc to ground setting the levels at 2/3 (Vcc) for pin-5 and 1/3 (Vcc) for pin-2. These levels can be changed by connecting an external resistance from pin-5 to

ground. Resistor R10 and potentiometer P3 have been connected for the same purpose.

The pulse width in the monoshot mode is given by:

1.1× (total charging resistance) × (charging capacitance)

This expression is valid when there is no external resistance connected from pin-5. The pulse width can be reduced by connecting an external resistance.

The HIGH and LOW times in the astable mode are given by:

HIGH-time = 0.69 × (charging resistance) × (charging capacitance)

LOW-time = 0.69 × (discharge resistance) × (capacitance)

Again the expressions are for no external resistance from pin-5. The HIGH-time can be made to decrease by connecting an external resistance from pin-5 to ground.

The circuit operates from +9V battery which makes the gadget portable.

The test gadget can thus be used to carry out the following tests with given timer IC 555:

1. The timer IC can be checked in the astable configuration.
2. The timer IC can be checked in the monostable configuration.
3. The capability of the RESET terminal to override all functions and rest the output to LOW can be checked.
4. The function of the control terminal to change the ON-time or the HIGH-time of the output waveform in case of astable mode of operation and the output pulse width in case of monostable mode of operation can be verified.

CONSTRUCTION GUIDELINES

The components' layout and the PCB layout as seen from component side are respectively shown in Figs.5.2 and 5.3. However the project can also be assembled on a general purpose PCB.

148

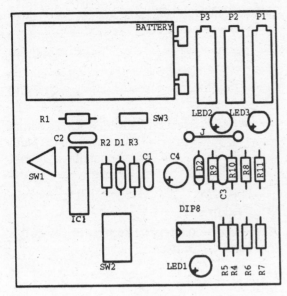

Fig. 5.2

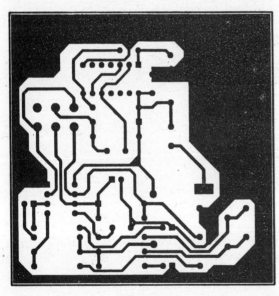

Fig. 5.3

PARTS LIST
Resistors and Potentiometers

R1, R2	: 22K, 1/4W
R4, R5, R11	: 3.3 K, 1/4W
R6	: 4.7K, 1/4W
R7	: 47 ohms, 1/4W
R8	: 150K, 1/4W
R9	: 47K, 1/4W
R10	: 1K, 1/4W
R3	: 10K, 1/4W
P1	: 1K (preset)
P2, P3	: 100K (preset)

Capacitors

C1, C3	: 0.01µF (ceramic disc)
C2, C6, C7	: 0.1µF (ceramic disc)
C4	: 10µF, 25V (electrolytic)
C5	: 100µF, 25V (electrolytic)

Semiconductor Devices

Diodes D1, D2, D3, D4	: 1N4001 or equivalent
LED-1, LED-2, LED-3	: Preferably of different colours
IC-1	: CD 4011B

Miscellaneous

1. 8-pin Dual-in-Line IC Socket
2. Fuse with holder, 1 Amp.
3. Switch SW1 (Microswitch)
4. Switch SW2 (DPDT switch) SW3 (Mains ON/OFF switch)
5. Transformer : 14-0-14, 500mA Mains transformer

NOTE: All resistors mentioned above are of carbon film or composition variety.

TESTING GUIDELINES

1. Insert the IC under test in the socket.
2. Set the DPDT switch in position-1-1.
3. Switch on the power supply.
4. LED-1 glows if the IC is healthy. LED-1 glows because the IC is presently wired as a monoshot and in the absence of any trigger, the output is LOW.
5. Give trigger pulse by pressing and releasing the switch SW1 once. You will observe the LED-1 getting extinguished and inturn the LED-2 becoming ON. This confirms that the output of the monoshot has gone HIGH. You will observe the LED-2 going OFF and LED-1 again becoming ON after some time. This will happen when the monoshot output goes

LOW again. Vary the preset P2 so as to change the resistance offered by the pot. Trigger the monoshot again. You will find that the LED-2 glows this time for a longer or a smaller time period depending upon whether you increased or decreased P2 resistance. While carrying out this step-4 test, keep the presets P1 and P3 in the maximum resistance position.

6. Trigger the monoshot again and before the expected HIGH-time is over, quickly decrease preset P1 resistance so as to bring the voltage at pin-4 below 0.8V. You will observe the output to go LOW (indicated by a glowing LED-1 and an extinguished LED-2).

7. Set preset P1 resistance again in the maximum resistance position. Set the preset P3 in the minimum resistance position. Trigger the monoshot. You will observe the monoshot going HIGH for a time period that is much less than what is dictated by the resistance offered by the series combination of R8 and preset P2 and capacitor C4. Infact for a fixed setting of this series combination, the output pulse width can be observed to vary for different values of P3 resistance by triggering the monoshot several times, once for each setting of P3.

8. Set the DPDT switch in position 2-2. The LEDs 1 and 2 will start glowing alternately with the timings determined by resistances in charge and discharge paths. The timer IC is now in astable mode.

9. The functions of RESET and CONTROL pins can be seen in this configuration too in a similar fashion like the one discussed above in the case of monoshot configuration.

IDENTIFYING THE PINS

1. The pin connection diagram of CD 4011B (which is a QUAD 2-input NAND) is shown in Fig.5.4.

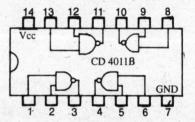

Fig. 5.4

150

OPAMP TESTER

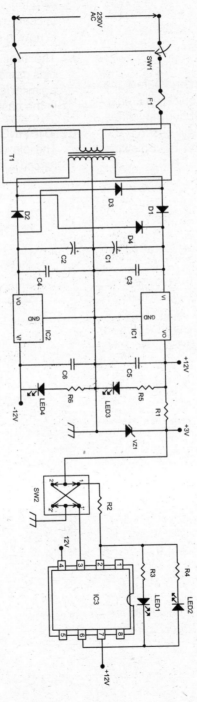

Fig. 6.1

OBJECTIVE

The objective of this construction project is to build a simple and easy to use Opamp Tester. This test gadget can be used to test the popular general purpose opamp type 741 and other such opamps that are pin to pin compatible to 741. These include the opamp type numbers such as LM 709, LM 201, MC 1439, LM 748, OP-02, LM 318, LM 356 etc. As an opamp finds its existence in almost every project of interest due to a large number of application circuits that can be built around opamps, a test gadget like the one hitherto described is certainly going to be an asset to an electronics experimenter or a hobbyist. Building this project will not only be another construction or learning exercise for them, it will become a very useful tool for them in the other projects they intend to construct. With this gadget available with them, they don't have to randomly replace the opamps in case the circuit they have built with so much of enthusiasm happens to use a few opamps and is not working. They will be able to test the opamp before declaring it fit for use. **One important point: Since the project has an educational value too, it could be a very good choice as a project for those doing diploma or an equivalent course in electronics.**

CIRCUIT DESCRIPTION

A careful look at the circuit diagram will tell you that the opamp under test can be wired either as an INVERTING AMPLIFIER (with GAIN equal to R3/R2) or as a NON-INVERTING AMPLIFIER (with GAIN equal to 1+R4/R2) depending upon the position of the DPDT switch. The input to the amplifier in the two cases is a 3VDC. The circuit has its own regulated power supply to generate (+12V) and (-12V) for the opamp from the mains. The power supply circuit consists of a transformer with a center tapped secondary winding followed by a conventional full wave rectifier circuit for both positive as well as negative supplies. Rectifiers are followed by simple single element capacitor filters. Diodes D1 and D4 constitute the full wave rectifier for the positive supply while the filtering action is provided by capacitor C1. Diodes D2 and D3 with the same center tapped secondary winding provide rectification for generating the

negative supply and capacitor C2 does the filtering. IC-1 is a +12 volt three terminal regulator of 78-series (7812 is the IC number) while IC-2 is a -12 volt three terminal regulator of 79-series (7912 is the IC number). Capacitors C3, C4, C5 and C6 are decoupling capacitors. These are used to decouple DC power supplies for high frequency noise, if any, present on the DC power supply line. Resistor R1 and Zener diode VZ1 generate 3VDC used as a test input to the opamp.

CONSTRUCTION GUIDELINES

The components layout and the PCB layout are respectively shown in Figs. 6.2 and 6.3.

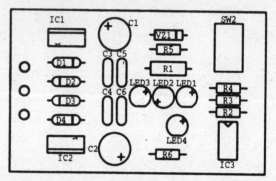

Fig. 6.2

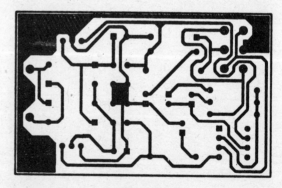

Fig. 6.3

PARTS LIST
Resistors

R1	: 470 ohms, 1/2 Watt
R2	: 1K, 1/4 Watt
R3	: 1K, 1/4 Watt
R4	: 1K, 1/4 Watt

R5　　　　　　: 2.2 K, 1/4 Watt
R6　　　　　　: 2.2 K, 1/4 Watt

Capacitors

C1　　　　　　: 100µF/35V (electrolytic)
C2　　　　　　: 100µF/35V (electrolytic)
C3　　　　　　: 0.1µF (ceramic disc)
C4　　　　　　: 0.1µF (ceramic disc)
C5　　　　　　: 0.1µF (ceramic disc)
C6　　　　　　: 0.1µF (ceramic disc)

Semiconductor Devices

IC-1　　　　　: Three terminal voltage regulator type 7812

IC-2　　　　　: Three terminal voltage regulator type 7912

Diodes
D1 to D4　　　: 1N 4001 or equivalent
LEDs
LED-1 and LED-2 : The two LEDs should preferably be of different colours

VZ1　　　　　: 3V, 400mW zener diode

Transformers

T1　　　　　　: Mains transformer (15-0-15, 250mA)

Miscellaneous

1. ON/OFF toggle switch (SW1)

2. Double Pole Double Throw (DPDT) switch (SW2).

3. Fuse, 500mA

4. 8-pin IC Socket (Dual-In-Line type)

TESTING GUIDELINES

1. Switch on the test gadget. Measure the regulated +12V, -12V and +3V DC. Ensure that all the DC voltages are available.

2. Keep the DPDT switch (SW2) in position 1-1.

3. Switch off the power supply.

4. Insert the opamp (Take a good opamp) in the IC socket meant for the purpose.

5. Switch on the power supply. LED-1 glows indicating that the opamp is functioning properly in the inverting amplifier configuration. LED-2 should not glow while the switch SW2 is in position 1-1.

6. Change the DPDT switch to position 2-2. LED-1 extinguishes and LED-2 starts

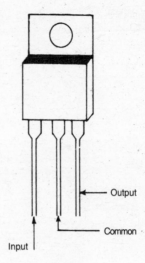

Fig. 6.4

glowing. This confirms the operation of the opamp in the non-inverting mode.

7. Switch off the power supply.

8. Remove the opamp from the test socket.

9. Remember that a bad opamp will not work in either of these configurations. But even if the opamp exhibits a behavior where it works in one and not both of these configurations, it should still be rated as a bad IC.

IDENTIFICATION OF PIN CONNECTIONS

The pin connection diagrams of three terminal regulators are shown in Figs.6.4 (for 7812) and 6.5 (for 7912).

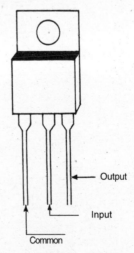

Fig. 6.5

153

MULTI-PURPOSE POWER SUPPLY

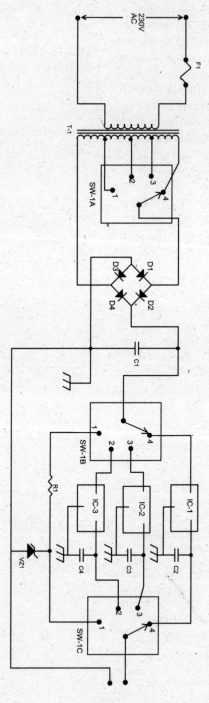

Multi-Purpose Power Supply

Fig. 7.1

OBJECTIVE

Here we intend to build a multi-purpose regulated power supply that will serve as a very useful alternative to our multiple needs of different battery eliminators to operate gadgets like Transistor sets, Audio Casette Recorders and so on and so forth. The circuit shown in Fig. 7.1 produces regulated output DC voltages of 3V, 6V, 9V and 12V that are selectable one at a time with the help of a rotary switch. Each one of the outputs is capable of delivering a load current of 500mA. and can take care of wide fluctuations in the input AC. Infact, the output voltage remains at its nominal value for an input of 230VAC ± 60 volts. It may be mentioned here that almost all battery eliminators available in the market for the purpose produce an unregulated output i.e. the output voltage varies with fluctuations in the mains.

CIRCUIT DESCRIPTION

The circuit shown comprises of all the necessary circuit components needed for a conventional regulated power supply. The transformer T-1 is a mains transformer with a multiple secondary. The secondary winding has taps at 4.5V, 7.5V, 12V and 15V. Switch SW1 is a 3-pole, 4-throw rotary switch and it has been shown as split up into three parts in the circuit diagram, the three parts being SW-1A, SW-1B and SW-1C. This switch can be used to select the desired output voltage. It basically selects the appropriate secondary tap. Diodes D1 to D4 constitute full wave bridge rectifier and capacitor C1 is the filter capacitor. IC-1, IC-2 and IC-3 are three terminal regulators of 78XX series. These regulators produce a fixed regulated output depending upon the type number chosen provided that the input to the regulator is at least 2.5V more than the expected output voltage. The requirement of minimum input-output voltage differential explains why we have chosen higher secondary voltages to get a certain DC output. C2 to C4 are decoupling capacitors. **It may mentioned once again that SW-1A, SW-1B and SW-1C are the parts of the same switch. When SW-1A is on position-1, SW-1B and SW-1C are also on position-1.**

When the switch is on position-1, the input to the bridge rectifier is from 4.5V tap of the secondary winding. The filtered waveform across the filter capacitor has therefore an amplitude of 4.5 x 1.414 = 6.36 volts. SW-1B routes this DC voltage to R1-Vz1 combination and SW-IC routes the regulated DC voltage to the output. The operation is similar for the remaining positions of the rotary switch.

PARTS LIST
Resistors and Capacitors

R1	: 3.9 ohms, 2 watt
C1	: 1000µF, 25V (electrolytic)
C2, C3, C4	: 0.1µF (ceramic disc)

Semiconductor Devices and ICs

Diodes D1 to D4	: 1N4001 or equivalent
Zener diode, Vz1	: 3V, 2 watt
IC-1	: 7812
IC-2	: 7809
IC-3	: 7806

Miscellaneous

Transformer T-1	: 0-4.5-7.5-12-15, 500mA Mains Transformer
Fuse F1	: Tubular type 500mA fuse with Holder
SW2	: Mains Power ON/OFF switch
SW1	: 3-POLE, 4-THROW Rotary switch (Fig. 7.2)

Power supply terminals, solder wire, mains cord etc.

The PCB layout and the components layout are respectively shown in Figs. 6.3 and 6.4 .

NOTE : *In case IC-2 and IC-3 are not easily available, IC-2 (7809) can be replaced by a 7805 with two series connected silicon diodes of 1N 4001 type wired between the IC's common terminal and circuit GND. IC-3 (7809) can also be replaced by a 7805 with a 3.9V zener diode wired from the IC's common terminal to circuit GND.*

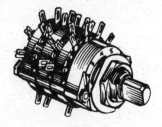

Fig. 7.2

155

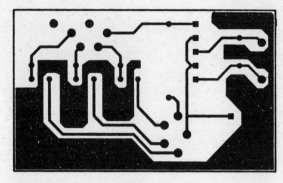

Fig. 7.3

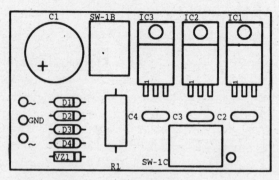

Fig. 7.4

TESTING GUIDELINES

The testing part of this project should ensure that the output voltages have correct nominal values, have the desired load current delivering capability and are nicely regulated. These things can be checked as per following guidelines:

1. Measure the output voltage in case of each of the rotary switch positions. The measured voltages should tally with the expected values in each one of the cases.

2. Repeat step: 1 this time connecting a resistive load across the output so as to deliver a current of 500mA. Remember you will have to change the resistance for each of the rotary switch positions. These resistances will be 6 ohms/2 watt, 12 ohms/5watt and 24 ohms/10 watt respectively for Positions 1,2,3 and 4 of the rotary switch SW-1.

3. The regulation part can be checked by varying the AC input to the power supply and monitoring the output voltage. Determine the input voltage range for which the output voltages maintain their values as constant.

LEAD IDENTIFICATION

Refer to Fig.7.5 for lead identification of IC-1, IC-2, IC-3 (all will have same pin configuration) and diode 1N4001.

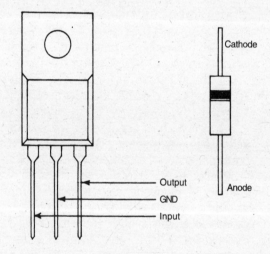

Fig. 7.5

PROJECT : 8

REGULATED DUAL POWER SUPPLY

Regulated Dual Power Supply

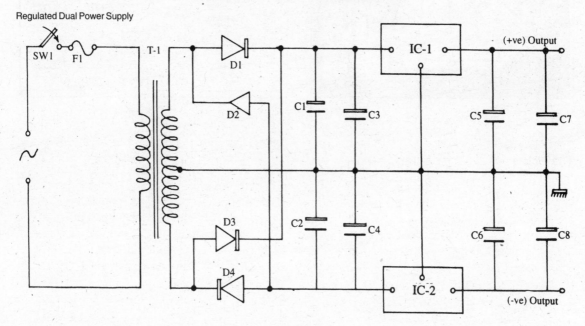

Fig. 8.1

OBJECTIVE

The objective here is to build a dual power supply that generates regulated +12 volts and -12 volts from 230VAC mains. Such a supply is a very common requirement in all those circuits that use opamps. Since opamps are very widely used in a variety of circuits of hobbyists' interests, construction of this project could serve as a very useful tool in testing all those circuits that need a dual supply. Each of the outputs in the circuit shown in Fig.8.1 has a current delivering capability of 250mA. You would also discover this circuit to be an integral part of the more complex circuits that are mains operable.

CIRCUIT DESCRIPTION

The unregulated AC/DC power supply part of the circuit consists of a transformer (T-1) that steps down 230VAC to 15 volts across a center tapped secondary winding i.e. 15VAC individually across the two halves of the secondary winding with

opposite polarities, diodes (D1) to (D4) that rectify the AC appearing across the secondary with (D1) and (D3) providing full wave rectification to produce a positive output, (D2) and (D4), providing full wave rectification to produce a negative output, capacitors (C1) and (C2) providing the filtering action. C3 to C8 are decoupling capacitors. IC-1 is a fixed output positive three terminal regulator whereas IC-2 is a fixed output negative three terminal regulator.

PARTS LIST
Capacitors
C1, C2	: 1000 µF, 50V (electrolytic)
C3, C4, C7, C8	: 0.1 µF (ceramic disc)
C5, C6	: 10µF, 50V (electrolytic)

Diodes
D1 to D4	: 1N4001 or equivalent

ICs
IC-1	: 7812
IC-2	: 7912

157

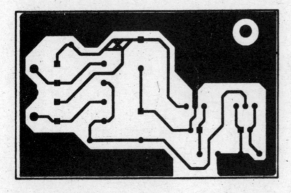

Fig. 8.2

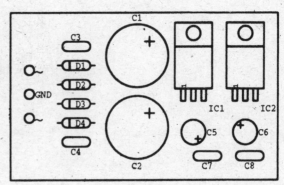

Fig. 8.3

Miscellaneous

Transformer T-1 : 15-0-15 volts, 250mA mains transformer.

Fuse F-1 : 500 mA tubular type with holder

Switch SW1 : Mains ON/OFF switch

Solder metal, wires, power supply terminals, mains cord

Figs. 8.2 and 8.3 respectively show the PCB layout as seen from component side and the components layout.

TESTING GUIDELINES

Testing part of this circuit is almost self evident. You have to only switch ON the AC power and then measure the two output regulated voltages with a multimeter. The load delivering capability of the supply can also be verified by connecting a resistance of 47 ohms, 5W across each of the two outputs as shown in Fig.8.4 and keeping the circuit ON for ten to fifteen minutes. See that the

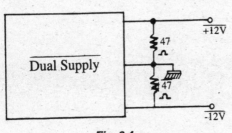

Fig. 8.4

transformer and IC regulators do not get excessively heated up and also that the regulated output voltages stay put. The regulation part can also be checked by feeding the AC input to the circuit from a VARIAC (Variable Autotransformer). You can verify that the DC outputs stay put at +12V and -12V for AC input right from 160V to 320V. The test set-up is shown in Fig.8.5.

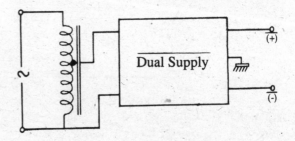

Fig. 8.5

IDENTIFYING THE LEADS

Refer to Figs.8.6 (a) to (c) for lead identification of IC-1, IC-2 and diodes D1 to D4.

OTHER VARIATIONS OF THE CIRCUIT

The same circuit configuration can be used to produce (+5V, -5V), (+9V, -9V), (+15V, -15V), (+18V, -18V) and (+24V, -24V). What you need to do is to use different type nos. for the two regulators and a different transformer. The table Table 8.1 gives the details.

158

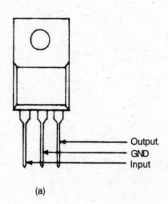

(a)

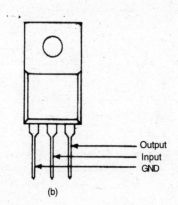

(b)

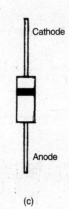

(c)

Fig. 8.6

Table: 8.1

Desired Output	T-1	IC-1	IC-2
+5V,-5V	7.5-0-7.5, 250mA	7805	7905
+9V,-9V	12-0-12, 250mA	7809	7909
+15V,-15V	15-0-15, 250mA	7815	7915
+18V,-18V	18-0-18, 250mA	7818	7918
+24V,-24V	24-0-24, 250mA	7824	7924

POSITIVE SUPPLY GENERATES — BOTH POSITIVE & NEGATIVE SUPPLIES

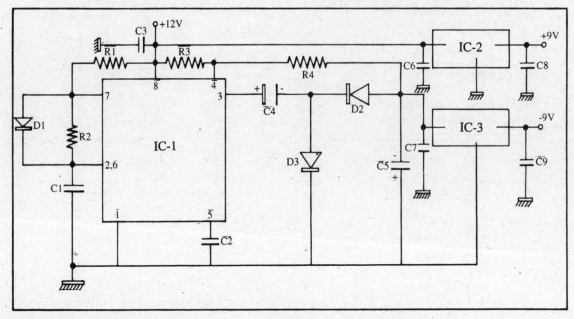

Fig. 9.1

OBJECTIVE

Quite often, the electronic circuit you want to build requires both positive as well as negative DC voltages for operation. The required DC voltages can be conveniently generated from the available AC mains but that would be possible only if you can tolerate your gadget operating from mains. In case of portable gadgets, what is usually available to you is only a single DC voltage from a battery source. This available voltage is usually 3V, 6V, 9V or 12V. In such cases, the negative DC voltage if needed requires to be generated from the available positive DC voltage.

The above circuit can be used to generate regulated DUAL SUPPLIES (+ve and -ve) from an available positive voltage. The circuit generates +9V and -9V from an input of +12V. The same circuit can also be used to generate dual supplies of any other magnitude with the only restriction that the unregulated input and regulated output differential voltage should be a minimum of 3V. Also since the absolute maximum value of Vcc for IC 555 is +18V and Vcc is nothing but the unregulated DC input in the present case, the circuit can be used to generate plus and minus voltages upto a maximum of about 12V as +15V is usually considered a safe maximum Vcc for IC 555. The desired positive voltage can be obtained by choosing proper three terminal regulator for IC-2. For desired negative voltage, you need to change both resistance R3 and regulator IC-3. The required modifications for some typical cases are given in Table 9-1.

Desired Function	R3	R4*	IC-2	IC-3
Generating +5V and -5V from available 9V battery	1K	1K	7805	7905
Generating +5V and -5V from available 12V battery	2.2K	1.6K	7805	7905
Generating +6V and -6V from available 9V battery	2.2K	2.47K	7806**	7906**

* R4 resistance value can be obtained by a parallel combination of appropriate resistors.

** In case, 7806 and 7906 are not available, 7805 can be used in place of 7806 by connecting two forward biased diodes in series from common terminal to ground. Similarly, 7905 can be used in place of 7906.

CIRCUIT DESCRIPTION

The generation of positive voltage is straightforward. It is basically choosing a proper three terminal regulator. The regulators for 5V, 9V and 12V are easily available. 6V can be generated by connecting two series connected forward biased diodes from the common terminal to ground instead of grounding the common terminal. In case you want to generate a voltage less than 5V, you may be required to replace IC-2 with resistor-zener diode combination.

IC-1 wired as an astable multivibrator and a positive clamper circuit constituted by capacitor C4 and diode D3 are the basic building blocks of positive to negative converter. The clamper circuit clamps the positive peaks of the pulse train at pin-3 of IC-1 to zero. Thus the clamped pulse train appearing across D3 switches between 0 and -V if the pulse train at pin-3 of IC-1 is switched between 0 and +V. Diode D2 and capacitor C5 provide rectification and filtration respectively.

We know that for IC timer 555 astable multivibrator to function, the RESET terminal (pin-4) should at least be at 0.8V. Voltage below 0.8 at pin-4 resets the output to LOW state. This property has been made use of in the present circuit to achieve some kind of load regulation and output voltage adjustment. The negative output voltage amplitude is the one for which voltage at pin-4 equals 0.8V.

The pulse train appearing at IC-1 output has an ON-time of $0.69R1C1$ and an OFF-time of $0.69R2C1$. These values have been so chosen as to produce a 10kHz pulse train with an ON-time of $10\mu S$ and an OFF-time of $90\mu S$. As a result, the clamped waveform across D3 stays at about -11V for 90% of the total time period. It may be mentioned here that the ON-time voltage level of the pulse train appearing at the output of IC timer 555 is usually 0.5 to 1 volt less than the Vcc.

IC-2 is a three terminal positive regulator of the type 7809. IC-3 is a three terminal negative regulator of the type 7909. Capacitors C6 to C9 are decoupling capacitors.

CONSTRUCTION GUIDELINES

The PCB layout and the components layout are respectively shown in Figs. 9.2 and 9.3.

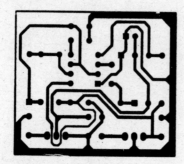

Fig. 9.2

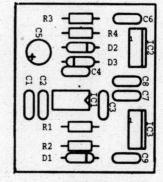

Fig. 9.3

PARTS LIST
Resistors

R1	:	1.5K, 1/4 Watt
R2	:	15K, 1/4 Watt
R3	:	1K, 1/4 Watt
R4	:	1.1K (1K + 100 ohms), 1/4 Watt

Capacitors

C1	:	0.01µF (polyester, mica)
C2	:	0.01µF (ceramic disc)
C3, C6, C7, C8, C9	:	0.1µF (ceramic disc)
C4	:	0.1µF (polyester, mica)

C5	:	10 µF (electrolytic)

Semiconductor Devices

Diodes D1, D2, D3	:	1N 4001 or equivalent
IC-1	:	IC timer 555
IC-2	:	Three terminal regulator, type 7809C
IC-3	:	Three terminal regulator, type 7909C

Miscellaneous

Solder metal, wires, power supply terminals etc.

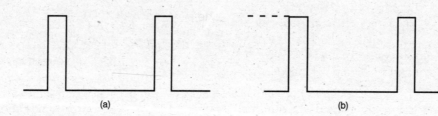

(a)

(b)

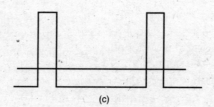

(c)

Fig. 9.4

162

TESTING GUIDELINES

If you can arrange for a general purpose oscilloscope, you can test different stages of this circuit. In the absence of an oscilloscope, you can only measure DC voltages at the input (pin-8 of IC 555), at the inputs of the two regulators (across C6 and C7) and at the outputs of the regulators (across C8 and C9). A comprehensive testing of the circuit can be carried out as follows:

1. Switch on the unregulated input to the IC 555.

2. Monitor the waveform at the output of the timer IC (pin-3 of 555). The waveform should look like what is shown in Fig.9.4 (a). If the ON and OFF timings of the waveform do not tally with the expected values, check for the resistor and capacitor values and connections in the charge and discharge paths. A permanently HIGH or LOW DC level at pin-3 of 555 is probably due to an improper grounding of pin-1. A shorted diode D1 gives almost zero OFF-time while an open diode D2 gives an ON-time larger than the OFF-time.

3. Monitor the waveform across diode D3. It should be like what is shown in Fig.9.4 (b). A shorted D3 practically gives a zero output while an open diode D3 would produce a waveform as shown in Fig.9.4 (c).

4. Measure DC voltages at the inputs of the two regulators. The expected values are +11V (at the input of IC-2) and -11V (at the input of IC-3). And if everything goes alright, then you can expect +9V at the output of IC-2 and -9V at the output of IC-3. Both the outputs have current delivering capability of 100mA each.

IDENTIFYING THE LEADS

Refer to Figs. 9.5 (a), (b) and (c) for identifying the leads of IC-2, IC-3 and diode 1N 4001.

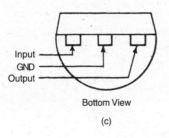

Bottom View

(c)

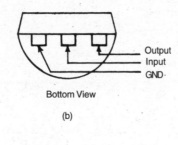

Bottom View

(b)

Fig. 9.5

PROJECT : 10

CAR BATTERY CHARGER

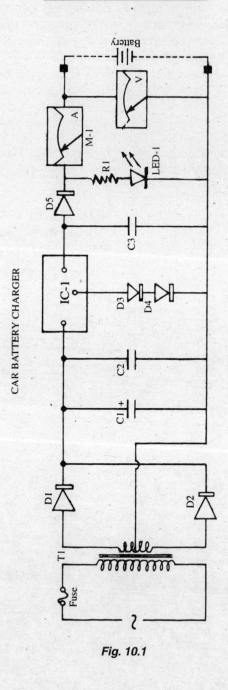

Fig. 10.1

OBJECTIVE

Here is a simple battery charger circuit, the one that can be used to charge 12 volt batteries of both the usual automobile type as well as the maintenance free sealed lead-acid type. The charger circuit being described here is quite compact and can be placed right on the top of the battery required to be charged. **In the event of your car battery misbehaving or having become weak, what you require in addition to this gadget is only the 230VAC mains. 230VAC point is quite conveniently available even if you are stuck somewhere on the roadside or elsewhere far away from a place where you can get your battery charged. This gadget could be one of the most important tools in your tool-kit and you could make use of this gadget to keep your battery healthy. Another significant point about this charger circuit is that it provides you a well regulated source of constant charging voltage. And that is what is recommended for charging of lead-acid batteries.** The gadget also provides to you metering of both voltage across the battery being charged as well as the charging current being drawn by the battery throughout the charging process. This tells you the status of the battery being charged as the time progresses.

CIRCUIT DESCRIPTION

The circuit is nothing but an AC/DC power supply that generates a regulated DC voltage of 13.2 volts from AC mains. Transformer T-1, Diodes D1 and D2 and Capacitor C1 constitute the unregulated power supply portion with D1 and D2 alongwith transformer providing voltage transformation and rectification and C1 providing the filtering action. IC-1 is a three terminal regulator of the type 7812. The common terminal of this regulator has been lifted to a potential of about 1.2 volts by the forward biased diodes D3 and D4 so as to give a regulated output voltage of 13.2 volts instead of 12V which would be the case if the common terminal was grounded. C2, C3 are decoupling capacitors. Diode D5 provides the charging path for the battery. The charging current flows from the power supply to the battery. The diode D5 also prevents the current to flow in the opposite direction i.e. from battery towards the power supply.

Meter M-1, which is a current meter, gives a continuous reading of the charging current. The current reading becomes zero when the battery is fully charged. Meter M-2 gives the reading of the voltage across the battery as it is being charged. A fully charged battery typically has an open circuit voltage of 12.5 volts or so.

CONSTRUCTION GUIDELINES

Refer to Fig.10.2 for PCB layout and Fig.10.3 for components layout. Lead identification of IC-1 is given in Fig. 10.6.

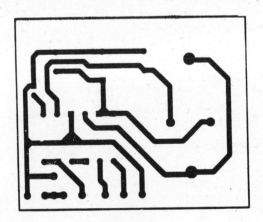

Fig. 10.2

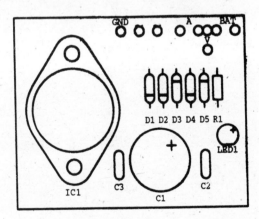

Fig. 10.3

PARTS LIST
Resistors and Capacitors
R1   : 2.2 K, 1/4 W
C1   : 1000 µF, 25V (electrolytic)
C2, C3   : 0.1 µF (ceramic disc)
Semiconductor Devices and ICs
Diodes D1, D2, D5 : BY 127
Diodes D3, D4   : 1N4001 or equivalent
IC-1   : 78T12 (It is 7812 in TO-3 package)
LED-1   : LED (Any Colour)
Miscellaneous
Meter M-1   : Ammeter 0-3A (Fig.10.4)
Meter M-2   : DC Voltmeter 0-15VDC (Fig.10.5)
Transformer T-1 : 15-0-15, 2A
Fuse F-1   : 1A tubular type with holder
Power supply terminals, solder metal, wires, mains power ON/OFF switch

Fig. 10.4

Fig. 10.5

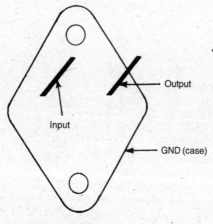

Fig. 10.6

TESTING GUIDELINES
Testing the assembled gadget is straightforward. Switch on the AC power. Measure the regulated DC output voltage across C3.13.2 to 13.4 volts appearing across C3 shows that the gadget is ready for use. Additionally, the load delivering capability of the charger can be ascertained by temporarily connecting a 6 to 10 ohms (25 watt) resistance across the output in place of the battery. Keep the gadget ON for at least ten minutes and see that there is no change in the regulated DC output voltage and also that there is no excessive heating of the transformer and regulator.

LEAD IDENTIFICATION OF MAJOR COMPONENTS
Fig.10.6 shows the pin connection diagram of IC 78T12:

Note: *Photographs shown in Figs. 10.4 and 10.5 are only representative ones to give an idea as to how the meters may look like.*

PROJECT : 11

AUTO-PROTECTION FOR TVs AND VCRs

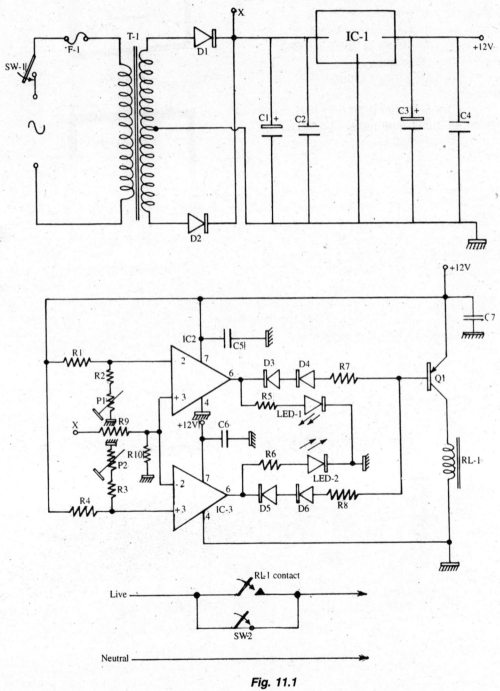

Fig. 11.1

OBJECTIVE

Here is a simple and easy to build electronic gadget that can protect your TV or VCR or any other similar mains operable system from the hazards of over and under voltages. In our country, voltage fluctuation as large as ± 40% is not unusual with the result that most of the faults in these systems are due to power supply failure. While TVs and VCRs are more likely to be damaged due to excessive voltage, Refrigerators or Fridges are severely affected by extremely low voltages. **Thus it is important to ensure that your system gets the correct AC mains voltage, of course, within a certain tolerance range which could be something like ±10%. Though most of the modern TV sets and VCRs have a power supply section that can take care of fluctuations in the AC mains over a reasonably large range, yet it is not advisable to operate your system (TV or VCR) under stress for a long time.** If an excessive voltage for instance persists for a long time, the power supply section of the system in question will be under stress for a long time. Not only this, the fluctuation could also go beyond the capability of the system's power supply section. Under these circumstances, the best alternative would be to switch off the mains supply to the system if the mains voltage exceeds or falls below predetermined limits. This is what this gadget precisely does. With this gadget, you can choose the upper and lower limits and it ensures that the mains reaches the system only when its amplitude is within the window selected by you. The gadget however also has a provision to bypass the gadget if you wish to do so.

CIRCUIT DESCRIPTION

The heart of the system is the window comparator constituted by two opamps (IC-2 and IC-3) along with peripheral components. The window comparator functions as follows: The output of each opamp depends upon the voltages present at its two inputs. The output is at GND potential when the negative input (voltage appearing at inverting input) is greater than the positive input (voltage appearing at non-inverting input) even by a few millivolts. The output voltage goes to +Vcc when the non-inverting input voltage is greater than the inverting input voltage. In the circuit shown, the voltage at the inverting input of the IC-3 and non-inverting input of IC-2 is equal to unregulated stepped down mains voltage. Infact the voltage at this point is representative of fluctuations in the mains voltage. The other inputs of the opamps (inverting input of IC-2 and non-inverting input of IC-3) are applied reference voltages generated from regulated +12V. The

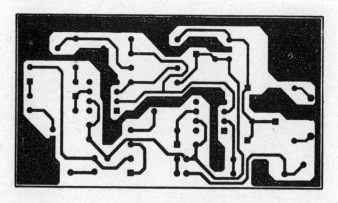

Fig. 11.2

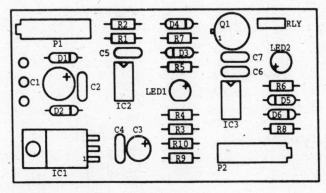

Fig. 11.3

reference voltage to IC-2 is set at +8V and the one to IC-3 is set at +6V. R9 and R10 are so adjusted that for the nominal mains input of 230 volts, the voltage at Point (Y) is +7V. Obviously, initially the output of IC-2 as well as IC-3 is at GND. Transistor Q1 as a result is in saturation i.e. it is fully conducting. Relay RL-1 is therefore actuated and its normally open contact closed. The relay contact opens when the voltage at point (Y) exceeds +8V or falls below +6V. In the present circuit, the upper limit can be set anywhere between 240V and 300V whereas the lower limit can be set anywhere between 160V and 200V. The mains voltage exceeding the upper limit or falling below the lower limit is also indicated by glowing LEDs. Switch SW-2 can be used to bypass the circuit.

The power supply portion of the circuit is nothing but a conventional transformer, full wave rectifier, capacitor filter configuration followed by a three terminal regulator of 78XX series (Type 7812) +12V acts as Vcc for transistor Q1 and the two opamps.

PARTS LIST
Resistors and Capacitors

R1	: 47K, 1/4W
R2	: 68K, 1/4W
R3	: 68K, 1/4W
R4	: 100K, 1/4W
R5, R6	: 3.3K, 1/4W
R7, R8	: 2.2K, 1/4W
R9	: 100K, 1/4W
R10	: 47K, 1/4W
P1, P2	: 47K (Preset)
C1	: 1000µF, 50V (Electrolytic)
C2, C4, C5, C6	: 0.1µF (Ceramic Disc)
C3	: 10µF, 25V (Electrolytic)

Semiconductor Devices and ICs

Diodes D1 to D6	: 1N 4001 or equivalent
LED-1 and LED-2	: preferably of different colours
Q-1	: Transistor type 2N2907
IC-1	: Three terminal regulator, Type 7812C
IC-2 and IC-3	: Opamp Type 741C

Miscellaneous

SW-1	: Mains ON/OFF switch
SW-2	: Toggle switch (Rated for mains voltage operation)
RL-1	: 12 volts DC relay with at least one SPST normally open contact
T-1	: 15-0-15, 250mA mains transformer
F-1	: 500mA fuse (tubular type) with holder

Mains lead, Solder, metal, 3-pin socket etc.

TESTING GUIDELINES

The gadget can be tested under simulated conditions by connecting an electrical bulb (60 watt or 80 watt) across the output in place of the actual system. The input to the system can be fed from a variac. The input can be varied and the input voltage limits which make the bulb go OFF seen. The test can be repeated for different settings of upper and lower limits and the results obtained compared with the ones theoretically expected.

LEAD IDENTIFICATION

Refer to Fig. 11.4 for lead identification of IC-1/IC-2/IC-3 and the diode 1N4001.

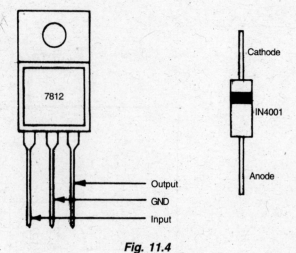

Fig. 11.4

ELECTRONIC REMINDER

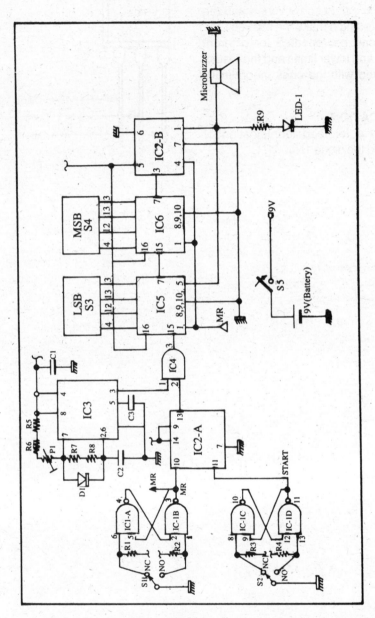

Fig. 12.1

OBJECTIVE

An easy to build gadget that could give you a reminder after the preset time after you press the start button is the project under discussion here. It is particularly useful in situations where you want to do something urgently but not immediately as you are busy doing something else and you would like to be reminded of that after some time. For instance, you have put something for cooking in the kitchen and you know that the next operation in cooking that dish is full 20 minutes away. So, you move to your bedroom and start reading some magazine. If you come across something engrossing to read, you would take your eyes off the magazine only after you get the burning smell of the dish being cooked. There can be many more similar situations. All you have to do in this reminder is to set the time in minutes with the help of two thumb wheel switches provided for the purpose and press the START button. Precisely after the time set by you is over, there is an audio as well as visual indication to remind you that the time you had set had elapsed. The gadget is portable and operates from a 9V battery.

If should attract both the House-wives as well as busy professionals.

CIRCUIT DESCRIPTION

The functional principle of this gadget is more easy to follow if we understand well different ICs being used here and the function of various terminals on each one of these ICs. The two counter ICs (designated IC-5 and IC-6 in Fig. 12.1) are the heart of this electronic reminder gadget. These are programmable UP/DOWN 4-bit Binary/Decade counters belonging to CMOS family of digital integrated circuits. These are programmable as the information present on the program inputs P0 to P3 is parallely loaded into the counter when the PL input is HIGH independent of the CP (Clock Pulse) input. These can be made to count either in the UP-Mode or the DOWN-Mode when the UP/Down input is HIGH or LOW. These can be wired as 4-bit binary counters (when BINARY/$\overline{DEC}$ input is HIGH) or decade counters (when BINARY/$\overline{DEC}$ input is LOW). The counter advances by one count on

every LOW to HIGH transition of the clock pulse. The terminal count (TC) output is usually HIGH. It goes LOW when the counter reaches its maximum count (if wired in the UP-Mode) or minimum count (if wired in the DOWN-Mode), and then HIGH again with the immediately following clock transition. The Clock Enable $(\overline{CE})$ input is an active low input as indicated by the bar i.e. the clock pulses will be enabled only when this input is LOW. Fig. 12.2 shows the internal schematic of counter IC CD4029B (IC-5 and IC-6) to facilitate better appreciation of what has been described above.

IC-2 (CD4013B) is a dual D-type flip flop IC with each D-flip flop inside CD4013B having independent DATA, CLOCK, SET and RESET inputs. The data bit (LOW or HIGH) on the D-input is transferred to the output on the LOW to HIGH transition of the clock input. SET and RESET are asynchronous inputs and are activated with a HIGH on these lines. This implies that when the SET input is at logic HIGH, the Q-output is HIGH irrespective of logic status of D-input and clock transitions. Similarly when RESET is HIGH, it overrides all other information and forces the Q-output to go to the LOW state.

IC-3 (a 555 timer IC) is wired as an astable multivibrator with the ouput waveform having a time period of one minute. For timing accuracy and stability, resistors (R5) and (R6) should preferably be metal film resistors and (C2) a tantalum capacitor. The output waveform's time period can be expressed as:

$$T = 0.69C_2 (R5+R6+R7+R8+P1)$$

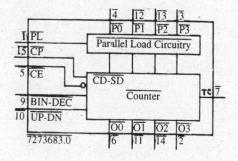

Fig. 12.2

172

IC-1 (CD4011B) is a Quad 2-input NAND i.e. the IC has four independent two input NAND gates. Two of these four NAND gates (IC-1A and IC-1B) with pull up resistors (R1) and (R2) constitute the debouncing circuit for microswitch (S1) that generates the Master Reset (MR) pulse everytime the switch is pressed and released. The other two NAND-gates (IC-1C and IC-1D) alongwith resistors (R3) and (R4) make up the other debouncing circuit for microswitch (S2) that generates the start pulse. With this background of different ICs being used here, the circuit operation can be explained as follows:

Initially, microswitches (S1) and (S2) are in a position that both MASTER RESET (MR) and START outputs are LOW. The first thing to do is to set the timing (in minutes) with the help of two BCD switches (also known as Thumbwheel switches) (S3) and (S4). If you select '5' in (S3) and '6' in (S4), the time delay is set at 65 minutes. The next step is to press and release the microswitch (S1). When this is done, a positive going pulse resets the flip flop IC, IC-2, and also loads the programmed time delay information into the counter ICs IC-5 and IC-6. Since the output of the IC-2A is initially LOW, the AND-gate is disabled and the clock pulses appearing at the output of timer IC are not allowed to reach the counter ICs. When we press and release (S2), IC-2A is clocked, its output goes HIGH; the AND-gate is enabled and the clock pulses are allowed to the clock input of IC-5. This is the time when the time delay begins. **To summarise, in order to use the gadget, set the time delay after which you would like to be reminded, press and release (S1) to be followed by a similar operation with (S2).**

We shall not go into the detailed operation of counter ICs but it would suffice to say that $(\overline{TC})$ output of IC-6 is normally HIGH and that it would go LOW and then HIGH again 65 minutes (if the time delay is set at 65 minutes) after the start. It is basically 65 clock cycles. Remember that the clock period here has been chosen to be equal to 1 minute. This pulse appearing at the $(\overline{TC})$ output of IC-6 clocks IC2-B whose output goes from LOW and HIGH and drives both the LED and the

microbuzzer ON. The output of IC-2B also forces Clock Enable $(\overline{CE})$ input of IC-5 to go HIGH and disable the clock. The LED and the Buzzer remain ON unless you reset the system. After the system is reset, the gadget is ready again for a fresh time setting.

The counters have been wired in DOWN COUNT mode as it is only then that the counter IC in LSB position completes its count cycle in a number of clock cycles equal to the number set in the LSB BCD switch and the counter connected in the MSB position completes its count cycle in a number of clock cycles equal to ten times the number set in MSB BCD switch. The time can be set in steps of one minute in this gadget. If the clock period is changed to say 2 minutes, the time resolution becomes 2 minutes whereas the maximum settable time delay increases from 99 to 198 minutes. **In essence, maximum time delay that is achievable with this circuit is 99 clock cycles with a resolution that is equal to period of one clock cycle.**

CONSTRUCTION GUIDELINES
Figs. 12.3 and 12.4 respectively show the PCB layout amd the components layout.

PARTS LIST
Resistors and Capacitors

R1, R2,	
R3, R4	: 22K, 1/4 Watt
R5	: 2.2M, 1/4 Watt (Metal film)
R6	: 680K, 1/4 Watt (Metal film)
R7	: 5.6M, 1/4 Watt (Metal film)
R8	: 220K, 1/4 Watt (Metal film)
R9	: 4.7K, 1/4 Watt
P1	: 100K multi-turn trimmer potentiometer
C1	: 0.1µF (Ceramic Disc)
C2	: 10µF, 16V (Solid Tantalum)
C3	: 0.01µF (Ceramic Disc)

Semiconductor Devices and ICs

D1	: 1N4001 or equivalent
LED-1	: LED (any colour you like) with holder
IC-1	: CD4011B
IC-2	: CD4013B
IC-3	: 555

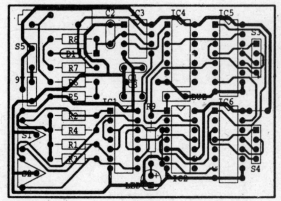

Fig. 12.3

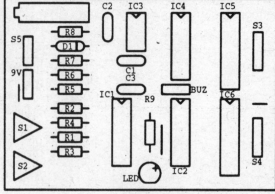

Fig. 12.4

IC-4   : CD4081B
IC-5, IC-6   : CD4029B

Other Components

S1, S2   : Miniature push button microswitches

S3, S4   : BCD switches (Thumbwheel switches) Fig. 12.5

S5   : ON/OFF switch

Microbuzzer, 9V Battery

Miscellaneous

IC Bases (8-pin, 14-pin, 16-pin), Multistrand wires, solder metal, suitable mounting cabinet.

CLOCK PERIOD ADJUSTMENT

For the given component values, the clock waveform at the output of 555 has a high time of 20 seconds and a low time of 40 seconds. In fact, for a high time of 20 seconds, the total charging resistance (R5+R6+P1) is required to be 2.9 mega-ohms. P1 can be adjusted to get (R5+R6+P1) equal to 2.9 mega-ohms. Total discharge resistance required for a 40 seconds low time is 5.8 mega-ohms. The total discharge resistance connected in the circuit is 5.82 mega-ohms which should be fairly accurate. **Discrepancy if any should be corrected by readjusting P1 to get an overall time of 1 minute. That is what is important. The high and low times individually are not important, it is the total time period that must precisely be one minute.**

Fig. 12.5

PIN CONNECTION DIAGRAMS OF ICS

Pin connection diagrams of CD4011B, CD4013B, CD4081B and CD4029B are shown in Figs. 12.6(a), (b), (c) and (d) respectively.

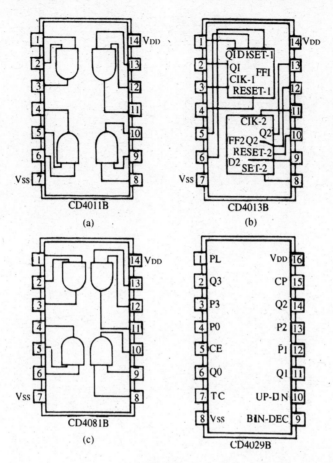

Fig. 12.6

AUTO SWITCH ON FOR TV

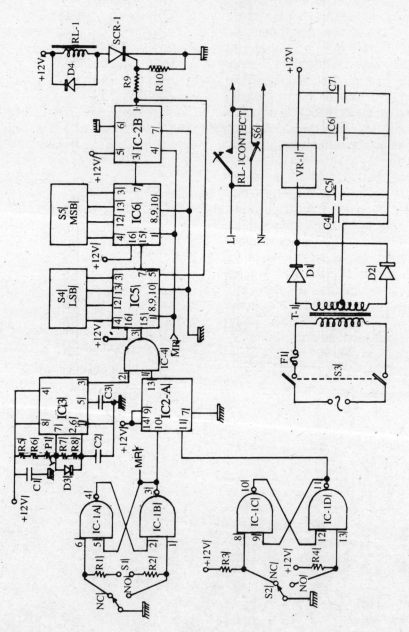

Fig. 13.1

OBJECTIVE

Believe it or not, there are numerous occasions when you have switched on your TV set to watch a specific program of your interest and you found out that there are still a few more minutes to go. The options before you are to either remain glued on to the TV set and wait for your program or switch off the TV set and then switch it on again after sometime. The first option is boring and with the second, you always run the risk of missing a part of the program if you get busy in something else and forget to switch it on in time. Here is a very simple and interesting gadget that could be very easily mounted on your electrical switchboard and which can be used to perform the auto switch on function for your TV set (or for that matter any other mains operated system) at a time programmed by you. With this gadget, you could set a timing of 99 minutes maximum with a resolution of one minute. **For instance, if you want that your TV set should automatically switch on fifteen minutes from now, all you have got to do is to set 15 in the BCD switches, reset the gadget and press start. Remember that you have to keep the ON/OFF switch on your TV set in the On-position. The gadget can also be bypassed if you so desired with the help of a switch provided on the gadget itself.**

CIRCUIT DESCRIPTION

The circuit shown in Fig. 13.1 is identical to the one described in case of Electronic Reminder gadget of the previous project except for addition of a power supply section that generates +12VDC for circuit operation and the output of IC-2B driving an SCR to energise a relay rather than a microbuzzer and an LED as in case of reminder gadget. The ICs used are the same. IC-1 is a Quad 2-input NAND wired as two independent debouncing circuits, IC-2 is a dual D-type flip flop, IC-3 is a 555 timer generating clock pulses at a rate of one clock pulse per minute, IC-5 and IC-6 are programmable Binary/Decade UP/DOWN counters, IC-4 is a Quad 2-input AND gate. All these ICs alongwith their pin designations and functions have already been discussed at length in project-12 and shall not be repeated here. The auto switch on gadget operates as follows:

Initially, both MASTER RESET (MR) and START outputs are LOW. Set the time in minutes from the BCD switches S4 and S5 after which you want your gadget (TV, VCR etc.) to switch on. Having programmed the time delay, press and release (S1) to apply the reset pulse. The positive going reset pulse resets flip flop IC (IC-2) and also loads the programmed time delay information into counter ICs, IC-5 and IC-6. Since the output of IC-2A is initially LOW, the AND-gate is disabled and the clock pulses are not allowed to reach the clock input terminal of counter IC-5 when we press and release (S2), IC-2A is clocked and its output goes HIGH, the AND-gate is enabled and the clock pulses are allowed to the clock input of IC-5. This is the time when the time delay begins. Also, as the power to the TV set or VCR is through the normally open relay contact, the system remains off. We shall not go into the detailed operation of counter ICs but it would suffice to say that ($\overline{TC}$) output of IC-6 is normally HIGH and that it would go to LOW state and then HIGH again when the preset time delay has elapsed. This pulse appearing at ($\overline{TC}$) output of IC-6 clocks IC-2B whose output goes from LOW to HIGH. This LOW to HIGH transition triggers the SCR thus energising relay coil RL-1. The normally open relay contact closes and the system is switched on. The output of IC-2B also forces the Clock Enable ($\overline{CE}$) input of IC-5 to go HIGH and disable the clock. The system remains on unless you reset the system.

The counters have been wired in the DOWN count mode as it is only then that the counter IC in LSB position completes its count cycle in a number of clock pulses equal to the number set in the LSB BCD switch. The counter connected in MSB position then completes its count cycle in a number of clock pulses equal to ten times the number set in the MSB BCD switch. This gives a total time delay equal to the time period of (N) clock pulses where (N) here is the decimal number preset with the help of BCD switches (S4) and (S5). As the clock period is one minute, the time here can be set in steps of one minute. **In essence, maximum time delay that is achievable from the gadget is 99 clock cycles'**

period with a time resolution equal to period of one clock cycle:

The power supply section is a conventional step-down transformer, two-diode full wave rectifier (using a transformer with a center tapped secondary winding) and a capacitor filter configuration followed by a 12V output three terminal regulator.

CONSTRUCTION GUIDELINES

Figs. 13.2 and 13.3 respectively show the PCB layout and the components layout.

PARTS LIST
Resistors and Capacitors

R1, R2, R3, R4	: 22K, 1/4 Watt
R5	: 2.2M, 1/4 Watt (Metal film)
R6	: 680K, 1/4 Watt (Metal film)
R7	: 5.6M, 1/4 Watt (Metal film)
R8	: 220K, 1/4 Watt (Metal film)
R9	: 1.5K, 1/4 Watt
R10	: 220Ω, 1/4 Watt
P1	: 100K multiturn trimmer potentiometer
C1	: 0.1µF (Ceramic Disc)
C2	: 10µF, 16V (Tantalum)
C3	: 0.01µF (Ceramic Disc)
C4	: 1000µF, 25V (Electrolytic)
C5, C7	: 0.1µF (Ceramic Disc)
C6	: 10µF, 16V (Electrolytic)

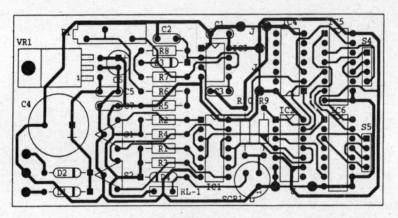

Fig. 13.2

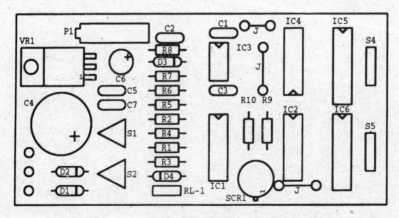

Fig. 13.3

178

Semiconductor Devices and ICs

D1 to D4	:	1N4001 or equivalent
IC-1	:	CD4011B
IC-2	:	CD4013B
IC-3	:	555
IC-4	:	CD4081B
IC-5, IC-6	:	CD4029B
SCR-1	:	OE101 or equivalent
VR-1	:	Three terminal Regulator, Type 7812

OTHER COMPONENTS

S1, S2	:	Miniature push button microswitches
S3	:	Mains power ON/OFF switch
S4, S5	:	BCD switches (Thumb–wheel switches)
S6	:	ON/OFF switch (230VAC, 1A)
RL-1	:	12DC Relay with at least one normally open contact
T-1	:	Mains transformer (Primary: 230VAC Secondary: 14-0-14, 250mA)
F-1	:	Fuse (0.5A) with holder

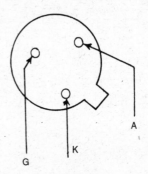

Fig. 13.4

Miscellaneous

IC Bases (8 pin, 14-pin, 16-pin), Multistrand wires, Solder metal, Suitable mounting cabinet, etc.

CLOCK PERIOD ADJUSTMENT, PIN CONNECTION DIAGRAMS

Clock period should be precisely adjusted to one minute. The adjustment guidelines are the same as a explained in case of Project: 12. The pin connection diagrams of different ICs being used have already been given in Project: 12. Pin connections for the SCR are shown in Fig. 13.4.

ALL ELECTRONIC ANALOG CAPACITANCE METER

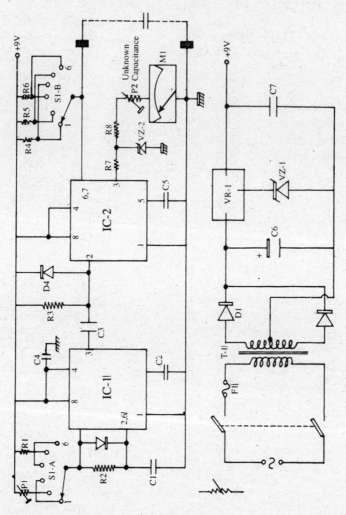

Fig. 14.1

OBJECTIVE

The circuit shown in Fig. 14.1 is that of a simple analog capacitance meter built around IC 555. It operates from a 9V battery and a provision for mains operation is also there. This test gadget can be used to measure capacitance values over a range from 0.0001μF to 100μF.

CIRCUIT DESCRIPTION

The operational principle of this capacitance meter is quite straightforward. It is built around two 555's, the first (IC-1) wired as an astable multivibrator and the second (IC-2) connected in the monoshot configuration and triggered by the 555 wired in the astable mode. There is a 2-pole

6 throw (2P6T) rotary switch that can be used to select the capacitance range. One half of this rotary switch has been wired in the astable multivibrator portion of the circuit and is being used to operate the astable multivibrator in two different frequencies, one for the first three capacitance ranges and the other for the remaining three capacitance ranges. The second part of the rotary switch is used to select appropriate resistance for the monoshot output timing circuit.

In the first three ranges, the values of R1 and R2 are such that the astable frequency is 10kHz. The waveform appearing at pin-3 of IC-1 has a high time depending on the setting of potentiometer P1. It should be set for a high time so as to give an overall time period of 100 µS. Now the frequency of the trigger pulses appearing at pin-2 of IC-2 wired as monoshot is a pulse every 100 µS for the first three ranges. For the first range, R4 is so chosen that it gives an output pulse width of 100µS for an unknown capacitance of 0.001µF so as to give full scale deflection in the meter. R5 is so chosen that it gives a pulse width of 100µS for an unknown capacitance of 0.01µF and R6 is so chosen that it gives a pulse width of 100µS for an unknown capacitance of 0.1µF.

In the fourth range, the astable time period becomes 100mS with the result that R4, R5 and R6 respectively give pulse widths of 100mS for unknown capacitance values of 1,10 and 100µF. Thus we get the following six capacitance ranges:
1. 0.0001µF to 0.001µF
2. 0.001µF to 0.01µF
3. 0.01µF to 0.1µF
4. 0.1µF to 1.0µF
5. 1.0 µF to 10 µF
6. 10µF to 100 µF

In nutshell, the unknown capacitance is being measured in terms of varying duty cycle and hence the average value of the waveform at the monoshot output. To get a continuous waveform at the output of the monoshot, it is triggered by an astable output. Two very important points to be borne in mind while constructing this project are:

1. The astable output frequencies should be set very precisely. Preferably, metal film resistors should be used in place of R1 and R2. Monoshot timing resistors R4, R5 and R6 should also be preferably of metal film variety.

2. The gadget should be calibrated by first choosing a range from the first half and connecting an appropriate capacitance so as to give full scale deflection. Potentiometer P2 can be adjusted to give full scale deflection. The calibration process can be repeated as cross check by choosing a range from the second half. Precision capacitors should be used for calibration purpose.

PARTS LIST
Resistors and Capacitors

R1	: 1M, 1/4W (Metal film)
R2	: 1K, 1/4W (Metal film)
R3	: 10K, 1/4W (Carbon film)
R4	: 100K, 1/4W (Metal film)
R5	: 10K, 1/4W (Metal film)
R6	: 1K, 1/4W (Metal film)
R7	: 330 ohms, 1/4W (Carbon film)
R8	: 3.3K, 1/4W (Carbon film)
P1	: 1K preset
P2	: 10K preset
C1	: 0.1µF, 25V (Polystyrene or Polyester)
C2	: 0.01µF (Ceramic disc)
C3	: 0.01µF (Ceramic disc)
C4	: 0.1µF (Ceramic disc)
C5	: 0.01µF (Ceramic disc)
C6	: 100µF, 25V (Electrolytic)
C7	: 0.1µF (Ceramic disc)

Semiconductors and ICs

D1 to D4	: 1N 4001 or equivalent
VZ-1	: 3.9V, 400mW zener diode
VZ-2	: 5.6V, 400mW zener diode
VR-1	: 7805C (Three terminal regulator)
IC-1, IC-2	: 555C

Miscellaneous

T-1	: Mains transformer, Primary: 230V,

Secondary: 9-0-9V, 250mA

Fuse : 1A rating
S1 : 2P6T rotary switch (Fig. 13.2)
S2 : Mains ON/OFF switch
Meter : 1mA F.S.D. meter
Mains power cord
Knob for the rotary switch
Solder wire

CONSTRUCTION GUIDELINES

Figs. 14.3 and 14.4 respectively show the PCB layout and the components, layout for the circuit diagram of Fig. 14.1.

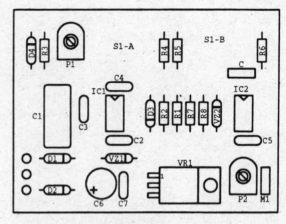

Fig. 14.4

Fig. 14.2

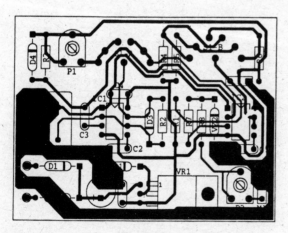

Fig. 14.3

TESTING GUIDELINES

1. The gadget can be tested by measuring the capacitance value of a large number of capaciors in different range setting positions. You can try the following values: 0.0001µF, 0.00022µF, 0.00033µF, 0.00047µF, 0.001µF, 0.0022µF, 0.0033µF, 0.0047µF, 0.01µF, 0.022µF, 0.033µF, 0.047µF, 0.1µF, 0.22µF, 0.33µF, 0.47µF, 1µF, 2.2µF, 3.3µF, 4.7µF, 10µF, 22µF, 33µF, 47µF, 100µF.

2. If you find that the capacitance meter is not showing any deflection in any of the range settings or in any one range setting, it is suggested that the waveforms at the output of astable multivibrator and the monoshot be checked and verified. In case the output of astable portion does not appear, check whether pin-1 is properly grounded and pin-5 shows a DC voltage of 2/3 Vcc i.e. 6V. Also check Vcc i.e. +9V at pin-8 and pin-4. Component level checking should start only after that. In case astable portion is functioning normally and still there is no monoshot output, check pin -1 to be at ground potential, pin-5 at +6V, pins 4 and 8 at +9V for the 555 wired as a monoshot. If these voltages are present and the monoshot is refusing to work, check the trigger waveform at pin-2.It should be Vcc (i.e. +9V) to Ground (or atleast less than 1/3Vcc) going pulse. Component level troubleshoting should begin only after that.

FULLY AUTOMATIC EMERGENCY LIGHT

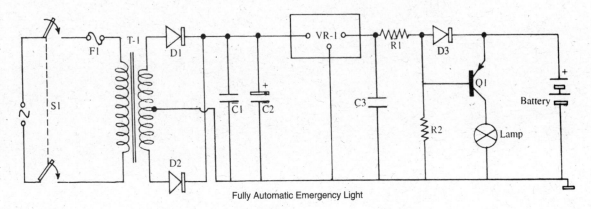

Fully Automatic Emergency Light

Fig. 15.1

OBJECTIVE

The objective is to build a fully automatic emergency light that remains off in the normal circumstances and switching on automatically in the event of mains power failure. Such gadgets are very useful when used in places such as electricity meter box or the place where the various cut outs are located. The other useful places for these gadgets are cupboards and other dark corners where a little bit of light in case of power failure is of great utility. Another gadget that had similar application but was not automatic was discussed earlier in one of the projects. In that case, one needed to switch on the light manually at the location where the gadget is located. It causes a little bit of inconvenience when reaching that place in complete darkness is itself a big problem.

CIRCUIT DESCRIPTION

The circuit operates as follows: In case mains power is available, it is rectified, filtered and regulated to produce 9VDC. T-1 is the step-down transformer, diodes D1 and D2 constitute the full wave rectifier alongwith the center tapped secondary winding, C2 is the filter capacitor and

VR-1 is a 9V three terminal regulator. C1 and C3 are decoupling capacitors. This 9V is used to provide constant current charging for the 6V battery (5, 1.2V, Ni-Cd cells in series). Diode D3 is forward biased during charging. The forward biased diode D3 ensures that the emitter potential of transistor is less than that of its base potential. As a result, transistor (Q1) remains in cut-off. (R1) is so chosen that the charging current for the Ni-Cd battery pack is about 100mA. To sum up, in the presence of mains power, transistor (Q1) is OFF and the battery is charged from the DC supply produced from mains.

In case of mains failure, the anode voltage of diode (D3) falls below the cathode voltage of (D3). D3 becomes reverse biased, the base emitter junction of (Q1) is forward biased and it conducts. The lamp is lighted. Thus as long as mains power is absent, the lamp gets its power from the battery. The time period for which the lamp could be maintained in the lighted state depends upon the capacity of the battery. The lamp extinguishes automatically when the mains power is restored. The charge drained out of the battery during mains power OFF condition is now replenished again.

CONSTRUCTION GUIDELINES

Figs. 15.2 and 15.3 respectively show the PCB layout and the components layout.

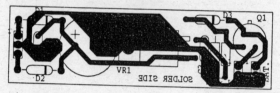

Fig. 15.2

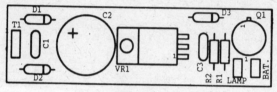

Fig. 15.3

In case, the three terminal regulator type 7809 is not available, as it is not a commonly used value, the same could be simulated from a 5V regulator (type 7805) as per the circuit configuration shown in Fig. 15.4. That is, what you have to do is to connect a 3.9V zener diode from common terminal of the regulator to ground instead of grounding the common terminal.

PARTS LIST
Resistors & Capacitors

R1	: 27Ω, 1/2W
R2	: 470Ω, 1/4W
C1, C3	: 0.1μF (Ceramic disc)
C2	: 1000μF, 16V (Electrolytic)

Semiconductor Devices

D1, D2, D3	: 1N4001 or equivalent
Q1	: 2N2907
VR-1	: Three terminal regulator, Type No. 7809

Other Components

S1	: Mains power ON/OFF switch
F1	: Fuse (0.5A rating) with holder
T-1	: Mains transformer Primary : 230VAC Secondary : 12-0-12, 250mA
Lamp	: 6 VDC Lamp
Battery	: 5×1.2V, 2Ah Ni-Cd Cells

Miscellaneous

Multistrand wires, suitable mounting cabinet, solder metal, mains lead etc.

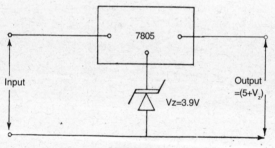

Fig. 15.4

PROJECT : 16

PORTABLE ELECTRONIC RESISTANCE METER

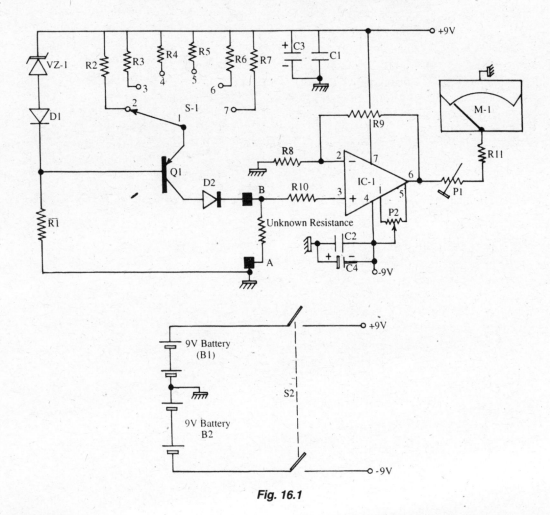

Fig. 16.1

OBJECTIVE

A simple, easy to build portable all electronic resistance meter that can be used to accurately measure resistances upto a maximum of 1MΩ is the project under construction here. The circuit operates from twin 9V batteries. The resistance meter has a linear scale and the zero resistance point appears on the extreme left end of the scale. **Another significant feature of this meter is that it can be used to measure resistances without actually taking them out of the circuit.** It has six

different selectable ranges that permit resistance measurement in decades of (i) 0 to 10Ω (ii) 10Ω to 100Ω (iii) 100Ω to 1K (iv) 1K to 10K (v) 10K to 100K and (vi) 100K to 1M

CIRCUIT DESCRIPTION

The measurement of resistance in this meter is in terms of voltage developed across the unknown resistance due to a constant current flowing through it. The voltage is directly proportional to the unknown resistance value if the current is constant. Different resistance ranges have been achieved by changing the amplitude of constant current i.e. the current remains constant only for a given resistance range. Also, the constant current amplitude is so chosen that in a given resistance range, it produces a voltage of 0.5V for the highest value of resistance in that range. That is, if you have selected a range of say 1K to 10K, then the amplitude of constant current for this range will be 50μA. This enables the user to use the meter without taking the components out of the circuit as 0.5V would not operate any of the silicon semiconductor devices (Diodes, Transistors etc.)

The constant current source is constituted by transistor (Q1), diodes (D1) and (D2), Zener diode (VZ1), resistors (R1) to (R7). Resistor (R1) provides bias current for the zener diode (VZ1) and diode (D1). The amplitude of constant current is given by VZ1 divided by the resistance appearing in the emitter lead of (Q1) as the drop across (D1) cancels the (VBE) drop of (Q1). VZ1 is a 5V zener diode and the resistors (R2) to (R7) are so chosen that the amplitudes of constant currents in six different range settings of switch (S1) are 50mA, 5mA, 500μA, 50μA, 5μA and 500nA. Six different ranges are (i) 0 to 10 ohms (ii) 10 ohms to 100 ohms (iii) 100 ohms to 1000 ohms (iv) 1K to 10K (v) 10K to 100K and (vi) 100K to 1M. That is, 10Ω, 100Ω, 1000Ω, 10K, 100K and 1M resistors produce 0.5V across them and give full scale deflection in six different range settings. Resistors (R2) to (R7) should be precision resistors (±1% or better) as the accuracy of the instrument largely depends upon precision of these resistors.

IC-1 is an opamp and is wired as a non-inverting amplifier with a gain of (1+R9/R8). The gain has been chosen to be (11) to produce 5.5 V at the opamp output for a full scale deflection in the meter. (C1) (C2), C3 and C4 are power supply decoupling capacitors. (P2) is the offset adjust potentiometer for the opamp. This potentiometer is used to calibrate the meter to read zero when a zero (or a short) resistance is connected between the unknown resistance terminals. (P1)

is used to calibrate the full scale deflection end of the meter.

CALIBRATION

Connect a small piece of wire between the unknown resistance terminals to simulate a zero resistance. Select any of the resistance ranges. Potentiometer (P2) is adjusted to get a zero reading on the meter. Choose 10K full scale deflection range and connect a 10K, ±0.5% or ±1% resistor in place of shorted wire. Adjust (P1) to get full scale deflection on the meter. The meter is calibrated. If you have any difficulty in getting a precision 10K resistor for calibration, you could choose one from a general purpose resistor lot that is within ±0.5% of 10K.

CONSTRUCTION GUIDELINES

Figs. 16.2 and 16.3 respectively show the PCB layout the components layout.

PARTS LIST
Resistors and Capacitors

R1	: 330Ω, 1/4W
R2	: 100Ω, 1/4W (Metal film)
R3	: 1K, 1/4W (Metal film)
R4	: 10K, 1/4W (Metal film)
R5	: 100K, 1/4W (Metal film)
R6	: 1M, 1/4W (Metal film)
R7	: 10M, 1/4W (Metal film)
R8	: 1K, 1/4W
R9	: 10K, 1/4W
R10	: 10K, 1/4W
R11	: 1K, 1/4W
P1, P2	: 10K, Multiturn trimmer potentiometer
C1, C2	: 0.1μF (Ceramic disc)
C3, C4	: 10μF, 16V (Electrolytic)

Semiconductor Devices and ICs

D1, D2	: 1N4001 or equivalent
VZ1	: 5V, 400mW zener diode
IC-1	: opamp 741
Q1	: 2N2907

Other components

Battery	: Two 9V batteries
S1	: Rotary switch with one pole and at least six throws

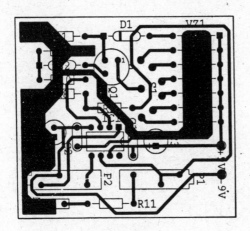

Fig. 16.2

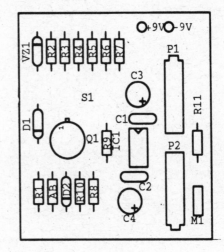

Fig. 16.3

S2	:	DPDT switch
Meter	:	Meter with 1mA f.s.d.

Miscellaneous

8-pin D.I.L. IC base (1 No.), Multistrand wires, solder metal, leads with crocodile clips, suitable mounting cabinet.

DIGITAL STOPWATCH

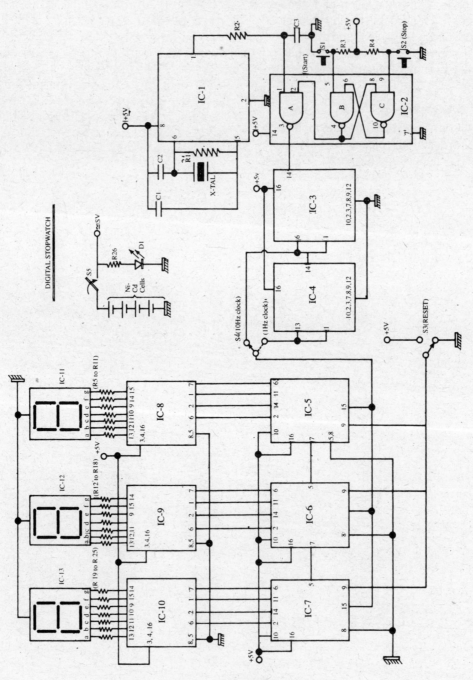

Fig. 17.1

OBJECTIVE

The project under construction here is a DIGITAL STOPWATCH that could count time upto a maximum of 99.9 seconds with a resolution of 0.1 sec (or in steps of 0.1 sec.) or upto a maximum of 999 seconds with a resolution of 1 second. This has been possible by having two clock frequency options, a 10Hz clock and a 1Hz clock. This gadget can be used to accurately measure short time intervals.It is portable and operates from four rechargeable Ni-Cd cells.

CIRCUIT DESCRIPTION

IC1 (MM5369) is a popular IC used for generating clock pulses in digital time pieces. IC-1 alongwith resistors (R1), capacitors (C1) and (C2) and crystal generates a 60Hz clock signal at its output (Pin-1). This 60Hz clock signal is passed on to the clock input of IC-3 (CD4018B) via an arrangement of NAND-gates. It is easy to see that whenever the START switch is pressed momentarily, pin-4 and thus pin-2 of IC-2 goes HIGH which enables the NAND-gate designated IC-2A with the result that the clock signal is passed onto the IC-3 clock input. When STOP switch (S2) is pressed momentarily, the NAND-gate designated IC-2A is disabled due to pin-4 of IC-2 going LOW with the result that the clock pulses are not allowed to reach IC-3. IC-3 and IC-4 (CD4018B) are presettable divide by (N) counters where (N) could be 2, 3, 4, 5, 6, 7, 8, 9 or 10. IC-3 here has been wired as a divide by-6 counter by feeding (Q3) output to Data input of the IC. IC-4 has been wired as a divide-by-10 counter by feeding (Q5) output back to the Data input. With 60Hz clock input to IC-3, we get a 10Hz clock signal at IC-3 output which when fed to the IC-4 as the clock signal results in a 1Hz clock signal at the output of IC-4.

IC-5, IC-6 and IC-7 (CD4510B) are presettable UP/DOWN BCD decade counters.These counters are connected in cascade arrangement and can count upto a maximum of 999 clock pulses. When fed with a 1Hz clock, the maximum attainable time delay between start and stop operations is thus 999 seconds. Similarly, when the clock frequency is chosen to be 10Hz, the

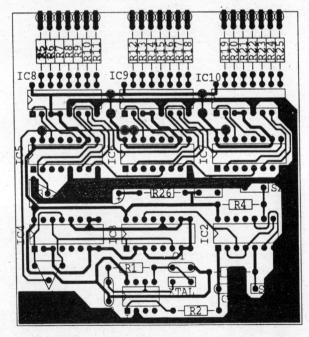

Fig. 17.2

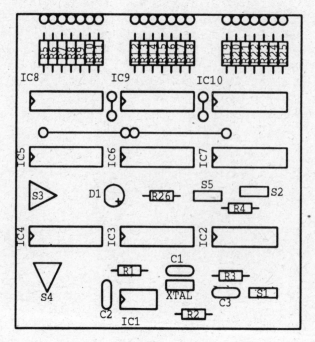

Fig. 17.3

maximum attainable time delay is 99.9 seconds. The RESET switch can be used to reset the counter to all zeros before start. Usually, the reset terminal is at GND, it is momentarily connected to +5V to reset the counter.

IC-8, IC-9 and IC-10 (CD4511B) are BCD to seven segment latch decoder drivers. IC CD4511B can directly drive seven segment LED displays of the common cathode variety.

IC-11, IC-12 and IC-13 (LT543) are seven segment displays of common cathode type. R5 to R25 are current limiting resistors.

CONSTRUCTION GUIDELINES
Figs. 17.2 and 17.3 respectively show the PCB layout and the components layout. Pin connection diagrams of CD4510B, CD4511B, CD4011B and LT543 are respectively shown in Figs. 17.4, 17.5, 17.6 and 17.7.

PARTS LIST
Resistors & Capacitors
R1	: 22M, 1/4W
R2, R26	: 1K, 1/4W
R3, R4	: 22K, 1/4W
R5 to R25	: 680Ω, 1/4W
C1, C2	: 33pF (Ceramic)
C3	: 0.0022µF (Ceramic)

Semiconductor Devices and ICs
D1	: LED
IC-1	: MM5369
IC-2	: CD4011B
IC-3, IC-4	: CD4018B
IC-5, IC-6, IC-7	: CD4510B
IC-8, IC-9, IC-10	: CD4511B
IC-11, IC-12,	
IC-13	: LT543 (Common cathode seven segment display)

Other Components
X-TAL	: 3.5795 MHz crystal
S1, S2	: Miniature push button microswitches
S3, S4	: SPDT switch
S5	: ON/OFF switch

Miscellaneous
IC Bases (14-pin, 16-pin), Nickel-Cadmium Cells (4 Nos.), Multistrand wires, solder metal, suitable mounting cabinet.

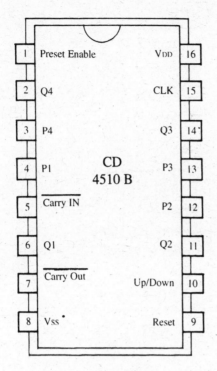

Fig. 17.4

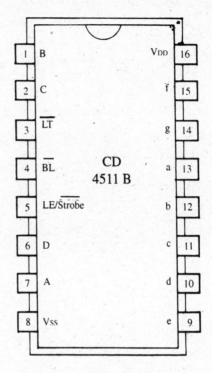

Fig. 17.5

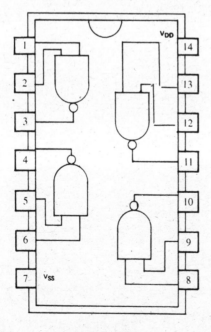

Fig. 17.6

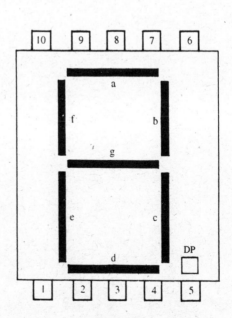

Fig. 17.7

191

31/2-Digit Voltmeter with LED Display

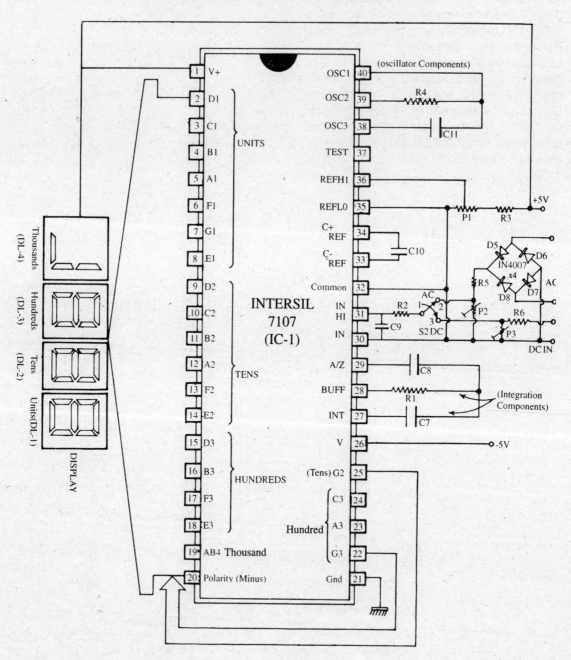

Fig. 18.1

192

OBJECTIVE

The objective here is to build a 31/2-digit digital voltmeter with a standard instrument sized LED display. It may be mentioned here that the IC type number ICL7107 is almost universally used for digital voltmeter applications and the circuit shown in Fig. 18.1 is basically what you would discover inside any digital panelmeter with a 31/2-digit LED display. The said voltmeter has been designed to operate from AC mains to generate regulated +5VDC and –5VDC for the circuit. Digital panel meters with an LED display usually operate from AC mains due to significant current drive requirement of LED displays. There is a separate power supply section (Fig. 18.2) that generates regulated +5VDC and –5VDC. **It is also worthwhile mentioning here that this circuit can also be used for the digital display of any electrical or non-electrical quantity that can be converted into a proportional DC voltage. Digital pH-meters, Pressure meters, Digital Thermometers etc. are all built around the basic circuit shown in Fig. 18.1.** The digital voltmeter circuit shown in Fig. 18.1 alongwith the power supply section of Fig. 18.2 can be used to measure DC voltages over a range of 0 to 1000 VDC. It also has a provision of measuring the AC mains voltage RMS value.

CIRCUIT DESCRIPTION

IC ICL7107 from INTERSIL is the heart of the system. Without going into the internal circuit details of this IC, it would suffice to mention here that the said IC is basically a dual slope integrating A/D converter with its own on-chip oscillator (that serves as the clock), reference, decoder and driver and it is capable of driving directly an instrument sized LED display of the common-anode type. The display reading depends upon the analog input voltage and the reference voltage. The reference voltage is so adjusted that the display reads the analog input directly. In the circuit shown in Fig. 18.1, switch S2 can be used to select DC or AC measurement. When the switch is on AC position, what is actually fed to the analog input terminals of the IC7107 is the rectified (full wave) AC input after the voltage divider arrangement constituted by resistor (R5) and potentiometer (P2). We shall discuss the adjustment of (P2) under the heading of CALIBRATION. Similarly, when the AC/DC select switch (S2) is on DC, what gets applied to the analog input terminals of the IC7107 is the DC input divided by the voltage divider arrangement constituted by (R6) and (P3). Adjustment of (P3) will be discussed when we discuss the calibration procedure.

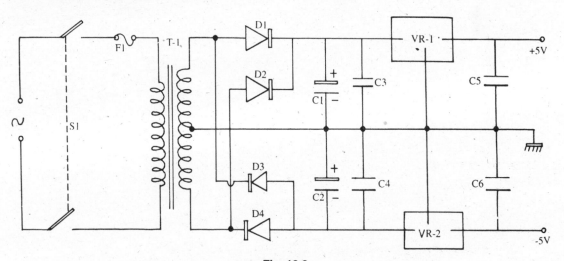

Fig. 18.2

The power supply section (Fig. 18.2) is a conventional AC/DC power supply using a step down center tapped mains transformer (T-1), full wave rectifier circuits (D1 and D2 for positive output, D3 and D4 for negative output) and capacitor filters (C1 for positive output and C2 for negative output). Regulation is achieved using three terminal regulators (VR-1 for positive output and VR-2 for negative output). C3 to C6 are decoupling capacitors.

CALIBRATION PROCEDURE
The calibration procedure is as follows:

1. Select the AC/DC switch (S2) to be on DC position, feed 1000 VDC from a high voltage power supply at DC IN terminals. Adjust potentiometer (P3) to get 2VDC at point-1 of the SPDT switch (S2). If 1000VDC is not available, a lower DC voltage can also be used and in that case, the divided voltage should also be proportionately reduced. For instance, for 100 VDC input, the divided voltage will be 200mV. In other words, (P3) should be so adjusted that (R6) and (P3) give a voltage division by a factor of 500.

2. Now, as a second step, adjust potentiometer (P1) so that the meter directly reads the DC input voltage.

3. Change the AC/DC select switch to AC position. Feed AC mains voltage at the AC IN terminals. Adjust potentiometer (P2) so that display directly reads RMS value of the AC input. Before feeding the AC mains, the RMS value of the AC mains should be checked independently with another voltmeter or multimeter with AC voltage measuring capability.

4. The voltmeter is now calibrated and ready for use.

5. The calibration of this voltmeter should be checked at regular intervals as it may get disturbed due to inherent change in the resistance values of voltage divider resistors.

You may be required to readjust different potentiometers to restore calibration.

CONSTRUCTION GUIDELINES
Figs 18.3 and 18.4 respectively show the PCB layout and the components layout.

PARTS LIST
Resistors and Capacitors

R1	: 470K, 1/4W
R2	: 1M, 1/4W
R3	: 22K, 1/4W
R4	: 100K, 1/4W
R5	: 1M, 1500V (You can also use three 330K, 1/2W resistors in series)
R6	: 2.2M, 1W, 1500V resistor
P1	: 1K Preset
P2, P3	: 10K Preset
C1, C2	: 1000µF, 16V (Electrolytic)
C3 to C6	: 0.1µF (Ceramic disc)
C7	: 0.22µF (Polyester)
C8	: 0.47µF (Polyester)
C9	: 0.01µF (Ceramic disc)
C10	: 0.1µF (Ceramic disc)
C11	: 100pF (Polyester)

Semiconductor Devices and ICs

D1 to D8	: 1N4007 or equivalent
VR-1	: 7805 (Three terminal regulator)
VR-2	: 7905 (Three terminal regulator)
IC-1	: ICL 7107
Display (DL-1 to DL-4)	: Common anode display type no. LTS-542

Other Components

S1	: Mains ON/OFF switch
S2	: SPDT switch, 230V, 1A
F1	: Fuse, 1A rating with fuse holder
T-1	: Mains transformer (Primary: 230VAC, Secondary: 7.5-0-7.5, 500mA)

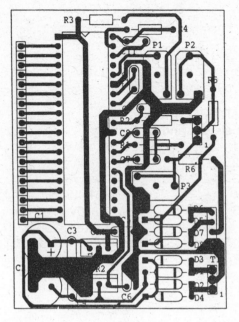

Fig. 18.3

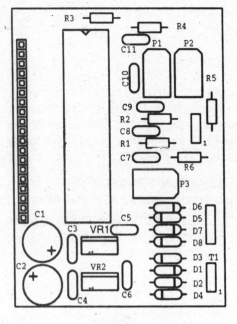

Fig. 18.4

Miscellaneous

Solder metal, multistrand wires, suitable mounting cabinet.

Pin Connection Diagram of Display

Fig. 18.5 shows the pin connection diagram of seven segment display type no. LTS-542.

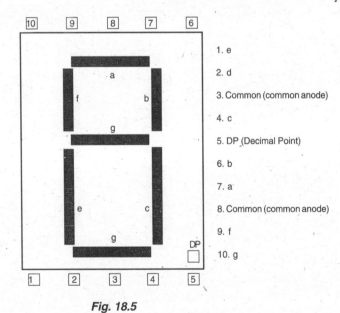

1. e

2. d

3. Common (common anode)

4. c

5. DP (Decimal Point)

6. b

7. a

8. Common (common anode)

9. f

10. g

Fig. 18.5

195

DIGITAL REACTION TIMER

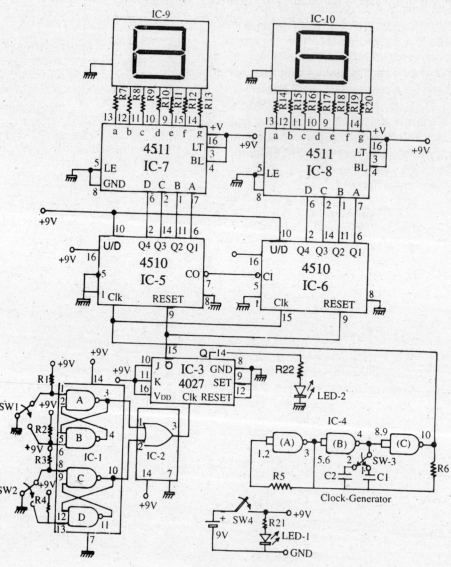

Fig. 19.1

OBJECTIVE

It is an ideal project for those who want to build something that not only teaches them something but also gives them lot of fun. As the title suggests, this gadget can be used to measure quantitatively the reaction time of an individual. The reaction time can be measured in two different settings. In the first setting, the reaction time can be measured upto a maximum of 99ms with a resolution of 1ms. In the second setting, the reaction time can be measured upto a maximum of 990ms with a resolution of 10ms. **You can try this gadget with your friends and relatives and find out how quickly they react to a given situation. You can try this with yourself too at different times and when you are in different states of mind and see the difference yourself.**

CIRCUIT DESCRIPTION

The circuit is basically a counter clocked by a clock generator having two different frequency selections of 100Hz and 1000Hz. There are two push buttons represented by microswitches SW1 and SW2. One of the push buttons to be held by the examiner is used to start the counter and the other push button to be held by the examinee is used to stop the counter. The display reading obviously gives the time interval between the start and stop operations and hence the reaction time. The display reads the reaction time in milliseconds directly if the clock is set at 1ms period and it reads one tenth of the reaction time in milliseconds if the clock is set at 10ms period.

The functioning of counter type 4510 has been explained in detail in the project DIGIKIT-III. The present circuit is nothing but a cascaded arrangement of two such counters thus extending the capability of the counter upto a maximum count of 99. Clock pulses are continuously applied to the counters' clock inputs. The RESET points of the counters are fed from the output of a J-K flip flop wired as a T-flip flop. Initially, the flip flop is kept in the HIGH output state so that the counter is reset to 00. Also, in this condition, LED-2 is OFF. The flip flop is made to toggle when the examiner presses the push button thus sending a pulse to the clock input of the flip flop. This removes the RESET condition from the counter

and it starts counting. The flip flop is again made to toggle and thus reset the counter by the examinee when he or she presses the push button provided to him or her. It may be mentioned here that the person under test has to press his push button only in response to the lighting of LED-2. LED-2 lights when the person who is the judge presses his push button.

The clock generator is a simple circuit built around three NAND gates in cascade. The frequency of this clock generator is given by

$$f = 0.56/RC$$

where $R = R5 = R6$ and $C = C1$ or $C2$

PARTS LIST
Resistors and Capacitors

R1 to R4	: 22K, 1/4W
R5, R6	: 560K, 1/4W
R7 to R20	: 680 ohms, 1/4W
R21, R22	: 3.9K, 1/4W
C1	: 0.1µF (Polyester)
C2	: 0.01µF (Polyester)

Semiconductors and ICs

LED-1 and LED-2	: Miniature LED
IC-1	: CD 4011
IC-2	: CD 4071
IC-3	: CD 4027
IC-4	: CD 4011
IC-5, IC-6	: CD 4510
IC-7, IC-8	: CD 4511
IC-9, IC-10	: LT 543 (Common cathode type seven segment display)

Switches

SW1, SW2	: Microswitches
SW3	: SPDT
SW4	: Miniature toggle switch

Miscellaneous

9V battery, solder metal, wires, IC bases

Figs. 19.2 and 19.3 respectively show the PCB layout and components layout.

TESTING GUIDELINES

The test gadget can be tested as per the following procedure:

1. Initially, keep the switch SW3 in position-1 so as to select 100Hz clock frequency. Check

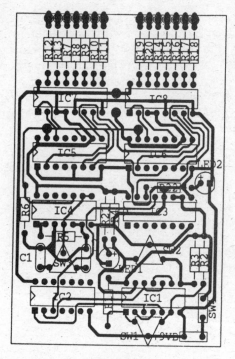

Fig. 19.2

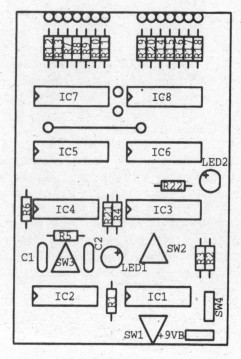

Fig. 19.3

that the LED-2 is OFF. If it is not so, press and release SW1 once.

2. Once the LED-2 is OFF, this ensures that the counter is in RESET mode. Now you are ready to check the reaction time.

3. Hold the microswitch SW1 in your hand and ask the other person (whose reaction time is to be determined) to hold the switch SW2. Instruct the other person to concentrate on the LED-2 and press the switch SW2 immediately when he sees the LED-2 glowing.

4. Now, press the switch SW1 without telling the other person. The reading on the display gives his reaction time in tens of milliseconds. That is, the actual reaction time is 10 × display reading.

5. If the person is too quick and the reaction time comes out to be less than or equal to 99ms, you can repeat the test by changing over the clock frequency to 1000Hz. This will give you a more accurate value.

198

HIGH FREQUENCY EMERGENCY FLUORESCENT LIGHT

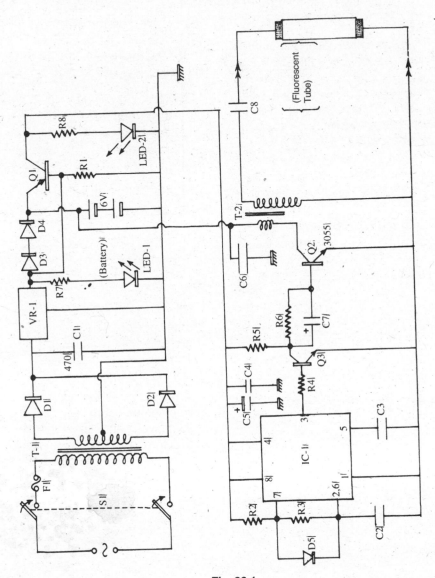

Fig. 20.1

OBJECTIVE

The objective here is to construct an emergency fluorescent light circuit that requires neither a choke nor a starter unlike conventional mains operable fluorescent light. Such emergency lighting units having different lighting power capabilities are available in abundance in the market. The circuit given here is simple and highly efficient. It operates from a 6V rechargeable battery (Lead-Acid type). The battery is trickle charged when the mains is present. The battery with a capacity of 6Ah (this is the battery used in this project) is capable of providing uninterrupted lighting for four hours in the absence of mains. The switchover is fully automatic i.e. when the mains goes OFF, the battery comes into the lighting circuit automatically and there is no requirement of manually switching on the light.

CIRCUIT DESCRIPTION

The emergency fluorescent lights are based on the principle of high frequency lighting. Typically, the frequency of the applied pulse train is around 30 to 35 kHz and the initial peak amplitude (when the light is not yet on) of the pulses is around 750 to 800 Volts. When the tube lights up, the peak amplitude falls to a value depending upon the output power delivery capability of the inverter circuit supplying high frequency pulse train to the tube. The circuit operation can be described as follows:

In the presence of AC mains power, the AC/DC power supply arrangement consisting of a step down transformer with center tapped secondary (T-1), the two diode conventional full wave rectifier constituted by diodes (D1) and (D2), the filter capacitor (C1) and the three terminal regulator (VR-1) generate regulated 9VDC which charges the battery through diodes (D3) and (D4). Since the emitter potential of transistor (Q1) is less than its base potential by two diode drops, (Q1) is surely in cut-off. As a result, no voltage appears at the collector of (Q1) and hence the drive circuit for the DC/AC inverter portion remains without its DC supply. The fluorescent tube (a 6 Watt, 9 inch tube in this case) stays OFF. To sum up uptill now, when ever AC power is ON, the battery is getting charged but is not supplying any power to the DC/AC inverter circuit feeding the fluorescent tube. LED-1 is ON and it indicates that mains is present. LED-2 is OFF and it tells that transistor (Q1) is in cut-off.

When the mains power is OFF, diodes (D3) and (D4) are reverse biased, transistor (Q1) conducts and the DC voltage is now available at the collector terminal of (Q1) and hence for the drive circuit of DC/AC inverter. Base of transistor (Q2) gets drive pulses and it is switched ON and OFF alternately. Basically, transformer (T-2), transistor (Q2) and the drive circuit constitute an externally driven DC/AC inverter of the flyback type. During every conduction time (when the output of 555 timer is LOW) of the transistor (Q2), energy is stored in the primary of the inverter transformer and during every OFF time (when the output of 555 timer is HIGH), the energy stored in the previous cycle is transferred to the secondary circuit. The inverter transformer has been so designed here that it produces a train of pulses with a frequency of about 30kHz and a peak amplitude of 750 volts. When such a pulse train appears across the tube, it lights up and the peak pulse amplitude drops to about 150 volts. Capacitor (C8) limits the tube current. The transformer and the drive circuit have been designed to feed a 6 Watt, 9 inch tube.

CONSTRUCTION GUIDELINES

The PCB layout the components layout are respectively shown in Figs. 20.2 and 20.3 respectively. Transformer (T1), Transformer (T2), Transistor (Q2) and the battery are not the part of the PCB. These are mounted separately. Transformer (T2) (the inverter transformer) is wound on a good quality ferrite rod (10mm diameter and 75mm long) usually seen in transistor sets. These are easily available in the market. The dots shown in the transformer windings indicate start of windings assuming that both primary and secondary are wound in same direction. Other details such as number of primary and secondary turns, the gauge of the wire to be used etc. are given in the parts list.

PARTS LIST
Resistors and Capacitors

R1	: 470Ω, 1/4W
R2	: 3.3K, 1/4W
R3	: 1.5K, 1/4W
R4	: 100Ω, 1/4W
R5	: 10Ω, 5W (Wirewound)
R6	: 4.7Ω, 2W
R7, R8	: 4.7K, 1/4W
C1	: 470µF, 16V (Electrolytic)
C2	: 0.01µF (Polyester)
C3	: 0.01µF (Ceramic disc)
C4, C6	: 0.1µF (Ceramic disc)

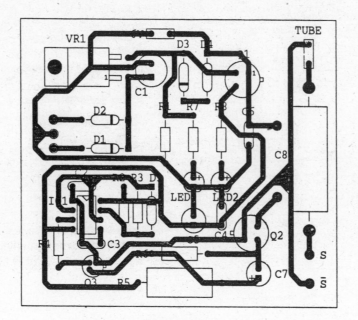

Fig. 20.2

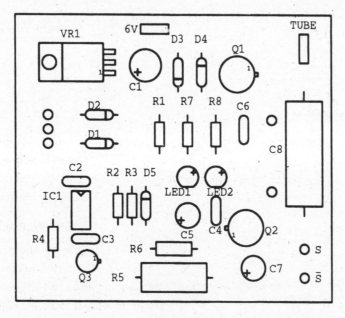

Fig. 20.3

C5	: 10µF, 16V (Electrolytic)
C7	: 2.2µF, 16V (Electrolytic)
C8	: 0.01µF, 1KV (Polyester)

Semiconductor Devices and ICs

D1 to D5	: 1N4001 or Equivalent
LED-1, LED-2	: Preferably two different colour LEDs
Q1	: SK100 or equivalent
Q2	: 2N3055
Q3	: 2N2222
VR-1	: Three terminal regulator type 7809
IC-1	: Timer 555

Other Components

1. S1 : Mains power ON/OFF switch
2. T-1 : Mains transformer, Primary : 230VAC, Secondary 9-0-9, 500mA
3. T-2 : Inverter transformer, Primary: Secondary:
   Core : 7.5cm long ferrite rod (Fig. 20.4)

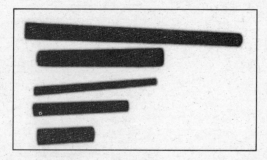

Fig. 20.4

Miscellaneous

6 Watt, 9 inch fluorescent tube with appropriate holder, 8-pin IC base, LED holders, multistrand wires, solder metal, mains power cord, suitable mounting cabinet etc.

Note: *The photograph of ferrite rods shown in Fig. 20.4 is only a representative photograph to give you an idea of how this component typically may look like.*

Visual AC Mains Voltage Indicator

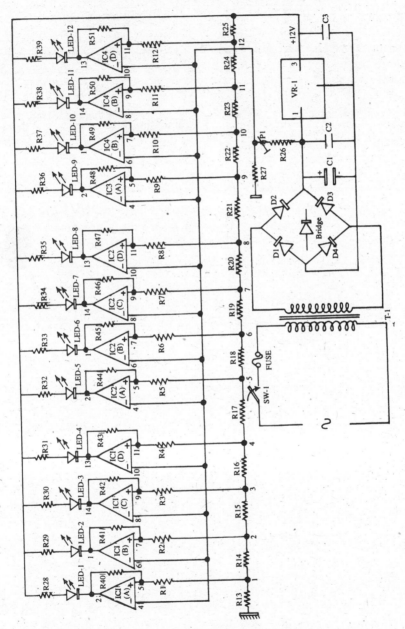

Fig. 21.1

OBJECTIVE

Wide fluctuations in the AC mains voltage is a very common problem in India. You should not be surprised if some one tells you that the voltage fluctuation could be as much as from 150 volts to 290 volts. **Although, majority of our electrical and electronic appliances and gadgets have some kind of voltage stabilisation internaly built-in, yet more than 90 percent of the faults in these gadgets occur due to these power fluctuations.** This simple test gadget can give you real time monitoring of the AC mains voltage in the form of glowing LEDs. It can give you the visible indication of AC mains voltage over a range of 170 volts to 280 volts in steps of 10 volts. There are 12 LEDs numbered from LED-1 to LED-12. For input AC mains voltage of less than 170 volts, all LEDs remain OFF. LED-1 glows when the voltage reaches 180 volts, LED-2 glows when the voltage reaches 190 volts. The number of LEDs that glow keeps increasing with every additional 10 volts increase. When the input voltage reaches 280 volts, all the 12 LEDs glow.

CIRCUIT DESCRIPTION

The circuit basically comprises of 12 voltage comparators built around opamp comparator IC type number LM 339. Each of the LM 339 has four comparators inside the IC. One of the inputs of all the comparators (the inverting input) is fed from the unregulated DC output whereas the other inputs (the non-inverting inputs) are applied reference DC voltages. Resistors R13 to R25 are so chosen that the reference voltages at points 1 to 12 are respectively 0.933V, 1.866V, 2.80V, 3.732V, 4.665V, 5.598V, 6.531V, 7.464V, 8.397V, 9.33V, 10.263V and 11.196V. P1 is so adjusted that when the input voltage is 230VAC, the DC voltage at the junction of R26-P1 series combination and R27 is 6.531 volts. All reference voltages have been generated from a regulated voltage of 12 volts. In all these comparators, whenever the voltage at their inverting input exceeds the voltage at their non-inverting input, the LED connected at the output glows.

CONSTRUCTION GUIDELINES

Figs. 21.2 and 21.3 respectively show the PCB layout and components layout.

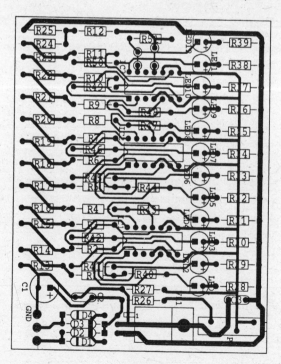

Fig. 21.2

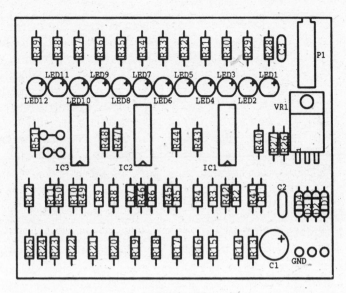

Fig. 21.3

PARTS LIST

Resistors and Capacitors

R1 to R12	:	100 ohms, 1/4W
R13 to R24	:	10K, 1/4W
R25	:	8.59K, 1/4W (Use a series combination of 8.2K and 390 ohms instead)
R26	:	15K, 1/4W
R27	:	10K, 1/4W
P1	:	10K Preset
R28 to R39	:	1K, 1/4W
R40 to R51	:	100K, 1/4W
C1	:	100µF, 50V (electrolytic)
C2, C3	:	0.1µF (Ceramic disc)

Semiconductors and ICs

LED-1 to LED-12	:	Miniature LEDs
Bridge Rectifier, B-1	:	Type 1B2 (The bridge can also be made using four rectifier diodes of the type 1N 4001
VR-1	:	Three terminal regulator, type 7812
IC-1, IC-2, IC-3	:	LM 339

Miscellaneous

Transformer, T-1	:	Mains transformer: Primary-230V, Secondary-15V Secondary current-250mA
Fuse	:	500mA rating
SW-1	:	Mains Power ON/OFF switch

Solder metal, Wires etc.

TESTING GUIDELINES

The test procedure has more or less been described during circuit description.

Following steps should however be followed for the calibration of the circuit.

1. Connect the input of the mains transformer to an auto-transformer (VARIAC). Set the auto-transformer voltage at precisely 170 volts. Verify the set voltage with the help of multimeter as the auto-transformer dial may not be properly calibrated.

2. Adjust the resistance of the preset P1 till only LED-1 glows. Remember that you have to gradually increase the resistance starting from the minimum and stop increasing it further the moment LED-1 glows.

3. The calibration can be further checked by increasing auto-transformer voltage beyond 170 volts. Gradually increase the voltage upto 280 volts and observe different LEDs glowing at 10 volt intervals as explained earlier.

205

5-IN-1 ALARM GADGET

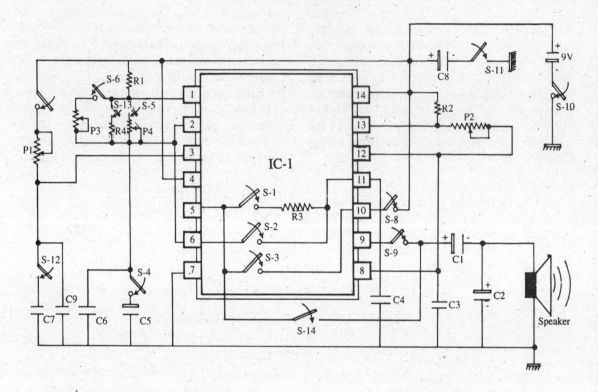

Switch positions	Type of Alarm
S10, S13 and S14 closed. Others open	Simple single tone alarm
S6, S7, S10, S12, S14 closed. Others open	A factory siren
S1, S4, S5, S9, S10 closed. Others open	An ambulance siren
S2, S4, S5, S9, S10, S11 closed. Others open	Police siren
S3, S4, S5, S9, S10 closed. Others open	Beeping siren

Fig. 22.1

OBJECTIVE

Here is a simple and very easy to build alarm/ siren producing gadget capable of producing five different types of siren tones. The gadget is built around a single IC 556 which is nothing but a dual IC timer 555. That is, it has two independent 555s within the same package. The type of siren can be selected from an appropriate combination of switches to be closed given in the accompanying table. The gadget could also be constructed using two 555s in place of one 556.

CIRCUIT DESCRIPTION

For a clear understanding of this circuit functioning, it is very important to identify those pins in IC556 that represent two independent 555's. IC555 has eight terminals namely the COMMON (Pin-1), TRIGGER (Pin-2), OUTPUT (Pin-3), RESET (Pin-4), CONTROL (Pin-5), THRESHOLD (Pin-6), DISCHARGE (Pin-7) and +Vcc (Pin-8). IC556 which is a 14-pin IC has two fully independent 555s with only a common supply and a common ground point. Its pin connection diagram as shown in Fig. 22.2 tells about the pin numbers for the different terminals of two 555s inside this IC. As is clear from this diagram, one of the 555's is represented by pins 1 to 7 and 14 with pin-7 being the ground pin and pin-14 the supply pin. The second 555 is available on pin numbers 7 to 14.

SIMPLE SINGLE TONE ALARM

With switches S10, S13 and S14 closed and all other switches open, the given circuit is reduced to a simple astable multivibrator configuration feeding the speaker. The astable multivibrator produces a waveform at the output that has a high time depending upon R1, R4 and C6 and a low time depending upon R4 and C6. The values for these components are so chosen that the frequency of the output waveform is about 4.5kHz. You would notice that the second 555 remains disconnected from the output side.

FACTORY SIREN

With switches S6, S7, S10, S12 and S14 closed and other switches open, the given circuit is once again an astable multivibrator built around one of the 555's. The high time this time depends upon the resistance R1, the resistance offered by potentiometer P3 and capacitance C6. The low time depends upon potentiometer P3 setting and capacitor C6. You would notice that there is an R-C network connected from supply to ground with the capacitor connected across control pin (Pin-3) of the 555 being used. The RC time constant is variable upto a maximum of 10 seconds. Thus as the circuit is switched on, voltage at the control pin rises towards Vcc with the time constant depending upon P1 setting and C7. This rising voltage changes the output frequency. Thus what we hear is a frequency modulated audio tone resembling that of the one from a factory siren. The second 555 is again not coming into picture.

AMBULANCE SIREN

With switches S1, S4, S5, S9 and S10 closed, the given circuit is reduced to a configuration where the first 555 wired as an astable multivibrator drives the control pin of the second 555 again wired as the astable multivibrator.

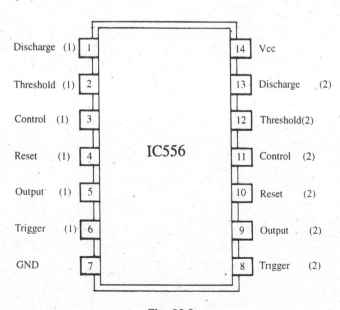

Fig. 22.2

The frequency of the first astable multivibrator is decided by R1, P4 setting and C5 while that of the second depends upon R2, P2 setting and C3 in addition to voltage being fed externally at its control pin (Pin-11). The second astable multivibrator operates on two different frequencies corresponding to two different voltage amplitudes present at its control pin due to the low and high portions of the waveform appearing at the output of first 555. Both frequencies of the second astable are much higher than the frequency of the first astable. The final result is therefore a siren with two different tones repeating alternately. The second astable sets the frequencies of these different tones and the first astable decides the durations of these tones.

POLICE SIREN

With the switches S2, S4, S5, S9, S10 and S11 closed and other switches open, the circuit that we get is again similar to what we have just seen in case of an ambulance siren with the only difference that the control pin of the second astable instead of being driven from the output of the first astable is fed from the trigger-threshold junction point of the first astable multivibrator. The more or less triangular waveform appearing at this junction continuously frequency modulates the output frequency of second astable output which feeds the speaker. The sound like a police siren is the result.

BEEPING SIREN

The circuit configuration is again similar to what we have seen in the two immediately preceding cases. In the present case, the output of the first astable multivibrator feeds the reset terminal of the second astable. The second astable output finally feeds the speaker. When the output of the first astable is high, the second astable functions normally and produces a tone. As the output of the first astable goes low, the second astable is reset and its output goes to zero. Thus result is a siren comprising of a repetitive seqence of presence and absence of tone.

Figs. 22.3 and 22.4 respectively show the PCB layout and the components layout.

PARTS LIST
Resistors and Capacitors

R1, R2	: 1K, 1/4W
R3	: 68K, 1/4W
R4	: 15K, 1/4W
P1	: 4.7K Preset
P2	: 100K Preset
P3	: 100K Preset
P4	: 4.7K Preset
C1	: 100µF, 25V (Electrolytic)
C2	: 10µF, 25V (Electrolytic)
C3, C4, C9	: 0.01µF (Ceramic Disc)
C5	: 1000µF, 25V (Electrolytic)
C6	: 0.01µF, 25V (Polyester)
C7	: 1000µF, 25V (Electrolytic)
C8	: 1000µF, (Electrolytic)

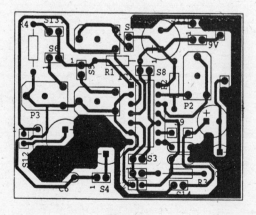

Fig. 22.3

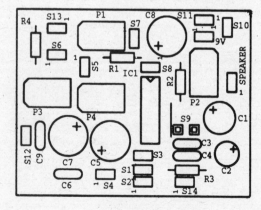

Fig. 22.4

208

Semiconductors and ICs
IC-1   : IC 556C
Miscellaneous
S1 to S9, S11 to S14: DIP switches, S10: Toggle switch, 8 ohm speaker

+9V battery Solder wire, multistrand wires etc.

TESTING GUIDELINES

1. The alarm gadget should be tested for its functioning in all the five different alarm settings separately by closing the appropriate set of switches and leaving the rest open. In all individual settings, check that you get an overall sound effect from the alarm that it is supposed to generate.

2. You would notice that S10 has got to be closed in all the five alarm settings. It is rightly so as it is the switch in series with the 9V battery. It is suggested that this switch be closed last of all after you have closed all other relevant switches when trying to test a particular alarm setting.

3. In case of those alarm settings which have potentiometers in the frequency determining portions, the effect of varying the potentiometer resistance on the output should be seen and the resistance should be set for the best overall effect.

PROJECT : 23

INNOVATIVE WAYS OF USING TIMER IC 555

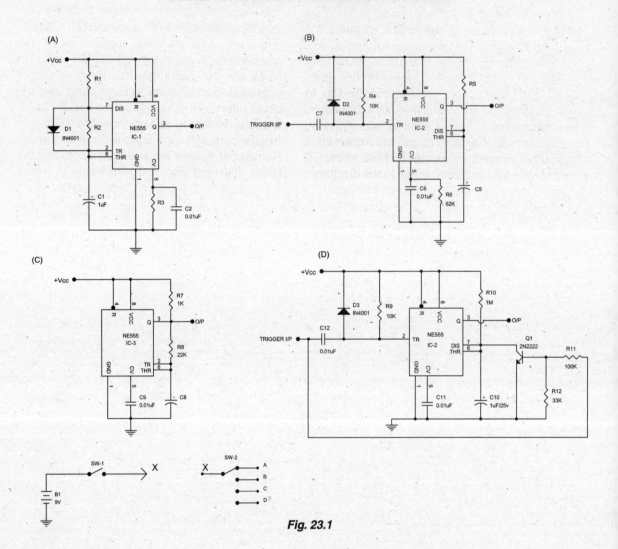

Fig. 23.1

OBJECTIVE

Timer IC 555 is versatile general-purpose linear integrated circuits and is thus the most widely used one. It is indeed a favourite with hobbyists. It is mostly used either as a monostable or an astable multivibrator. In this project activity, we shall present some modified circuits for monostable and astable operation of timer IC 555 and see for ourselves how these changes simplify design. In two of the four different circuits given here, the circuits have been so modified as to yield very simple and design friendly expressions for the monostable and astable operations. In case of modified astable circuit, the expressions for output frequency becomes $f = 1/RC$ where (R) is charge path resistance equal to the discharge path resistance and (C) is the capacitance. In a conventional astable circuit, this expression would be $f = 1/(1.38RC)$. In case of monostable circuit, the suggested modification changes the expression for output pulse width from $T = 1.1 RC$ to $T = RC$. Another circuit given here produces a 50% duty cycle free running output with the least component count. Yet another circuit transforms a conventional monostable circuit into a retriggerable monoshot. Retriggerable monoshot circuits are available as digital ICs. 74123 in TTL and 4098 in CMOS are examples. However these ICs offer a very limited source current capability. A retriggerable monoshot configured around IC 555 gives you a peak current sourcing capability of 200mA. The intention behind this project activity is to enable the experimenters experience new circuits and thus expand the horizon of their thinking.

CIRCUIT DESCRIPTION

Modified Astable Multivibrator

Refer to the astable part of Fig.6.1. The charge and discharge path resistances are respectively (R1) and (R2). The small modification to this circuit is in the form of (R3) connected from pin-5 of the IC to ground. In the absence of this resistance, the HIGH and LOW times of the output waveform would respectively be (0.69R1.CI) and (0.69R2.C1). If R1 = R2 = R and C1 = C, the expression for frequency of output waveform would be $f = 1/(1.38RC)$, an expression very inconvenient to handle.

It can be verified mathematically that a 5.6K resistance (R3 in this case) is connected from pin-5 to ground, the HIGH and LOW times of the output waveform will be given by relationships $T(HIGH) = 0.31R1.C1$ and $T(LOW) = 0.69R2.C1$. The frequency of the output waveform would then be given by $f = 1/RC$ provided R1 = R2 = R and C1 = C. In all those applications of 555 astable circuits, where individual HIGH and LOW times are not important, this modified circuit offers a distinct advantage. Even otherwise, the circuit offers a lot of academic interest. We leave it to the readers to find out how this additional resistance modifies the expression for frequency. Remember that we are able to change only the HIGH time and also that HIGH time in a 555 astable circuit is the time taken by capacitor to charge from 1/3(Vcc) to 2/3(Vcc). Now 1/3(Vcc) and 2/3(Vcc) are reference levels for lower and upper comparators inside the IC. Does this additional resistance change those levels?

Modified Monostable Ultivibrator

Refer to the monostable part of the circuit. A similar modification can be used for this circuit. It can be proved mathematically that connecting a 62K resistance from pin-5 to ground changes the output pulse width expression from $T = 1.1R5.C5$ to $T = R5.C5$. You can connect even a resistance of 68K without any noticeable error. Again we leave it to readers to find out for themselves reason for change in expression. Remember that in a 555 monoshot, the output pulse width is the time taken by the capacitor to charge from 0 to 2/3(Vcc).

Astable Circuit with 50% Duty Cycle

Refer to the relevant part of the circuit shown in Fig.6.1. It is a simple circuit that makes use of only 3 external components, 2 resistors and 1 capacitor, to construct a 50% duty cycle astable circuit. The design idea takes advantage of the fact that the output is HIGH during the charging process and LOW during the discharge process of the capacitor. In the present circuit, the capacitor discharges through the resistor (R8) and the output transistor connected to pin-3 inside the timer IC. It does not discharge through the discharge transistor connected to pin-7 of the IC, as is the case in conventional astable circuits. For best results (R8) should be 22K or greater. The frequency of the output waveform is given by $f = 1/(1.38R8.C8)$.

Retriggerable Monoshot

555-monoshot circuit can be transformed to a retriggerable monoshot by including a few additional external components. The circuit consists of a bipolar transistor (Q 1), whose base is connected to the trigger input. The collector is connected to pins 6 and 7 of the IC and the emitter is grounded. The HIGH time of the monoshot in this case is larger than the time interval between the trigger pulses. With the leading edge of every trigger input pulse, the transistor goes into saturation and the capacitor

discharges through the transistor. The capacitor starts charging again with the trailing edge of the trigger pulse input and the output remains HIGH.

The voltage across pin-6 never reaches 2/3(Vcc) as long as there are trigger pulses at pin-2 of the IC with inter-pulse duration shorter than the expected output pulse width. The output goes LOW after a time equal to (1.1R10.C13) after the trailing edge of the last received trigger pulse input as shown in Fig.23.2.

The design gives a retriggerable monoshot operation with an output current of 200mA, which is much higher than a few mA (typical) sourcing capability of digital retriggerable monoshot ICs.

Switch SW- 1 can be used to connect the battery voltage to any of the four circuits, one at a time.

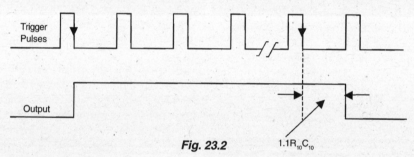

Fig. 23.2

$1.1R_{10}C_{10}$

CONSTRUCTION GUIDELINES

Figs.23.3 and 23.4 respectively show the PCB layout and components layout. This would help those who want to construct this project in a compact and packaged form. However, the circuit is simple enough to be constructed on a general purpose PCB.

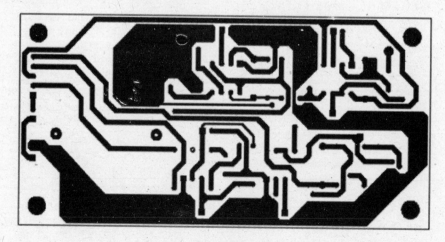

Fig. 23.3

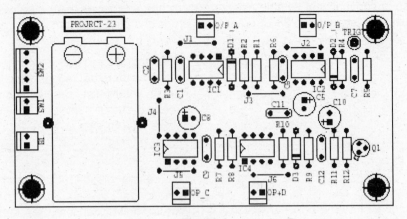

Fig. 23.4

PARTS LIST
Resistors

R 1, R2, R4, R5, R9   : 10K, 1/4 Watt

R3   : 5.6K, 1/4 Watt

R6   : 62K, 1/4 Watt

R7   : 1 K, 1/4 Watt .

R8   : 22K, 1 /4Watt

R10   : IM, 1/4Watt

R11   : 100K, 1/4 Watt

R12   : 33K, 1/4 Watt

Capacitors

C l, C5, C8, C13   : 1µF/25V (Tantalum)

C2, C3, C4, C6, C7,C9,

C10, C11, C12, C14   : 0.0lµF

Semiconductors and ICs

D1, D2, D3 (Diodes)   : 1N4001

Q1 (Transistor)   : 2N2222

IC-1 to IC-4   : Timer IC 555

Hardware Components

Battery, B-1   : 9V Battery

SW-1   : SP4T Rotary switch

Miscellaneous

Multistrand Wires, Solder Metal etc.

DIGI-KIT(I)-LOGIC GATE

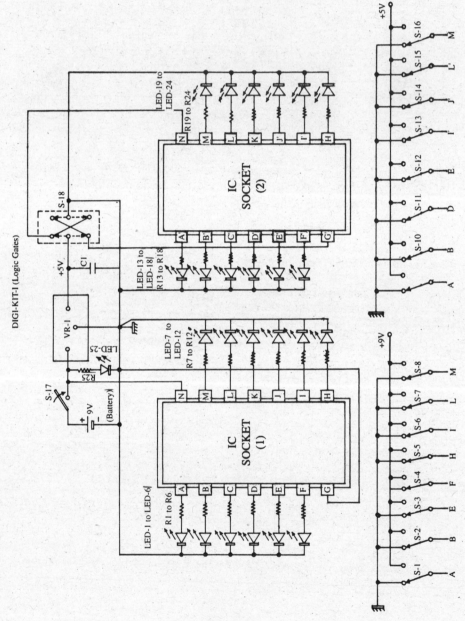

Fig. 24.1

OBJECTIVE

It is the first in the series of three projects that can be used to understand the functioning of general purpose digital integrated circuits. The present one is aimed at providing a check on the functioning of all 2-input logic gates of both TTL and CMOS families. **This project circuit has two-fold objective. You can practically verify the truth table of any 2-input logic gate belonging to either the TTL or the CMOS logic family. Secondly, this can also be used as a test gadget for checking the health of these logic gate ICs.** What is important here is that the given circuit arrangement has a provision for checking each one of the four logic gates inside the IC. It is not an unusual occurence where not all the four logic gates inside the same package have gone bad. Under such circumstances, it becomes essential to see the health of all the gates individually before the IC is declared dead. The circuit operates on a +9V battery and is thus portable.

CIRCUIT DESCRIPTION

There are two different IC sockets used for testing the TTL family logic gates and CMOS logic family logic gates. IC socket-1 is for testing CMOS logic gates (2-input gates) and the relevant circuit operates from +9V. IC socket-2 is for TTL gates and the circuit operates from a regulated source of +5V generated from +9V.

All Quad 2-input logic gates belonging to CMOS logic family have identical pin arrangement for different logic gates inside the IC. The type numbers are CD4011 (NAND), CD4081 (AND), CD4071 (OR), CD4001 (NOR), CD4030 (EX-OR) and CD4077 (EX-NOR). The internal logic arrangement of these ICs is depicted in Fig. 24.2(a). The IC is inserted in the socket in such a fashion that pin-1 of the IC is in position-A of the socket. Now each of the four gates can be applied any possible input combination. A logic '0' is applied by connecting the input to ground point and a logic '1' is applied by connecting the input to Vcc. There are LED indicators at the inputs and the outputs of all gates. A lighted LED indicates a logic '1'. The logic IC can be tested for its health by applying all possible input combinations to all gates and monitoring the outputs. Possible inputs are 00,01,10,11. The corresponding outputs in case of different logic gates are given in Table-24.1.

With the exception of Quad 2-input NOR gate, all other logic gates belonging to TTL family have identical pin connection arrangement in terms of input/output points, Vcc terminal and Ground terminal as shown in Fig. 24.2(b). Fig. 24.2(c)

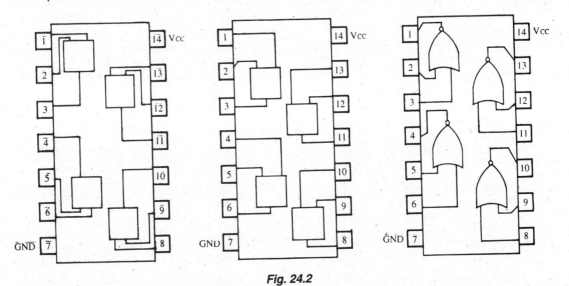

Fig. 24.2

Input		Output					
		AND	OR	NAND	NOR	EX-OR	EX-NOR
0	0	0	0	1	1	0	1
0	1	0	1	1	0	1	0
1	0	0	1	1	0	1	0
1	1	1	1	0	0	0	1

shows pin connections for TTL Quad 2-input NOR-gate. Connections shown for IC socket-2 are thus valid for all TTL logic Quad 2-input gates when pin-1 of the IC comes in position-A′ except for NOR gate. However, if the NOR gate is so inserted in the socket that pin-1 coincides with position-H′, then the circuit still remains valid provided Vcc and Ground points are also interchanged. This interchange of Vcc and ground connections can be done with the help of DPDT switch S18. The test procedure is the same as described in case of CMOS gates above.

So, remember that when you are trying your hand at NOR gates belonging to TTL family, do not forget to insert the IC in such a way that its pin-1 is inserted in position-H′ and its pin-14 coincides with G′.

Figs. 24.3 and 24.4 respectively show PCB layout and components layout.

PARTS LIST
Resistors and Capacitors
R1 to R12, R25 : 3.9K, 1/4W (Carbon film)

R13 to R24 : 2.2K, 1/4W (Carbon film)
C1 : 0.1μF, 25V (Ceramic disc)

Semiconductors and ICs
LED-1 to LED-25 : Miniature sized LEDs
VR1 : 78L05

Miscellaneous
Switches S1
to S17 : Miniature toggle switches
Switch S18 : Miniature DPDT switch
IC sockets, 1
and 2 : 14-pin IC bases
9V battery, solder metal, wires etc.

TESTING GUIDELINES
The testing guidelines have more or less been already discussed during circuit description. I may repeat here that the given circuit arrangement is both a logic gate truth table evaluer as well as a tester. Those who are absolutely new to the world of digital electronics can use this gadget to verify what they have already read about logic gates and those who are pretty familiar with logic gates and their functioning can use the same gadget for checking the health of these ICs.

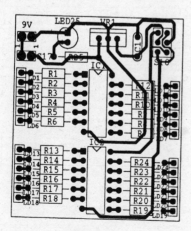

Fig. 24.3

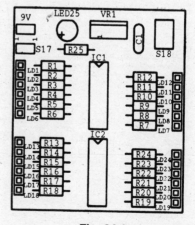

Fig. 24.4

PROJECT : 25

DIGI-KIT (II)-FLIP FLOPS

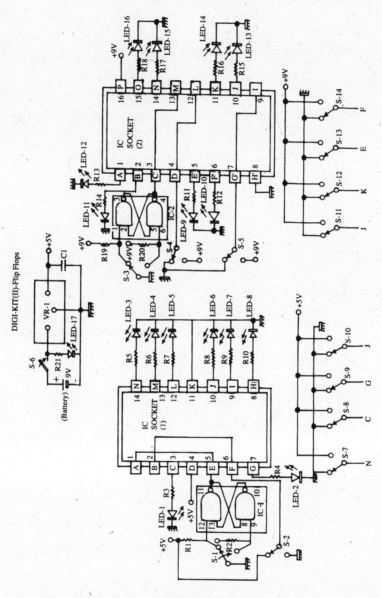

Fig. 25.1

OBJECTIVE

What we have learnt and gained by building project: 22 with reference to logic gates, the same we are going to learn about flip flops by building the present one. The philosophy of the two is more or less identical. Here too, the idea is to build a gadget that can expose the experimenters and hobbyists to the many functional capabilities of flip flops. Since a JK flip flop is the most widely used of all the flip flop types and also since it can be used to construct many other flip flops (D-type or T-type), we have chosen to base this circuit on the most popular JK flip flop type numbers in TTL and CMOS logic families i.e. 7473 (in TTL) and 4027 (in CMOS). Both are dual JK flip flops with CLEAR facilities. IC CD4027 has both PRESET and CLEAR facilities. Thus we can use this gadget to practically see PRESET, CLEAR functions in addition to verifying the truth table entries. The indication is again in the form of LEDs. LEDs have been connected across all input and output points.

CIRCUIT DESCRIPTION

The pin connection diagrams of ICs 7473 and 4027 are respectively shown in Figs. 25.2 (a) and (b). If we carefully look at the pin connection diagram of IC 7473 and the circuit arrangement around IC socket-1, we can observe the following:

(i) The clock inputs of the two flip flops in IC 7473 have been shorted and fed from the output of the debouncing circuit constituted by the two NAND gates of IC-1. It may be mentioned here that the debouncing circuit only generates a clean pulse at the output in response to operation of the microswitch S1. (ii) The CLEAR inputs of the two flip flops have also been joined together and connected to the pole of a SPDT switch S2. (iii) Pins 14, 3, 12 and 13 represent J, K, Q and $\overline{Q}$ of the first flip flop respectively. Pins 7, 10, 9 and 8 respectively represent J, K, Q and $\overline{Q}$ of the second flip flop. Now switches S7 to S10 can be used to apply either a logic '1' or a logic '0' to J and K inputs of the two flip flops. The truth table of J-K flip flop can thus be verified. LEDs have been connected across the inputs and outputs of the two flip flops to indicate the logic status.

From the pin connection diagram of IC 4027 and the circuit arrangement around IC socket-2, we can observe the following: (i) The clock inputs for the two flip flops have been tied together and fed from the output of the debouncing circuit. (ii) The RESET inputs of the two flip flops have also been tied together and connected to the pole of an SPDT switch S4. (iii) The SET inputs of the two flip flops have also been tied together and fed from a switch S5. Now J, K input of the two flip flops and also the SET and RESET inputs can be

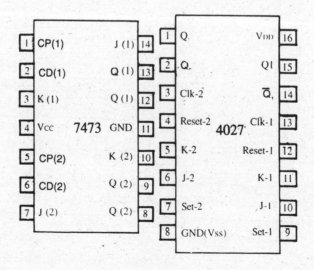

Fig. 25.2

applied either a logic '0' or a logic '1' depending upon the position of the corresponding switch. LEDs again indicate the logic status of the inputs and outputs.

PARTS LIST
Resistors and Capacitors
R1, R2 : 10K, 1/4W
R3 to R10 : 2.2K, 1/4W
R11 to R18, R21 : 3.9K, 1/4W
R19, R20 : 22K, 1/4W
C1 : 0.1µF (Ceramic Disc)

Semiconductors and ICs
LED-1 to LED-17 : Miniature LEDs
VR-1 : Three terminal regulator type 7805
IC-1 : 7400
IC-2 : 4011

Switches
S1, S3 : Microswtiches
S2, S4, S5, S7 to S14 : SPDT switch
S6 : Miniature toggle switch

Miscellaneous
9V battery, IC sockets (14-pin, 16-pin), wires, solder metal etc.

Note: All resistors are general purpose carbon film resistors.

The PCB and components layouts are respectively shown in Figs. 25.3 and 25.4.

TESTING GUIDELINES
The gadget can be tested on the following lines:

IC 7473
1. The Q and Q̄ outputs are respectively 0 and 1 if the RESET input is 0 irrespective of the J and K input logic status.

2. The output toggles (i.e. 0 becomes 1 and 1 becomes 0) when the J and K inputs are both 1 and the flip flop is clocked. The RESET input is logic '1'.

3. The Q and Q̄ outputs are respectively 1 and 0 when J and K inputs are respectively 1 and 0 and the RESET (or CLEAR) input is 1. The flip flop is then said to be set. The Q and Q̄ outputs are respectively 0 and 1 when J and K inputs are respectively 0 and 1 and the RESET input is 1. The flip flop is then said to be RESET or CLEARED.

4. The flip flop HOLDS the output when both J and K inputs are 0 and the RESET input is 1.

5. All output states change only on HIGH to LOW transition of the clock pulse.

6. That the flip flop responds to the HIGH to LOW transition of the clock pulses is evident from the clock pulse symbol on the pin connection diagram having a bar. A bar or a bubble on any of the inputs always indicates that the referred input is active when LOW.

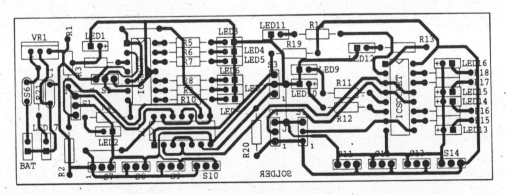

Fig. 25.3

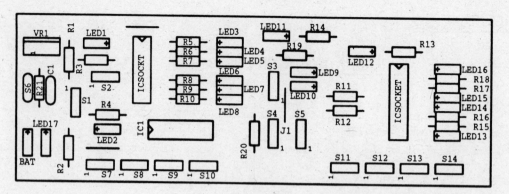

Fig. 25.4

IC 4027

The test procedure is similar to the one described above in case of IC 7473. The only differences are that the flip flop responds to LOW to HIGH transition of the clock pulses and the RESET and SET inputs are active when HIGH. This is indicated by absence of bars or bubbles in the symbols representing these functions.

DIGI-KIT(III)-COUNTERS AND DISPLAYS

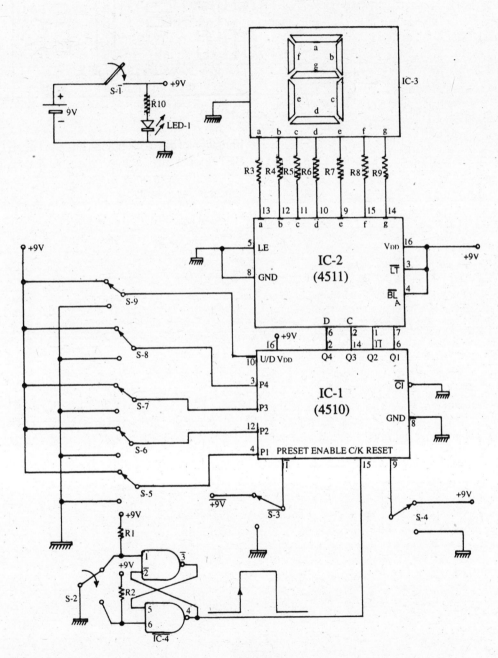

Fig. 26.1

221

OBJECTIVE

A counter whose outputs' logic status increments in steps on receiving clock pulses at its clock input is used for a variety of counting and timing applications. It forms the heart of digital clock circuitry and other similar timing devices. A 4-bit binary counter will count in its natural binary sequence from 0000 to 1111 in the first 15 clock cycles and then reset back to 0000 in the 16th clock cycle before repeating the sequence again. A decade counter will have ten different counter output states and a BCD decade counter is a special type of decade counter that counts from 0000 to 1001 and then resets. There are UP counters that count upwards i.e. every count increments the counter output and there are DOWN counters where the counter output decrements with every clock pulse. There are PRESETTABLE counters where any predetermined logic input loaded onto the program inputs can be made to appear at the output when desired. The counters also have a CLEAR facility where the counter output can be reset to 0000 (in case of 4-bit counters) when desired. Majority of the popular counter ICs have all the above facilities built into them. There are selection pins from where you can select the counter mode (UP/DOWN, PRESET-mode, CLEAR-mode). Construction of this simple project will enable you have a feel of different aspects of commonly used counter ICs. The counter chosen for the purpose is IC CD 4510 which is a BCD decade counter that has UP/DOWN, PROGRAM and CLEAR facilities.

CIRCUIT DESCRIPTION

The heart of this circuit is thus a BCD decade counter (Type number: 4510) whose output is fed to another IC (Type number: 4511) which is a decoder/driver IC. That is, it converts the BCD output of the counter into a decoded output for the seven segment display. For instance, initially, the counter output is 0000, the decoded outputs are such that the display segments a, b, c, d, e, f are lighted to display numeral '0'. Similarly, when the counter output is 0011, the decoded outputs are such that segments a, b, c, d and g are lighted to display numeral '3'. With the help of switches

S6 to S9, any desired logic input can be loaded onto the program inputs P1, P2, P3, P4. A logic '1' on the RESET input clears the counter to 0000. A logic '1' on the PRESET ENABLE input transfers the binary number present on the program inputs onto the output with the occurrence of the clock pulse. Infact all operations are performed with the occurrence of clock pulse. The clock here is a manual one and is generated by the microswitch followed by a debouncing circuit formed by NAND gates in IC-4. The UP/DOWN count-mode control pin designated $U/\overline{D}$ signifies that the counter would count in the forward mode when this pin is applied a logic '1' and it would count in the backward mode when it is applied a logic '0'. As an example, if the counter output (Q4 Q3 Q2 Q1) at a particular instant of time is (1000), then the next clock pulse will make it (1001) if the counter is in the UP-mode and 0111 if it is in the DOWN count mode.

PARTS LIST

Resistors

R1, R2	: 22K, 1/4W
R3 to R9	: 680ohms, 1/4W
R10	: 3.9K, 1/4W

Semiconductors and ICs

LED-1	: Miniature LED
IC-1	: CD4510
IC-2	: CD4511
IC-3	: LT543 (Common Cathode type LED 7-segment display)
IC-4	: CD4011

Switches

S1	: Miniature toggle switch
S2	: Miniature Microswitch
S3 to S9	: SPDT switches

Miscellaneous

IC bases (16-pin), 9V battery, solder metal, wires etc.

Figs. 26.2 and 26.3 respectively show the PCB layout and the components layout.

TESTING GUIDELINES

The project should be tested on the following lines:

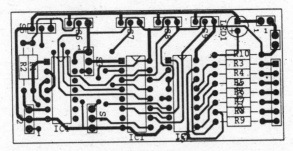

Fig. 26.2

1. Close switch S1 to connect 9V battery to the circuit. See that the LED-1 lights up indicating the appearance of 9V after the switch.

2. Keep switch S3 to GND position and switch S4 to 9V position. The seven segment display should read '0'.

3. Change the switch S4 to GND position. Keep switch S9 at 9V position thus selecting the UP-count mode.

4. Now press and release the microswitch S2 once thus sending one clock pulse. The display should read '1'.

5. Continue pressing and releasing the microswitch and you would notice that each clock pulse increments the seven segment display by one digit. Continue this exercise till you have reached '9'. The next press and release operation will change the display to '0' indicating that the counter has been reset and that it has completed its one count cycle.

6. Now change the switch S9 position to GND. Give a clock pulse from the micro switch. The display will show '9'. This indicates that the counter has now started counting backwards because a forward counting would have taken the display to '1'. Reverse counting is justified as we have already selected the DOWN count mode. The display readings corresponding to next four pulses will be 8, 7, 6 and 5.

7. Next, select any count mode (UP or DOWN) and let the display be at any count. Change the switch S4 over to position of 9V. You will find the display going to '0'. And once the switch S4 is kept at 9V position, the subsequent clock pulses have no effect on the display reading and it stays '0'.

8. Change the switch S4 back to GND position. Change the switch S3 to 9V position. Load any input to the program pins P1 to P4. Let us assume that (P4 P3 P2 P1) is (0 1 0 1). You will observe that the display changes to '5' on applying the next clock pulse.

Thus we have seen the functioning of all terminals one by one.

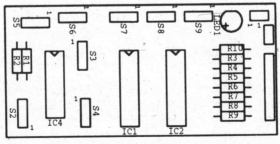

Fig. 26.3

AUTOMATIC NIGHT LIGHT

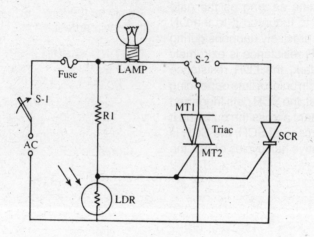

Fig. 27.1

OBJECTIVE

Here is an extremely simple circuit consisting of just four essential components to build a fully automatic self sensing night light.The light bulb used in the project could be the porch light that would go ON as the day light fades into a dark night. The same could also be used in the staircase or the open terrace. There is a provision for disconnecting AC supply to the input of the circuit in case you deliberately want the lamp to remain extinguished during night due to some reason or the other. One such instance could be when you are going out of the house during the daytime and you are not likely to return the same day. The above project is very inexpensive to construct and shall definitely interest many a hobbyists and electronics enthusiasts.

CIRCUIT DESCRIPTION

The circuit description is straightforward once operational principles of SCR and triac are clearly understood. We know that an SCR is a three terminal device with anode, cathode and gate as its terminals. It behaves as an open switch as long as the anode cathode voltage is less than the breakover voltage of the device. It behaves like a closed switch as the anode cathode voltage exceeds the breakover voltage. It can also be made to behave like a closed switch for an anode-cathode voltage less than the breakover voltage by giving a trigger pulse at the gate terminal. After that it continues to behave like that even after removal of the gate trigger. It goes back to the open state only when anode-cathode voltage is made zero or preferably negative. An SCR remains in the open state when anode is negative with respect to cathode. Triac behaves like a combination of SCRs connected in inverse parallel with the result that for both positive as well as negative anode cathode voltages, the triac can be made to switch to the ON state by applying an appropriate gate signal. Anode and cathode of an SCR are designated as MT-1 (Main Terminal-1) and MT-2 (Main Terminal-2) in case of triacs.

In the project circuit diagram of Fig. 27.1, let us assume that DPDT switch S-2 is in position-1 and it is day time. With sufficient light falling on the LDR, its resistance is very low, typically few tens of ohms. With switch S-1 closed, AC voltage rises from zero to a peak value of about 330 volts (=230×1.414) during all positive half cycles across anode-cathode of the SCR. The same voltage after division by the potential divider formed by R1 and the LDR appears at the gate. If the chosen SCR has a breakover voltage less than the peak value of the AC input, the SCR will remain in the open state as long as the gate voltage is inadequate to triggered it to the ON state. And this is what precisely happens during daytime when the LDR resistance is extremely low. As it becomes dark, the LDR resistance increases and at a certain point of time depending upon the darkness level, the SCR gets triggerred and the AC input appears across the bulb and it lights up. Since in the case of SCR, the SCR is active only during positive half cycles of AC, the bulb would give somewhat reduced light intensity.But then it gives you a longer lamp life and reduced drain on the AC power. There is no such limitation in case of triacs. You can notice a distinct increase in the brightness level of the lamp by switching S-2 to position-2. Another interesting point here is that for any chosen position 1 or 2, time of switch ON can be adjusted by varying resistance R1. Switch S-1 can be used to permanently disable the circuit.

PARTS LIST
Resistance

R1	:	10M, 1/2W (carbon film)
LDR	:	
SCR	:	Any 2A 600V SCR such as OE206, SN206, 2N 2601, TY 6004
Triac	:	Any 2A, 600V triac such as SPT 6M, 2N 5757
Lamp	:	60W lamp

Switches

S-1	:	Mains ON/OFF switch
S-2	:	DPDT switch
Fuse	:	3A rating

Miscellaneous
Mains cord, solder wire, lamp holder, appropriate housing for lamp and the circuit card etc.

Figs. 27.2 and 27.3 respectively show the PCB layout and the components layout. The LDR should be mounted on the chassis so as to face the environment.

TESTING GUIDELINES
1. Initially keep the Switch S1 open and Switch S2 in position-1.
2. Place the gadget in a position so that adequate light is falling on the LDR. You could do it inside the room by switching on all lights or outside in the open where you want to finally instal the same. The idea is that you should try to simulate light conditions for which you have made the gadget.
3. Connect the mains power cord and close switch S1.
4. The lamp should stay extinguished. It should not light up.
5. If it lights up, you might have to increase resistance R1 further till under light conditions, the lamp does not light up.
6. In case the lamp remains OFF which is the desired state, then cover the top face of the LDR by hand or by an opaque paper.The lamp should now light up. The lamp should again extinguish when you remove your hand or the piece of paper away.
7. Repeat the above steps by keeping the switch S2 in position-2. You can notice an increase in intensity of light from the lamp from what you observed in case of SCR. The reasons are obvious.

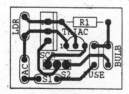

Fig. 27.2

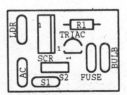

Fig. 27.3

225

PROJECT : 28

SOUND OPERATED LIGHT

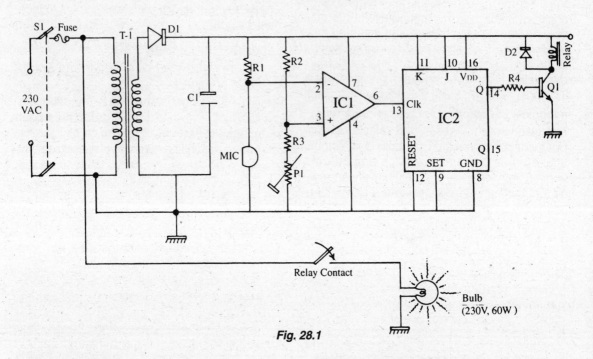

Fig. 28.1

INTRODUCTION

Here is a simple to understand and easy to build gadget that could be used to switch on the lights with the sound of a clap or the sound of opening of a door or even clicking sound of key in the lock. If properly installed, it could serve a very useful purpose in checking burglars' intrusion. The gadget has a sensitivity adjust control so that the gadget can be made to operate at the intended sound level. Gadget getting triggered by a whisper and the gadget not responding to even a loud bang, both are undesirable situations. The proposed gadget is designed to switch on and off alternately. That is, if one sound pulse switches the light on, another one will switch it off. It is a desirable feature when you have installed this gadget with the sole aim of switching the lights on and off at will without having to go to the switchboard. Even if the intention is to keep the burglars away, alternate switching of lights could really frighten them away.

CIRCUIT DESCRIPTION

The heart of the system is a J-K flip flop (IC2) whose ($\overline{Q}$) output state is used to drive the relay coil. The flip flop wired as a TOGGLE FLIP FLOP in turn is clocked by the output of an opamp (IC1) wired as a voltage comparator. The electric bulb gets its AC input through relay contact.

Transformer T-1, diode D1 and capacitor C1 constitute the conventional AC/DC power supply generating +12VDC. The non-inverting input of the opamp is applied a reference voltage produced by R2, R3 and the preset P1. Preset P1 can be used to adjust the reference voltage. The voltage at the inverting input is the same as that across the microphone. in the absence of any sound, this voltage is almost equal to the full DC voltage (=12VDC) with the result that the output of opamp is initially low. The J-K flip flop (IC2) has been wired as a toggle flip flop and its ($\overline{Q}$) output is initially low. Transistor (Q1) is in cut-off and the relay remains de-energised. The AC power input

226

connected to the bulb via relay contact thus does not reach the bulb and it remains extinguished.

In the presence of sound pulse, current flows through the microphone and the voltage across the microphone goes down from +12VDC due to the potential divider arrangement formed by R1 and the microphone. If the sound level is adequate so as to bring the voltage at the inverting input below the reference voltage at the non-inverting input, the opamp output goes high for a duration depending upon the duration of sound pulse. This positive going pulse triggers the flip flop and it toggles. ($\overline{Q}$) output goes high and the relay is energised with the result that relay's normally open contact closes and the bulb is lit. Another sound again toggles the flip flop and the relay contact opens. The bulb extinguishes again. Thus the bulb lights up and extinguishes alternately if there are recurrent sound pulses.

CONSTRUCTION GUIDELINES

The PCB layout and the components layout are respectively shown in Figs. 28.2 and 28.3.

PARTS LIST
Resistors and Capacitors

R1	: 10K, 1/4W
R2	: 1K, 1/4W
R3	: 470Ω, 1/4W
R4	: 2.2K, 1/4W
P1	: 1K Preset

C1	: 1000µF, 50V (Electrolytic)

Semiconductors

D1, D2	: 1N4001 or equivalent
Q1	: 2N2222
IC1	: 741
IC2	: CD4027B

Other Components

Transformer, T-1	: 12V, 250mA Mains transformer

Condenser Microphone

Relay	: 12VDC Relay with at least one normally open contact
Fuse	: 0.5A with holder
Switch	: S1 (Mains ON/OFF switch)

Miscellaneous

Solder metal, multistrand wires, suitable cabinet etc.

TESTING GUIDELINES

The only critical parameter that is required to be carefully set and then verified is the SENSITIVITY ADJUST. A higher value of reference voltage means a smaller sound level needed to force a change of state at the opamp output as in that case the voltage across the microphone needs to change by a smaller amount. A smaller reference voltage requires a louder sound. The reference voltage should be so adjusted (with the sensitivity adjust preset) as to produce the desired effect with intended sound level. Repeated tests should be carried out to establish the gadget reliability and that it does not trigger on false alarms.

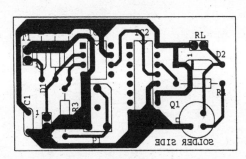

Fig. 28.2

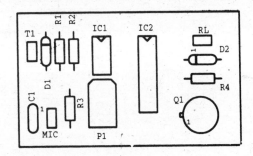

Fig. 28.3

PROJECT : 29

SIMPLE MUSICAL BELL

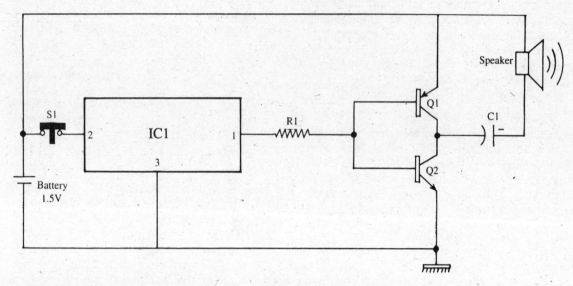

Fig. 29.1

CIRCUIT DESCRIPTION

A simple musical doorbell circuit is shown in Fig. 29.1. The circuit is built around IC UM66T32S, a popular type number used for constructing musical greeting cards. The IC can directly drive a microbuzzer but needs a driver stage to operate the speaker. IC UM66 comprises a ROM memory of 64 notes and has a built-in oscillator and a

PARTS LIST
Resistors and Capacitors

R1	: 2.2K, 1/4W
C1	: 220µF, 16V (Electrolytic)
Q1	: BC158
Q2	: BC148
IC1	: UM66
S1	: Push-Button Microswitch

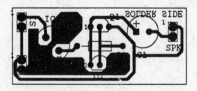

Fig. 29.2

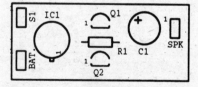

Fig. 29.3

preamplifier. Transistors Q1 and Q2 constitute the complementary symmetry audio amplifier that generates sufficient drive power for the speaker. Switch (S1) is a microswitch with normally closed contact connected in the circuit. The switch is pressed to open the contact momentarily.

8 ohm speaker, 1.5 volt cell, wires, solder metal etc.

Figs. 29.2 and 29.3 respectively give the PCB layout and components layout.

ELECTRONIC DICE

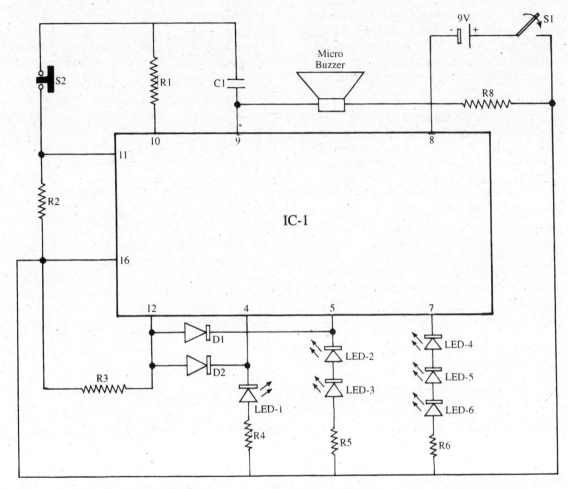

Fig. 30.1

Counter output Status			LEDs ON	Number indicated
Pin-4	**Pin-5**	**Pin-7**		
0	0	0	ALL	6
0	0	1	LED-1, LED-2, LED-3	3
0	1	0	LED-1, LED-4, LED-5, LED-6	4
0	1	1	LED-1	1
1	0	0	LED-2 to LED-6	5
1	0	1	LED-2, LED-3	2
0	0	0	ALL	6

OBJECTIVE

Here is a simple, easy to construct and a single chip based Electronic dice circuit. The dice comprises of six LEDs marked LED-1 to LED-6 (Fig. 30.1). The dice action is provided by lighting of a combination of LEDs. Number of LEDs that glow indicates the numeral. The LEDs that would glow corresponding to numerals 1 to 6 are given in the tabular form. The electronic dice circuit operates from a 9V battery and is small enough to be assembled in an audio cassette cover.

CIRCUIT DESCRIPTION

The heart of this simple electronic dice circuit is the CMOS IC 4060B which is 14-stage binary ripple counter with an on-chip oscillator that requires just one resistor (R1) and one capacitor (C1) to be connected external to the IC to complete the oscillator circuit. The oscillator output here serves as the clock input to the binary counter. The counter advances by one count in its natural binary count sequence each time it is clocked and the change of state of counter output occurs on HIGH to LOW transition of the clock pulse. The oscillator frequency in terms of (R1) and (C1) is given by:

$$f = \frac{1}{2.2R_1C_1}$$

and is approximately 2000Hz for the chosen component values. The oscillator is initially disabled as long as the push button is not pressed. The counter outputs are all in logic '0' state and all the six LEDs are ON. Press the push button (S2) to operate the dice. As the push button is pressed and the contact is made, the oscillator is enabled and the counter starts counting. The selected counter outputs (pins 4, 5 and 7) change from 000 to 101 and then reset to 000 to repeat

the sequence. Pin-7 represents the LSB and pin-4 the MSB. Remember that the counter resets to 000 after 101 and does not advance to 110 due to R3, D1 and D2. As the counter tends to advance to 110 from 101, D1 and D2 are both reverse biased and pin-12 (reset terminal) goes HIGH momentarily to reset the IC. For all other counts (000 to 101), either D1 or D2 or both are forward biased. Also remember that a HIGH on the reset terminal in this IC resets the counter.

So, the counter counts repetitively as long as the push button is kept pressed. Also the microbuzzer sounds as long as the counter is counting. As the push button is released, the counter stops counting any further and holds the state existing immediately prior to releasing the button. Depending upon the counter state, a certain combination of LEDs glow indicating any numeral from 1 to 6. Resistors R4, R5 and R6 are there to limit the current through LEDs.

CONSTRUCTION GUIDELINES

Figs. 30.2 and 30.3 respectively show the PCB layout and the components layout. It may however be mentioned once again that most of the projects including the present one were assembled using a general purpose PC board easily available in the market for the purpose of testing. So, if you are not good at making PCB layouts or etching of PC cards, you should not feel discouraged or disappointed. You could still try this and also the other projects given in this book.

PARTS LIST
Resistors and Capacitors

R1	:	470K, 1/4W
R2	:	2.2M, 1/4W
R3	:	100K, 1/4W
R4	:	1K, 1/4W
R5	:	680Ω, 1/4W

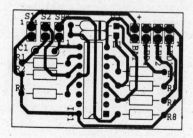

Fig. 30.2

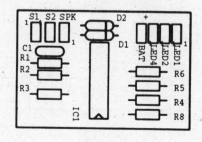

Fig. 30.3

230

R6   : 470Ω, 1/4W
R7   : 2.2K, 1/4W

C1   : 470pF

Semiconductor Devices
D1, D2   : 1N4001 or equivalent
LED-1 to LED-6 : Red LEDs
IC1   : CD4060B

Other Components
1. Microbuzzer: Any microbuzzer capable of operating from 9VDC. (Fig. 30.4)
2. 9V Battery
3. S1: ON/OFF switch

4. S2: Push Button type microswitch or ON/OFF switch

Miscellaneous
Solder metal, multistrand wires, suitable mounting cabinet etc.

PIN CONNECTION DIAGRAM OF CD4060B
To familiarise the constructor with the inside features of IC4060B, the pin connection diagram of the IC is given in Fig. 30.5. This is to allow the constructor understand better the function of this counter IC so that he does not follow the connections blindly.

Fig. 30.4

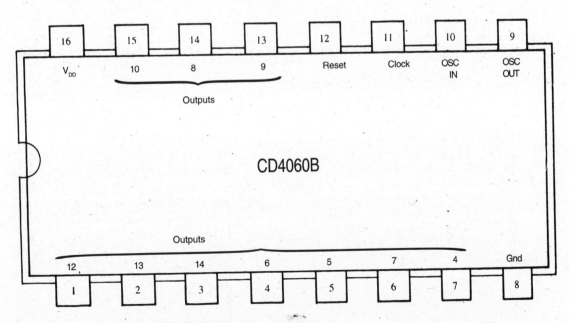

Fig. 30.5

231

BICOLOUR DANCING LIGHTS

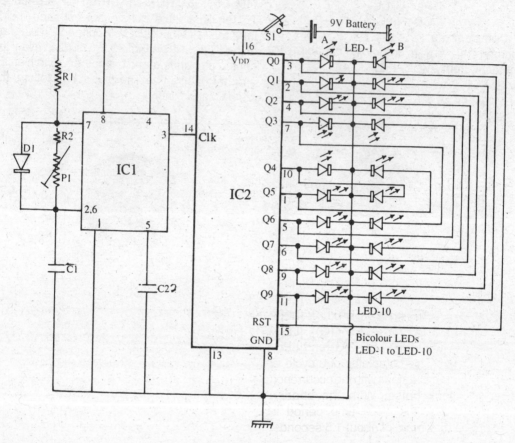

Fig. 31.1

INTRODUCTION

Here is a simple sequential running light circuit constructed with bicolour LEDs. While in operation, red and green portions of bicolour LEDs seem to be running in opposite directions i.e. when LED-1 is emitting in Red, LED-10 is emitting in green and all other LEDs are OFF. Following this, LED-2 and LED-9 simultaneously emit in Red and Green respectively and the process goes on. The circuit has a provision for varying the speed with which the two different colours move.

CIRCUIT DESCRIPTION

IC4017B is the heart of the system. It is a CMOS 1-of-10 decade counter/decoder with (Q0) to Q9) being the decoded outputs. Timer IC 555 has been wired as an astable multivibrator to generate clock pulses for the counter IC. It is this astable multivibrator frequency that decides the speed with which the LEDs switch ON and OFF. With the first clock pulse, (Q0) output goes HIGH while all other decoded outputs are LOW. This lights up the red portion of LED-1 (Bicolour LEDs used here have a common cathode and two anodes. One of the anodes when positive with respect to the

232

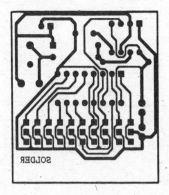

Fig. 31.2

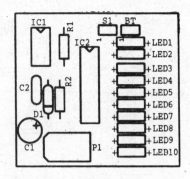

Fig. 31. 3

common cathode, the LED emits red whereas the other anode when positive with respect to the common cathode, the LED emits in Green) and the green portion of LED-10. With the second clock pulse, (Q1) goes HIGH, which all other outputs are LOW. LED-2 emits in red and LED-9 emits in green while all other LEDs are OFF. Similarly with the third, fourth, fifth, sixth, seventh, eighth, ninth and tenth clock pulses the pairs of LEDs that glow are [LED-3(R), LED-8(G)], [LED-4(R), LED-7(G)], [LED-5(R), LED-6(G)], [LED-6(R), LED-5(G)], [LED-7(R), LED-4(G)], [LED-8(R), LED-3(G)], [LED-9(R), LED-2(G)] and [LED-10(R), LED-1(G)]. This completes one cycle of running light. Next cycle starts with the occurrence of eleventh clock pulse. With the chosen component values, the clock time period is variable upto a maximum of about 1.5 seconds.

PARTS LIST
Resistors and Capacitors
R1, R2	:	10K, 1/4W
P1	:	1M potentiometer (LIN)
C1	:	2.2µF, 16V (Electrolytic)
C2	:	0.01µF (Ceramic disc)

Semiconductors
D1	:	1N4001 or equivalent
LED-1 to LED-10	:	Common cathode Bicolour LEDs

IC1	:	555
IC2	:	CD4017B

Miscellaneous
1. 9V Battery
2. Solder wire, multistrand wires
3. Knob for the potentiometer
4. Chasis for mounting PCB, battery, switch etc.
5. ON/OFF switch (S1)

Note: All resistors are carbon film or carbon composition resistors.

The PCB layout the components layout are respectively shown in Figs. 31.2 and 31.3. (Fig. 31.4) shows pin connection diagram of IC4017B.

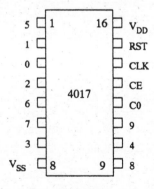

Fig. 31.4

PROJECT : 32

MOVING LIGHTS

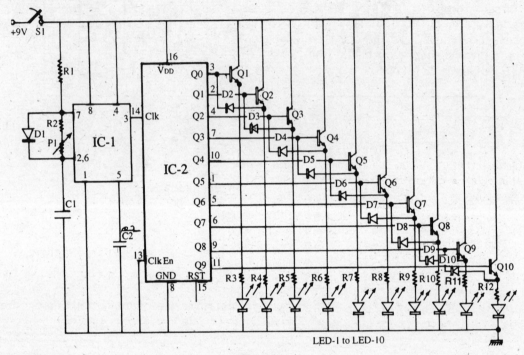

Fig. 32.1

INTRODUCTION

In essence, the project circuit is similar to the one described in case of the immediately preceding project. Both are based on CMOS IC CD4017B decade counter/decoder driven by a clock waveform generated by Timer IC 555 wired as an astable multivibrator. The two projects differ in the circuitry following the decoded outputs and subsequently in the lighting effects produced.

CIRCUIT DESCRIPTION

The circuit is built around CD4017B which is a 1-of-10 decade counter/decoder. The clock waveform is generated by timer IC 555 wired as the astable multivibrator with the time period of the clock waveform equal to 0.69 (R1+R2+P1) × C1. Q0, Q1, Q2.......Q9 are the decoded outputs. Q0, Q1, Q2....... Q9 decoded outputs go HIGH for one clock period with the occurrence of first,

second, third, ... tenth clock pulses respectively. This completes one count cycle and after that the process repeats.Now let us analyse the lighting effect produced as a result of changing decoded outputs.

When (Q0) goes HIGH, transistor (Q1) conducts and LED-1 lights up. With the second clock pulse, (Q1) goes HIGH, transistor (Q2) conducts and LED-2 lights up. With the conduction of transistor (Q2), diode (D2) gets forward biased and the LED-1 remains lit. With the third clock pulse, (Q3) conducts, LED-3 is lighted up. LED-2 also remains lit due to diode (D3) getting forward biased. Thus different LEDs are lit in sequence one after the other till we have all the ten LEDs lit with the tenth clock pulse. This completes one count cycle. You can observe that in the absence of diodes D2, D3....... D10, various LEDs are lit in

234

sequence one at a time i.e. first clock pulse only lights LED-1, second clock pulse lights only LED-2 and so on.

Another important point here is that if you decide to use less than 10 LEDs, you can do so without any problem provided that you connect the immediately following decoded outputs to RESET terminal. For example, if you use only five LEDs, then you must connect (Q5) output (Pin-1) to RESET terminal (Pin-15) of 4017B.

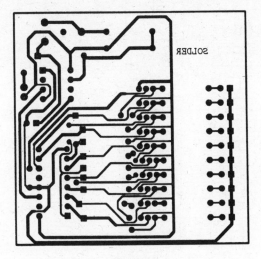

Fig. 32.2

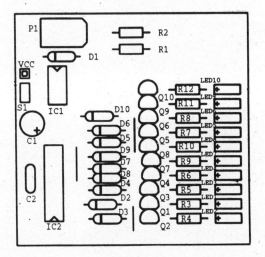

Fig. 32.3

With the chosen component values, the clock time period is adjustable upto a maximum of about 1.5 seconds. Resistors R3 to R12 are connected to limit current through LEDs.

CONSTRUCTION GUIDELINES
The PCB layout and the components layout are respectively shown in Figs. 32.2 and 32.3.

PARTS LIST
Resistors and Capacitors
R1, R2	: 10K, 1/4W
R3 to R12	: 1K, 1/4W
P1	: 1M Potentiometer (LIN)
C1	: 2.2 µF, 16V (Electrolytic)
C2	: 0.01µF (Ceramic Disc)

Semiconductor Devices and ICs
D1 to D10	: 1N4001 or equivalent
Q1 to Q10	: 2N2222
LED-1 to LED-10	: Red or Green LEDs with holders
IC1	: 555
IC2	: CD4017B (Figs. 32.4)

Miscellaneous
Switch, S1	: ON/OFF switch, 9V Battery, Solder Metal, Multistrand wires, Suitable cabinet

Note: All resistors are general purpose carbon film or carbon composition resistors.

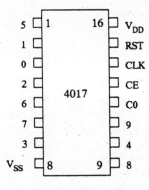

Fig. 32.4

235

SOUND OPERATED INTRUDER ALARM

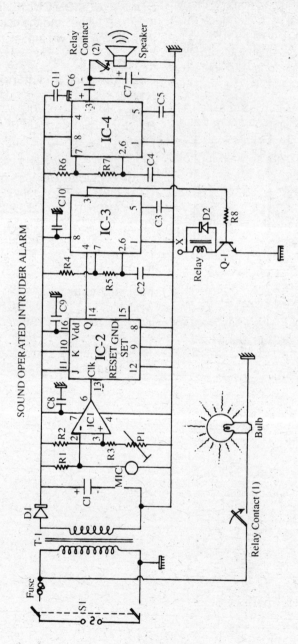

Fig. 33.1

INTRODUCTION

This project is a modification of the previously discussed SOUND OPERATED LIGHT gadget. The present circuit has been designed to make it a true burglar's alarm that operates automatically picking up sounds like those of opening of a door, the clicking sound of a key in the lock etc. The gadget provides both flashing light and an intermittent audio tone indications.

CIRCUIT DESCRIPTION

Upto the flip flop output, the circuit is identical to the earlier project. Initially, the opamp output and also the ($\overline{Q}$) output of the flip flop are low. 555 timer (IC3) that is wired as an astable multivibrator is reset due to the reset terminal (Pin-4) being held low. Transistor (Q1) is in cut-off and the relay coil stays de-energised. Both the normally open contacts of the relay are thus open. One of these contacts (marked relay contact-1) keeps the lamp extinguished whereas the other (marked relay contact-2) disconnects the output of another timer IC (IC4) also wired as an astable multivibrator from reaching the speaker.

In the presence of a sound pulse, there is a positive going pulse at the opamp output which clocks the flip flop. The output state of the flip flop toggles (It becomes high if initially low and vice versa). The (Q) output of the flip flop thus goes high and stays so till there is another sound pulse. This high output enables the astable multivibrator built around IC3. The output of this astable drives the relay coil on and off. The on and off time periods are given by:

On-time = 0.69 (R4+R5)C2
Off-time = 0.69 R5 C2

With the chosen component values, on and off times are 1.4 and 0.7 seconds respectively. When the relay coil is energised, relay contact-1 passes on the AC power to the bulb and it lights up. Relay contact-2 allows the output of astable multivibrator built around IC4 to the speaker and there is an audio tone. The frequency of this tone is given by:

$$f = \frac{1}{0.69[(R6+R7\,C4)+R7C4]}$$

It is about 500 Hz for the chosen component values. Thus, there is a flashing light and an intermittent audio tone as long as flip flop output is high. With another sound pulse, flip flop output goes low, the bulb extinguishes and the tone vanishes.

CONSTRUCTION GUIDELINES

The PCB layout the components layout are shown in Figs. 33.2 and 33.3 respectively.

PARTS LIST

Resistors and Capacitors

R1, R6, R7	: 10K, 1/4W
R2	: 1K, 1/4W
R3	: 470Ω, 1/4W
R4, R5	: 470K, 1/4W
R8	: 2.2K, 1/4W
P1	: 1K preset
C1	: 1000µF, 25V (Electrolytic)
C2	: 2.2µF, 25V (Electrolytic)

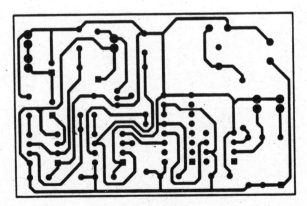

Fig. 33.2

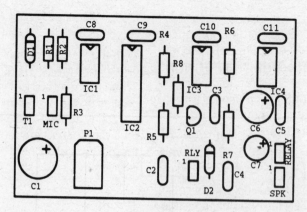

Fig. 33.3

C3, C5	: 0.01µF (Ceramic disc)	
C4	: 0.1µF (Polyester)	
C6	: 100µF, 16V (Electrolytic)	
C7	: 10µF, 16V (Electrolytic)	

Semiconductor Devices

D1, D2	: 1N4001 or equivalent
Q1	: 2N2222
IC1	: 741
IC2	: CD4027B (Fig.33.4)
IC3, IC4	: 555

Other Components

Transformer, T1	: 12V, 250mA Mains transformer
Speaker	: 4 ohms speaker
Relay	: 12VDC Relay with at least two normally open SPST contacts
Bulb	: 60W electric bulb
Fuse	: 0.5A rating with holder
Switch S1	: Mains ON/OFF switch

Miscellaneous

IC Bases (three 8-pin bases, one 14-pin base), solder metal, multistrand wires, suitable cabinet.

TESTING GUIDELINES

The gadget should be tested on similar lines as explained in case of earlier gadget. Again, sensitivity adjust control should be carefully set. Repeated testing should be done to ensure that there are no false triggers and that the gadget responds when intended with almost 100 percent reliability.

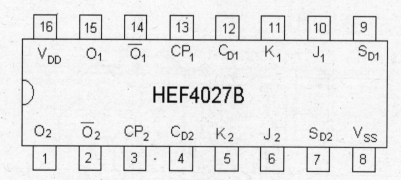

Fig. 33.4

Cooler Pump Protection cum Humidity Control Gadget

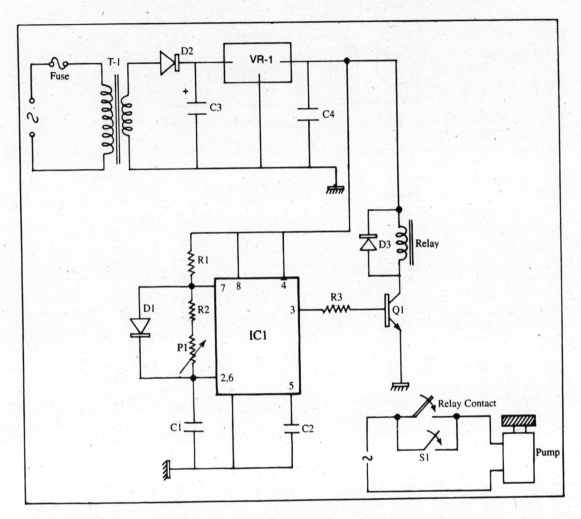

Fig. 34.1

INTRODUCTION

The desert cooler pumps packing off mainly due to excessive heating during summer peaks and also because they are forced to run almost continuously with very little breathing time is not very uncommon. Another shortcoming with these coolers is excessive humidity produced which forces majority of us to abandon the coolers with the onset of rains with the result that coolers are found effective and are used only during dry hot climate. Yet another problem faced particularly with low water capacity coolers is that you may suddenly discover at past mid night that there is no water in the cooler tank. All these problems could be overcome if the cooler pump was operated in a duty cycle while the fan was run continuously. Typically, the pump may be kept on for say two minutes and then switched off for a time ranging from four to eight minutes depending upon environmental temperature. This not only enhances pump life but also controls humidity. In addition, the cooler runs for a longer time for a given quantity of water. It may also be stressed that the operation of the pump in the ON/OFF fashion would not decrease the cooling effect. Infact, with humidity control, cooling effect is better.

CIRCUIT DESCRIPTION

The circuit is pretty straightforward. It is built around IC timer 555 wired as an astable multivibrator whose high time drives the relay ON and whose low time switches it OFF. The cooler fan gets the AC input directly whereas the cooler pump gets it via relay's normally open contact.

When the 555 output is high, the transistor conducts and the relay is energised. Normally open contact closes and the pump gets AC input. When the output goes low, the transistor goes to cut-off, the relay is de-energised and the pump is OFF. The high time of the 555 output waveform is given by (0.69R1 C1) and the low time is given by [0.69 (R2+P1)C1]. The given component values produce a fixed high time (the working time of the pump per cycle) of approximately 2 minutes and a selectable low time (the time for which the pump remains OFF per cycle) variable from about 3 minutes to 8 minutes. Switch S1 across the relay contact can be used to bypass the relay contact in case you desire to run your pump contineously.

PARTS LIST

Resistors and Capacitors

R1, R2	: 1M, 1/4W
R3	: 2.2K, 1/4W
P1	: 2.2M potentiometer (LIN)
C1	: 220µF, 25V (Electrolytic)
C2	: 0.01µF (Ceramic disc)
C3	: 1000µF, 25V (Electrolytic)
C4	: 0.1µF, (Ceramic disc)

Semiconductors

D1, D2, D3	: IN4001 or equivalent
VR-1	: Three terminal regulator, type 7812
IC-1	: 555

Miscellaneous

Relay	: 12VDC relay with at least one normally open contact

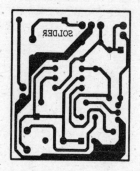

Fig. 34.2

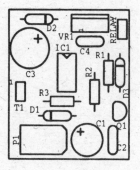

Fig. 34.3

Transformer, T-1 : 12V, 250mA Mains transformer
Fuse : 0.25A rating
Switch, S1 : Simple ON/OFF toggle switch (230V, 1A rating)

All resistors are general purpose carbon film or composition resistors.

CONSTRUCTION GUIDELINES

The PCB layout and the components layout are respectively shown in Figs. 34.2 and 34.3. The assembled unit should be mounted on the inside of the front panel near the usual controls of the cooler. The cabinet should be adequately sealed with some epoxy such as Araldite so that moisture does not get inside the unit. Fig. 34.4 shows the interconnections of the gadget and the cooler. Four wires are brought out from inside the unit. The AC input for the cooler (also going to the cooler fan through the regulator) also goes to the input of the gadget. The other two wires brought out after the relay contact serve as the AC input for the cooler pump. The third wire (earth wire) of the AC input is usually connected to the cooler body and gets automatically connected to the gadget body once the gadget is mounted on the cooler body.

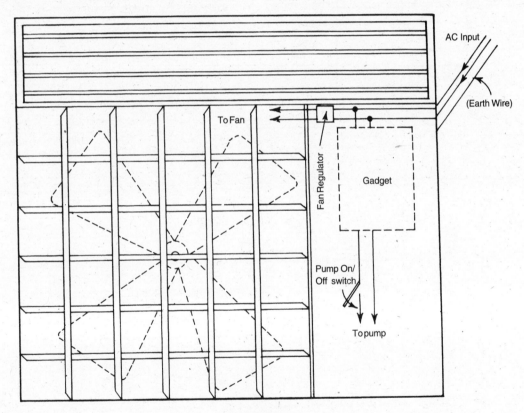

Fig. 34.4 (a)

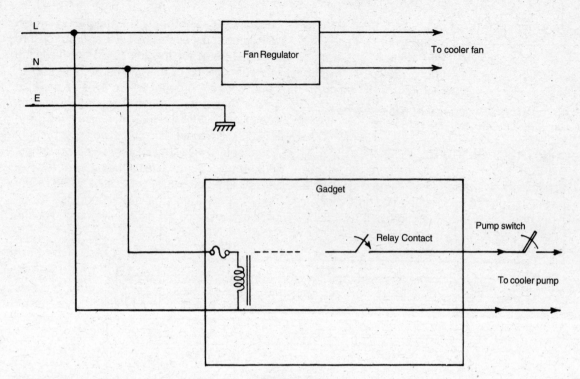

L

N

E

Fan Regulator

To cooler fan

Gadget

Relay Contact

Pump switch

To cooler pump

Fig. 34.4 (b)

242

PROJECT : 35

CUPBOARD LIGHT

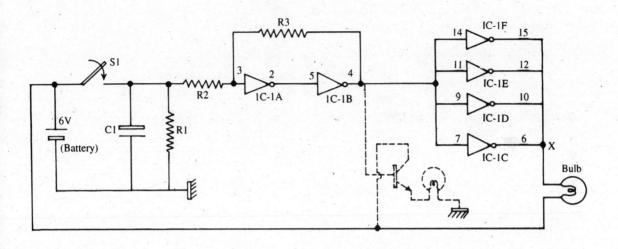

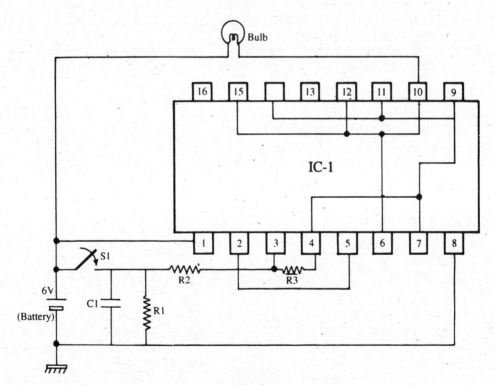

Fig. 35.1

INTRODUCTION

Here is a simple circuit that could temporarily illuminate your cupboard or other such usually dark places whereas mains connection is either not possible or not worthwhile. The circuit is nothing but a battery operated light with an in-built auto shut-off.

CIRCUIT DESCRIPTION

The circuit is built around a single hex inverter CMOS IC type no. CD4049B. Two of these six inverters inside the IC (designated IC-1A and IC-1B) along with resistors (R2) and (R3) constitute the Schmitt trigger.

When the switch (S1) is momentarily pressed, the voltage across capacitor (C1) rises to +6V almost instantaneously. The schmitt output goes HIGH which forces the output of four parallel connected inverters (IC-1C to IC-1F) go LOW thus switching ON the lamp. To sum up, when the switch (S1) is pressed and released, the lamp lights up. Now the capacitor (C1) has already started discharging through resistor (R1) and the moment the voltage across it decreases to a value that is treated as LOW state, the voltage at point (X) goes HIGH thus switching off the lamp. With the given component values, the lamp would remain ON for about two minutes. The time is given by 1/4 (R1 C1). The inverters IC-1C, 1D, 1E and 1F have been connected in parallel to increase

the current sinking capability. Note that when the lamp is ON, the lamp current would flow through the conducting output stages of these inverters inside the IC. For a larger lamp current, a transistor switch should be used in place of parallel connected inverters (shown dotted in the circuit diagram).

PARTS LIST

Resistors and Capacitors

R1, R3	: 10M, 1/4W
R2	: 1M, 1/4W
C1	: 47μF, 16V (Electrolytic)

Semiconductors

IC-1	: CD4049B (Fig. 35.4)

Miscellaneous

Switch, S1	: Push Button Microswitch
1.5V cells	: 4 nos
16-pin DIP IC base	: 1
Bulb	: 6V, 50mA

All resistors are of carbon film or carbon composition variety.

CONSTRUCTION GUIDELINES

PCB layout and components layout diagrams are respectively shown in Figs. 35.2 and 35.3. Fig. 33.4 shows pin connection diagram of IC CD4049B.

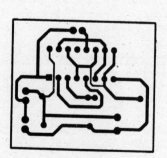

Fig. 35.2

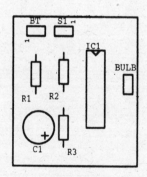

Fig. 35.3

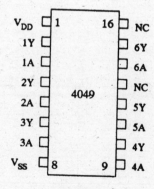

Fig. 35.4

244

PROJECT : 36

THE UNUSUAL MOTOR

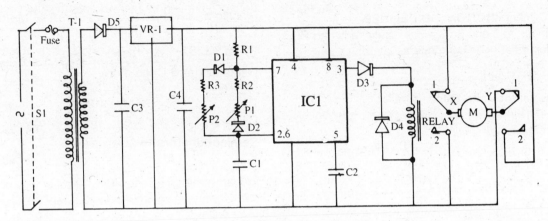

Fig. 36.1

INTRODUCTION

A simple and easy to construct circuit that can provide a bidirectional drive to a DC motor is given here. The circuit is pretty straightforward. The time and consequently the angular movement of the motor in the two directions can be controlled by two independent potentiometers. This simple drive circuit has numerous applications. It can be effectively used to drive the wind shield wiper in automobiles. It can be used to create a number of fun games for the kids by attaching different kinds of things such as toys, roulette wheel etc. to the motor shaft and trying various timing combinations.

CIRCUIT DESCRIPTION

The circuit operation is straightforward. The output of an astable multivibrator drives a relay coil that has atleast one DPDT (Double Pole Double Throw) or two SPDT (Single Pole Double Throw) contacts. The DC motor has been connected between the two poles of the relay contacts. The relay contacts are so wired as to reverse the DC supply to the motor when the contacts changeover.

The astable multivibrator is constructed around timer IC 555. It produces a square waveform at the output with its high time given by

$$0.69 (R1+R3+P2) C1$$

and its low time given by

$$0.69 (R1+R2+P1) C1$$

The high and low time periods can be varied respectively by varying potentiometers P2 and P1. For the chosen component values, the high and low times are adjustable from about 1 second to 8 seconds separately. When the 555 output is low, the relay is de-energised and the relay contacts are in position 1-1 with the result that X-terminal of the motor is positive with respect to the Y-terminal (X and Y are only designations) and the motor rotates in one direction (say clockwise). When the 555 output is high, the relay is energised and the contacts changeover to position 2-2. As a consequence, DC supply to the motor reverses in polarity. The motor starts rotating anticlockwise. Diodes D3 and D4 are there to protect the timer IC from positive and negative spikes generated due to relay coil switching.

The circuit operates on 12VDC generated from mains using a conventional AC/DC power supply. VR-1 is a three terminal regulator of the type 7812. Diode D5 provides rectification while C3 is the filter capacitor. T-1 is a 12V mains power transformer.

CONSTRUCTION GUIDELINES
Figs. 36.2 and 36.3 respectively show the PCB layout and the components layout.

PARTS LIST

Resistors and Capacitors
R1	: 1K, 1/4W
R2, R3	: 10K, 1/4W
P1, P2	: 100K potentiometer (LIN)
C1	: 100µF, 25V (Electrolytic)
C2	: 0.01µF (Ceramic disc)
C3	: 1000µF, 25V (Electrolytic)
C4	: 0.1µF (Ceramic disc)

Semiconductors
D1 to D5	: 1N4001 or equivalent
VR-1	: Three terminal regulator type 7812 (Fig. 36.4)
IC-1	: 555

Other Components
Transformer, T-1	: 12V, 250mA Mains transformer
Relay	: 12VDC Relay with at least one DPDT or two SPDT contacts
Motor	: 12VDC Motor
Fuse	: 0.5A rating (with holder)
Switch S1	: Mains power ON/OFF switch

Miscellaneous
Solder metal, multistrand wires, knobs for potentiometers, suitable mounting cabinet, 8-pin IC Base for IC-1.

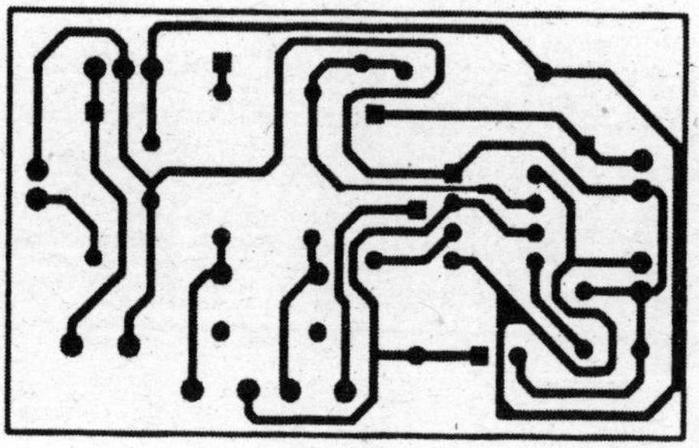

Fig. 36.2

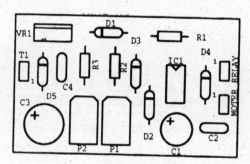

Fig. 36.3

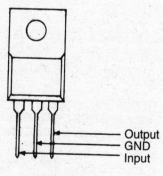

Fig. 36.4

246

TRANSISTOR TESTER

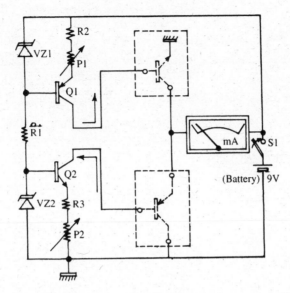

Fig. 37.1

INTRODUCTION

Here is an extremely simple circuit that can be used to test bipolar junction transistors. It can be used to test both NPN and PNP transistors. In addition to testing the transistors for any defect, this easy to build test gadget can also be used to measure the (hFE) of a given healthy transistor (NPN or PNP). Two different sets of three terminals each have been brought out on the front panel, one for testing NPN and the other for testing PNP transistors. Bringing out such terminals instead of using a specific transistor socket facilitates testing of transistors in any package style. Also (hFE) measurement can be carried out for a wide range of transistors starting with low (hFE) power transistors to high (hFE) small signal transistors. An (hFE) as high as 1000 can be measured with this gadget.

CIRCUIT DESCRIPTION

The heart of the circuit are two constant current sources built around transistors (Q1) and (Q2).

(Q1) is a PNP transistor and the constant current flows in the emitter lead. The same constant current flows out of the collector lead. The magnitude of constant current is given by:

$$\frac{VZ1 - 0.6}{(R2 + P1)}$$

In this circuit, (P1) is adjusted to get a constant current of 10µA. The second current source is built around NPN transistor (Q2) and the magnitude of constant current is given by:

$$\frac{VZ2 - 0.6}{(R3 + P2)}$$

Again (P2) is adjusted to get a constant current of 10µA. Here too, almost same constant current flows into the collector lead of (Q2).

This constant current (provided by Q1-circuit if the transistor under test is an NPN one and by Q2-circuit if the transistor under test is a PNP one) is fed to the base of transistor under test. This current multiplied by the (hFE) of the transistor

247

under test flows in the collector lead and is indicated by the meter. This is true as the transistor under test is always operating in the non-saturated mode. Maximum value of (hFE) that can be measured depends upon the full scale deflection of the meter. The meter can infact be directly calibrated to read the (hFE) of the transistor. The (hFE) check provides an automatic check for the functioning of the transistor.

CONSTRUCTION GUIDELINES

The PCB layout and the components layout are respectively shown in Figs. 37.2 and 37.3.

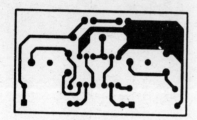

Fig. 37.2

PARTS LIST

R1	: 1K, 1/4W
R2, R3	: 470K, 1/4W
P1, P2	: 100K Preset
Vz1, Vz2	: 5.6V, 400mW zener diodes
Q1	: 2N2907
Q2	: 2N2222
Meter	: 10mA F.S.D.
S1	: ON/OFF switch

Miscellaneous

9V Battery, solder metal, multistrand wires, suitable mounting cabinet.

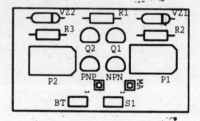

Fig. 37.3

31/2-DIGIT VOLTMETER WITH LCD DISPLAY

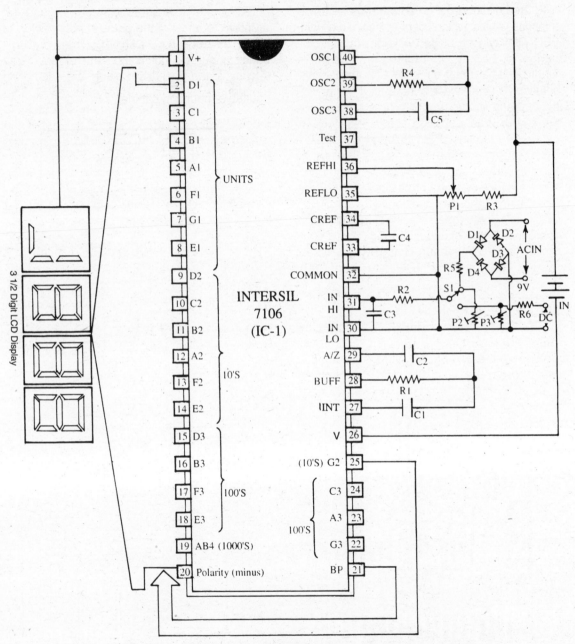

Fig. 38.1

OBJECTIVE

The 31/2-digit voltmeter project discussed earlier (Project-18) was a mains operable one. The basic IC (ICL7107) that could drive directly instrument sized LED seven segment displays needed +5VDC and –5VDC for its operation and also the current requirement from these power supplies (which is significant when we are using LED displays) prohibited us from making this gadget a battery operable one. It may be mentioned here that it may not be an optimum solution to use a battery here as it is not only the current requirement but also the need to generate +5VDC and –5VDC from the available battery voltage. If you are looking for a portable digital multimeter, the solution lies in using an LCD display which has a relatively much lower current requirement and interestingly the IC (Type No. ICL7106) that can directly drive a 31/2 digit LCD display requires a single 9VDC supply for its operation. For a change, the digital voltmeter under construction has voltage measurement ranges of 0 to 2000 VDC and 0 to 500V (RMS) AC.

CIRCUIT DESCRIPTION

Fig. 38.1 shows the circuit diagram. It is identical to the one shown in Fig. 18.1. ICL7106 is also identical to the ICL7107 except for a couple of differences in the pin designation. Firstly pin-21

in ICL 7106 is not the GND terminal (Pin-21 is GND terminal in ICL 7107) here, it is the BP (Back Plane) terminal and it has to be connected to the Back Plane input of the LCD display. Secondly, the positive terminal of the battery is connected to the REF HI input (Pin-36) through a potentiometer to adjust the reference and the negative terminal of the battery is connected to the negative supply input (Pin-26). The operational principle of this circuit is the same as described in case of the previous project. The calibration procedure is also similar. Here for DC calibration, you have to adjust potentiometers (P3) for a division factor of 1000 (for a 1000 VDC input, the divided voltage will be 2V) with the fixed resistance (R6). (P1) is then adjusted to make it direct reading on DC voltages. Once the DC calibration is over, potentiometer (P2) is adjusted to set the division factor for AC voltages in such a way that the gadget is direct reading on AC voltages also.

CONSTRUCTION GUIDELINES

Figs. 38.2 and 38.3 respectively show the PCB layout and the components layout.

PARTS LIST

Resistors and Capacitors

R1	: 470K, 1/4W
R2	: 1M, 1/4W
R3	: 22K, 1/4W

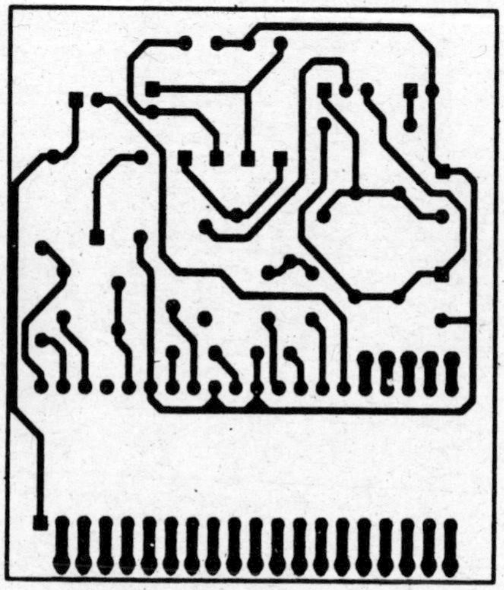

Fig. 38.2

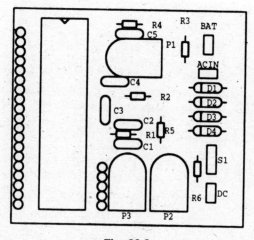

Fig. 38.3

R4	: 100K, 1/4W
R5	: 2.2M, 1500V resistor
R6	: Use two 2.2M, 1500V high voltage resistors in series.
P1	: 1K multi-turn trimmer
P2	: 10K multi-turn trimmer
C1	: 0.22µF (Polyester)
C2	: 0.47µF (Polyester)
C3	: 0.01µF (Ceramic disc)
C4	: 0.1µF (Ceramic disc)
C5	: 100pF (Polyester)

Semiconductor Devices and ICs

| D1 to D4 | : 1N4007 or equivalent |
| IC-1 | : ICL 7106 |

| Display | : 31/2-Digit LCD display |

Other Components

| S1 | : SPDT (230V, 1A) switch |

Miscellaneous

40-pin dual-in-line IC socket (for ICL 7106), multistrand wires, solder metal, suitable mounting cabinet, 9V Battery etc.

PIN CONNECTION DIAGRAM

Pin connection diagram of 31/2-digit LCD display is shown in Fig. 38.4. With this information, the display can be wired to the ICL 7106 display terminals without any problem.

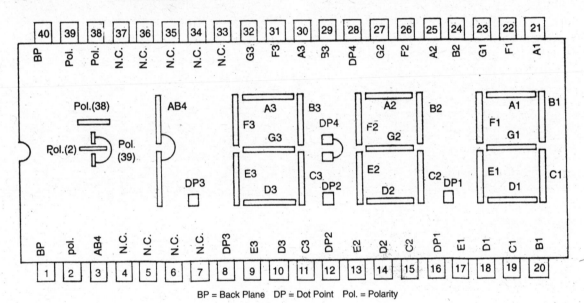

BP = Back Plane   DP = Dot Point   Pol. = Polarity

Fig. 38.4

DIGITAL THERMOMETER

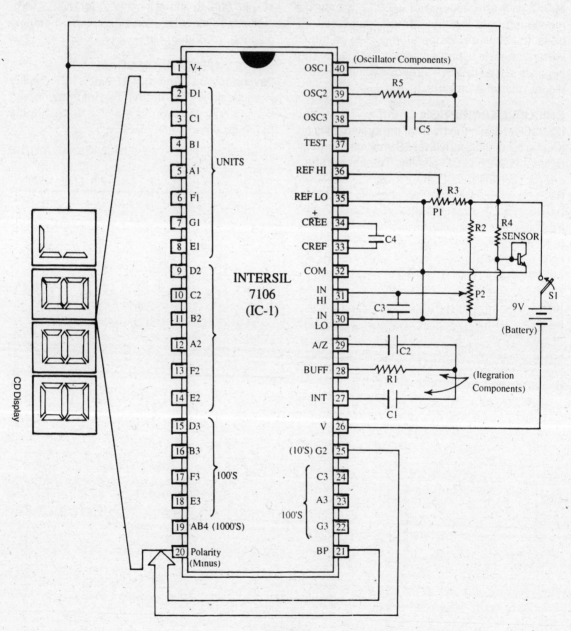

Fig. 39.1

OBJECTIVE

Here is a simple, easy to build and an attractive digital thermometer circuit that would measure temperature in centigrade over a range of 0°C to 100°C with an accuracy of ±0.1°C. It may be mentioned here that the same circuit could be used to measure temperatures over a much larger range if a proper sensor is there. The circuit is similar to those already explained in the digital voltmeter projects.

CIRCUIT DESCRIPTION

ICL7106 is again the heart of the system. It is an analog to digital converter IC that can directly drive a 31/2-digit LCD display. The temperature sensor is constructed from a silicon transistor 2N2222 with its collector terminal shorted to the base terminal to make it a two terminal device. The basis of temperature measurement is the fact that the base-emitter junction voltage of a silicon transistor has a temperature co-efficient of about $-2mV/°C$ i.e. the junction voltage reduces at a rate of 2mV for every degree centigrade rise in temperature. The sensor's base emitter junction here has been biased at a current of about 0.4mA through resistance (R4). The junction voltage varies as much as 200 mV over the temperature range of 0°C to 100°C. It is this junction voltage that is converted into a digital display.

CALIBRATION OF THERMOMETER

Calibration is achieved in a two step procedure:

1. In the first step, the sensor is placed in ice water (Put four or five cubes of ice in a container and dip the sensor cap so that it is surrounded by ice from all sides). Adjust potentiometer (P2) so that the display reads 000.0.

2. In the second step, dip the sensor's metal portion in boiling water and adjust potentiometer (P1) so that the display reads 100.0.

The thermometer is calibrated and ready for use.

CONSTRUCTION GUIDELINES

Figs. 39.2 and 39.3 show respectively the PCB layout and the components layout.

PARTS LIST

Resistors and Capacitors

R1	: 47K, 1/4W
R2	: 220K, 1/4W
R3	: 100K, 1/4W
R4	: 22K, 1/4W
R5	: 100K, 1/4W
C1	: 0.22µF (Polyester)
C2	: 0.47µF (Polyester)
C3	: 0.01µF (Ceramic disc)
C4	: 0.1µF (Ceramic disc)

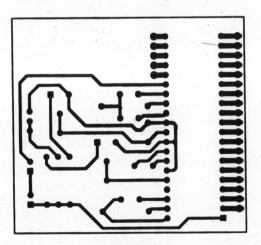

Fig. 39.2

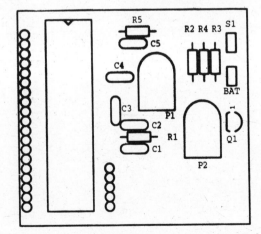

Fig. 39.3

| C5 | : 100pF (Polyester) |
| P1, P2 | : 100K, Multi-turn trimmers |

Semiconductor Devices and ICs
| Sensor | : Transistor 2N2222 with its collector-base shorted |
| IC1 | : ICL 7106 |

Other Components
Display	: 31/2-digit LCD Display
Battery	: 9V Battery
S1	: ON/OFF switch

Miscellaneous
40-pin D.I.L. IC socket, multistrand wires, shielded wire, solder metal, suitable mounting cabinet etc.

MAKING THE SENSOR

The temperature sensor, as mentioned earlier, is constructed from a silicon NPN transistor or its equivalent by shorting its collector base terminals. A piece of shielded wire should be used to make connections between the sensor and the circuit (Refer to Fig. 39.4). The length of shielded wire to be used depends upon the distance between the sensor location and the gadget. Also, sensor leads should not be exposed and some epoxy such as araldite should be used to insulate the sensor leads so that sensor coming in contact with water does not short the leads. We have shown here the cut-view of the shielded cable to expose the shield and the centre conductor.

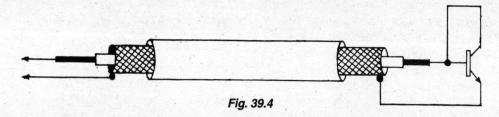

Fig. 39.4

ALL ELECTRONIC THERMOSTAT FOR FRIDGE

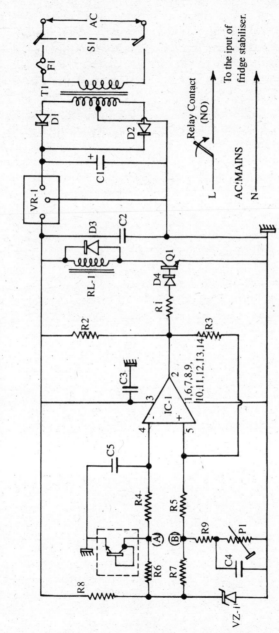

Fig. 40.1

OBJECTIVE

Here is a simple and easy to build electronic circuit that would automatically turn on and turn off your fridge at the two preset temperature extremes. Typically in a fridge, the temperature inside the deep freezer usually varies between – 2°C and –12°C i.e. the fridge becomes ON when the temperature inside the freezer becomes – 2°C and it becomes OFF when the temperature reaches –12°C. The extreme temperatures to some extent depend upon the fridge setting usually provided in terms of numbers 1 to 9. In the thermostat circuit shown in Fig. 40.1, the two temperature extremes as well as the difference between the two temperatures, known as temperature hysterisis, can be set independently with ease. The above thermostat is certainly more precise and reliable.

CIRCUIT DESCRIPTION

The AC mains voltage instead of going directly to input of automatic voltage stabiliser used with the fridge is routed through the normally open contact of the relay RL-1. Obviously, the ON/OFF duty cycle of the fridge can now be controlled by controlling the closing or opening of the relay contact which in turn can be controlled from the relay coil. When the relay coil is energised which is the case when transistor (Q1) conducts or is turned ON, the relay contact is closed and the fridge gets AC power and starts cooling. The DC voltage required for operating the relay coil control circuitry (12VDC in this case) is generated from AC only by using a conventional AC/DC power supply arrangement of a stepdown transformer (T-1), full wave rectifier (constituted by D1 and D2), a filter capacitor (C1) and a three terminal regulator (VR-1). As there must always be a minimum of 3V differential between the unregulated input and the regulated output in a three terminal regulator to maintain regulation, we have used a 14-0-14 mains transformer to guarantee a regulated DC voltage for a mains voltage of 230V ±60V. (C1) and (C2) are decoupling capacitors commonly used at the input and output of three terminal regulator. The temperature control circuitry functions as follows:

IC-1 is an opamp comparator. It is basically a quad comparator and we are making use of one of the four comparator circuits. It has been wired in the circuit as a voltage comparator with hysterisis. The non-inverting input of the comparator is applied a reference voltage derived from a zener diode. Resistor (R8) provides biasing current to the zener diode (VZ-1). The zener diode voltage is then divided by the potential divider arrangement provided by (R7), (R9) and (P1). (C4) is the decoupling capacitor to bypass AC noise if any. Between the inverting input and ground is connected the temperature sensor. The temperature sensor is nothing but a silicon NPN transistor with its collector shorted to its base. We are making use of the temperature dependent characteristics of the base emitter junction. You would remember that this junction voltage decreases by 2mV for every degree rise in the temperature of its body. Sensor fabrication and calibration are discussed separately. Potentiometer (P1) is adjusted to set the reference voltage at a value equal to the sensor's junction voltage corresponding to the less negative temperature of the two temperature extremes (–2°C in our case). Now let us assume that the temperature inside the freezer is –2°C or more negative than –2°C but less negative than –12°C. The voltage at the non-inverting input of the comparator which is equal to the reference voltage (corresponding to a voltage equivalent of –2°C) plus the fraction of the voltage fed back through potential divider (R3) and (R5). The fedback voltage in our case is 20mV whenever the comparator output is HIGH and zero whenever it is LOW. Now 20mV corresponds to a temperature change of 10°C. Therefore, as long as temperature is less negative than –12°C, the voltage at the non-inverting input is greater than that at the inverting input, the comparator output is HIGH, transistor Q1 saturates and the relay coil is energised. The fridge is on. When the temperature tends to go below –12°C, comparator output goes LOW and the relay coil is de-energised. The fridge is off. When the comparator goes LOW, the feedback voltage of 20mV vanishes and the voltage at the non-inverting input corresponds to a temperature of –2°C. So, the temperature cycles between –2°C and –12°C. To summarize, the reference voltage setting (Potentiometer P1) decides the less negative of the two temperature extremes whereas the temperature hysterisis and subsequently the more negative of the two temperatures depends upon the voltage divider arrangement formed by (R3) and (R5). If (T) is the desired temperature hysterisis then

$$T \text{ (in degrees)} = \frac{3000R5}{(R3 + R5)}$$

SENSOR FABRICATION AND CALIBRATION

The sensor is fabricated by shorting the collector and base leads of transistor 2N2222 and bringing out two leads from the base collector common point and the emitter. The sensor is mounted on the side wall of the freezer with some epoxy (like araldite). The connections from the sensor to the circuit should be made with a shielded cable or a twisted pair of wires if shielded cable is not available. The sensor leads should be fully insulated from each other and from the transistor

body using some epoxy so that the water deposition on the sensor does not short the leads. Also, preferably, the sensor's metallic body should be housed in a ceramic block and the ceramic block should be affixed to the freezer body. The sensor should be fitted in the ceramic block quite tightly so that there is complete thermal contact. Remember that ceramic is a very good thermal conductor and an electrical insulator.

The sensor can be calibrated by bringing it in full contact with ice water and at the same time biasing its base emitter junction at about 100µA using a series resistance and a suitable voltage. The junction voltage thus observed corresponds to a temperature of 0°C. The junction voltage corresponding to any other temperature can then be determined from the figure of temperature co-efficient (−2mV/°C).

CONSTRUCTION GUIDELINES

Figs. 40.2 and 40.3 show the PCB layout and the components layout respectively.

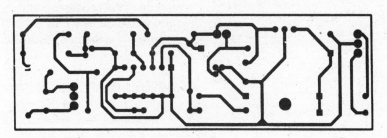

Fig. 40.2

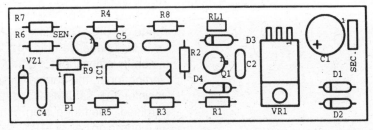

Fig. 40.3

PARTS LIST

Resistors and Capacitors

R1, R2	: 3.9K, 1/4W
R3	: 10M, 1/4W
R4	: 10K, 1/4W
R5	: 33K, 1/4W
R6	: 47K, 1/4W
R7	: 15K, 1/4W
R8	: 470Ω, 1/4W
R9	: 1K, 1/4W
P1	: 1K, Multi-turn trimer
C1	: 1000μF, 25V (Electrolytic)
C2, C3, C4	: 0.1μF (Ceramic disc)
C5	: 1μF (Solid tantalum preferably)

Semiconductor Devices and ICs

D1, D2, D3, D4	: 1N4001 or equivalent
VZ-1	: 5.6V zener diode, 400mW rating
VR-1	: Three terminal regulator type 7812
Q1	: 2N2222
Sensor	: Constructed from 2N2222 as explained (Fig. 38.4).
IC-1	: LM339

Other Components

T-1	: Mains transformer, Primary : 230VAC Secondary: 14-0-14, 250mA
S1	: Mains power ON/OFF switch with built-in Neon
F1	: Fuse with holder, fuse rating 0.5A

Miscellaneous

Solder metal, multistrand wires, suitable mounting cabinet, 14-pin D.I.L. IC socket, shielded cable etc.

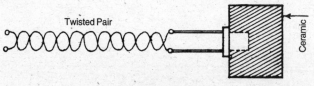

Fig. 40.4

PROJECT: 41

INVISIBLE INTRUDER ALARM

INVISIBLE INTRUDER ALARM

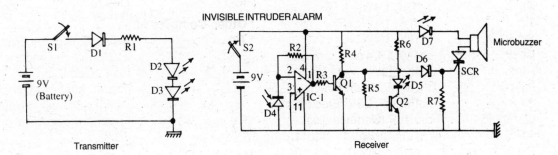

Fig. 41.1

OBJECTIVE

Here is an ultra compact intruder alarm system based on the detection of an intrusion caused by the interruption of an infra-red (which is invisible to human beings) light beam being emitted by an infra-red LED and falling on a matched photo-diode. Both the transmitter and the receiver portions separately operate from 9V batteries. The transmitter and receiver gadgets can be mounted in an aligned position on the two sides of a door to check intrusion or even on the two facing walls of inside of a locker to give you an alarm whenever an unauthorised person attempts a mischief. The gadget has a provision of both audio as well as visible indications. The audio indicator (microbuzzer) and the visible indication (LED) can be remotely located away from the location of gadget also.

CIRCUIT DESCRIPTION

The circuit comprises of a transmitter module and a receiver module. The transmitter module generates the required current drive for the infra-red light emitting diode and the receiver module once aligned with the transmitter module senses any interruption of the light beam caused by an intruder to activate the alarm. In the transmitter, the current through the light emitting diode is being controlled by resistance (R1). The current here is about 60mA.

In the receiver module, which during normal operation is aligned to the transmitter, the light beam emnating from the LEDs is directly falling on the photo diode in the receiver. The opamp (IC-1) has been wired as a current to voltage converter i.e., it converts the photo-induced current into an equivalent voltage at the opamp output. This voltage switches the transistor (Q1) ON. To summarise, when the transmitter and receiver modules are perfectly aligned and the light beam is falling on the receiver, transistor (Q1) is fully conducting and is in saturation.

Once transistor (Q1) is ON, its collector is at ground potential ($\cong$0.2V more precisely) which keeps both the transistor (Q2) and the SCR in the OFF-state. In nutshell, as long as the infra-red light beam from the transmitter is falling on the receiver photo detector, transistor (Q2) and the SCR are in OFF-state with the result that LED (D7) doesn't glow and the microbuzzer too doesn't get the supply. Now let us see what happens when there is an intrusion and the light beam is interrupted. Transistor (Q1) goes to cut-off. Transistor (Q2) conducts and also the SCR fires. LED (D7) glows and the microbuzzer produces a sound. The SCR stays ON if once fired even if the gate drive is removed. Therefore, the micrbuzzer continues sounding the alarm and LED (D7) continues to glow even after the beam interruption is over and light beam path between transmitter and receiver is restored. Switch S2 needs to be opened momentarily to reset the system and get it ready to detect the next intrusion. LED (D5) can be used to align the transmitter and receiver modules.

ALIGNMENT

The procedure to be followed for aligning the transmitter and receiver modules is as follows:

The status of LED (D5) when switches S1 and S2 are closed tells about the system alignment. When the system is out of alignment, the light beam does not fall on the photo detector thus simulating the conditions of an intrusion. As a result, LED (D5) glows. The two modules should be so aligned that the LED (D5) extinguishes.

CONSTRUCTION GUIDELINES

Figs. 41.2 and 41.3 respectively show the PCB layout and the components layout.

PARTS LIST

Resistors

R1   : 68Ω, 1W
R2   : 10M, 1/4W
R3   : 1K, 1/4W
R4   : 470Ω, 1/4W
R5   : 4.7K, 1/4W
R6   : 4.7K, 1/4W
R7   : 100Ω, 1/4W

Semiconductor Devices and ICs

D1, D6   : 1N4001 or equivalent
D4   : Photo diode, Type No. TIL81
D2, D3   : Infra-red emitting diode Type No. TIL34
D5, D7   : LEDs (D7 red and D5 green)
Q1, Q2   : 2N2222
SCR   : OE101 or equivalent (Any SCR with 100V breakdown voltage and 1A forward current ratings)
IC-1   : LM324 (Quad opamp)

Other Components

Microbuzzer, 9V battery, 14-pin D.I.L. IC socket, two miniature ON/OFF switches (S1 and S2).

Miscellaneous

Multistrand wires, solder metal, suitable mounting cabinet for transmitter and receiver etc.

Fig. 41.2

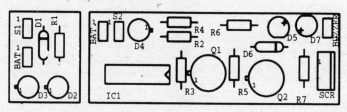

Fig. 41.3

PIN CONNECTION DIAGRAMS

Pin connection diagrams of LM324, infra-red emitting diode TIL34 and photo diode TIL81 are respectively shown in Figs. 41.4(a), (b) and (c).

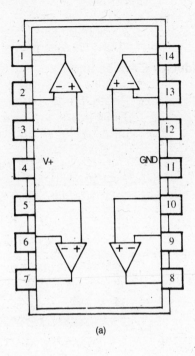

(a)

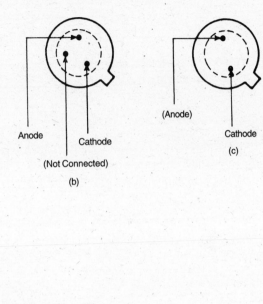

(b)

(c)

Fig. 41.4

ELECTRO-MECHANICAL COUNTER

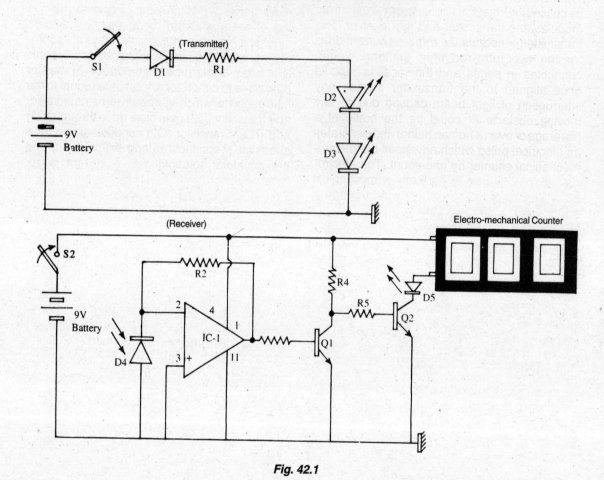

Fig. 42.1

OBJECTIVE

Here is a simple gadget that can be used as an incremental counter. The gadget has numerous applications. It can be used to count the number of bottles passing over the conveyer belt or even the number of people passing through a certain entrance. In its application, the transmitter and receiver portions are aligned with each other and infra-red light beam generated by the transmitter is directly falling on the photo diode in the receiver. Whenever the infra-red light beam is interrupted, the electro-mechanical counter advances by one count. In a typical application of counting of bottles passing over a moving conveyer belt, the transmitter and receiver portions are located on the two opposite sides of the belt and aligned with each other to establish a continuous light beam path. The light path is interrupted every time a bottle moves across it. The number of bottles passing over a period of time is thus known from counter reading. The gadget may also be used on the entrance to an exhibition or a fete to determine the number of people coming to see the exhibition or fete. But here the gadget works only when the entrance gate allows only one person at a time to pass through.

CIRCUIT DESCRIPTION

The circuit like the invisible intruder alarm discussed in Project : 41 consists of two separate modules, the transmitter and the receiver. The transmitter generates the required current drive for the two infra-red light emitting diodes connected in series and the receiver module once aligned to the transmitter senses any interruption of light beam caused due to any moving obstacle (it could be the bottle of a beverage or even a human being) and generates an electrical pulse which advances the electro-mechanical counter by one count. The electro-mechanical counter is basically a mechanical counter actuated by current flowing through a solenoid integral to the counter.

In the transmitter module, the current through the light emitting diodes is being controlled by resistance (R1). The current has been set at 60mA. Two identical infra-red emitting diodes have been connected in series to increase the light output to facilitate a larger range between transmitter and receiver locations.

In the receiver module, which during normal operation is aligned to the transmitter, the infra-red beam emitted by diodes (D2) and (D3) is directly falling on the photo diode in the receiver. The opamp (IC-1) has been wired as a current to voltage converter i.e. it converts the photo induced current into an equivalent voltage at the opamp output. This voltage switches the transistor (Q1) on. Once transistor (Q1) is on, its collector is approximately at ground potential ($\cong 0.2$ volt more precisely) which keeps transistor (Q2) in the off-state with the result that the electro-mechanical incremental counter stays at its initial setting. Now let us see what happens when this light beam is interrupted temporarily. Transistor (Q1) goes to cut-off for a short time (equal to the time period for which light beam remains blocked) and transistor (Q2) gets base drive through (R4) and (R5). Transistor (Q2) conducts again for a short time (it conducts as long as (Q1) is off) and the counter's solenoid gets a current pulse. Consequently, it increments by one count. If the light beam remains blocked continuously which doesn't happen in the intended application of the circuit, the counter would keep on incrementing at a steady rate. Again LED (D5) can be used to help in aligning transmitter and receiver modules.

ALIGNMENT

Alignment procedure is similar to the one described in Project : 41. LED (D5) glows as long as the two modules are not aligned. It extinguishes when they are properly aligned.

CONSTRUCTION GUIDELINES

Figs. 42.2 and 42.3 respectively show the PCB layout and the components layout.

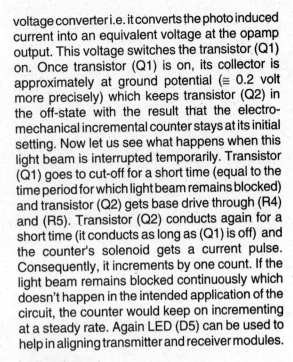

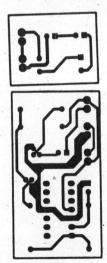

Fig. 42.2

Fig. 42.3

PARTS LIST

Resistors

R1	: 68Ω, 1W
R2	: 10M, 1/4W
R3	: 1K, 1/4W
R4	: 470Ω, 1/4W
R5	: 4.7K, 1/4W

Semiconductor Devices and ICs

D1	: 1N4001 or equivalent
D2, D3	: Infra-red emitting diode, Type TIL34
D4	: Photo diode, Type TIL81
D5	: LED
Q1, Q2	: 2N2222
IC-1	: LM324 (Quad opamp)

Other Components

Two 9V batteries, two ON/OFF switches (S1 and S2), Electromechanical incremental counter (Fig. 42.4) 14-pin dual-in-line IC socket.

Miscellaneous

Multistrand wires, solder metal, suitable mounting cabinets for transmitter and receiver modules.

PIN CONNECTION DIAGRAMS

Pin connection diagrams of Quad opamp LM324, infra-red emitting diode TIL 34 and photo diode TIL81 were given in Project : 41.

Fig. 42.4

SIMPLE LASER-BASED INTRUDER ALARM

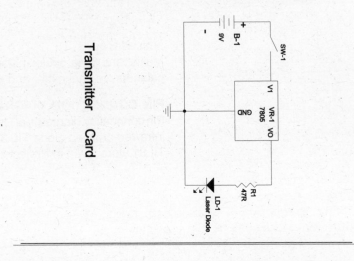

Transmitter Card

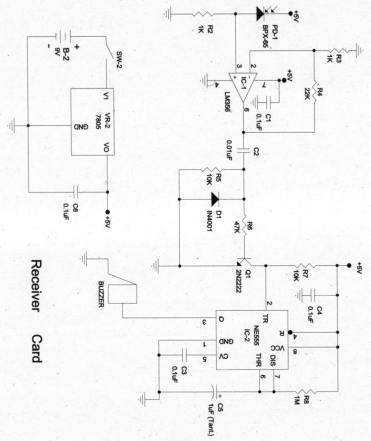

Receiver Card

Fig. 43.1

OBJECTIVE

The objective of this exercise is to build a simple laser-based intruder alarm gadget that could very conveniently be used at the entrance of a certain hall or any other similar location to protect the same from unauthorized access as and when desired. For example, such a gadget could be used at the main entrance and then activated during the night time. The same could also be used at the entrance of a place where you have kept your valuables and so on.

The concept of this project, as you will see, can be extended further to build a perimeter protection system where this gadget would be used to protect the perimeter of a building or any other precious location from unauthorized intrusion. A cascade arrangement of multiple gadgets could also be used to extend the range of the system. All these ideas are separately discussed in subsequent projects.

Also, familarization with this circuit would enable you understand better the simple laser-based communication gadget discussed in a subsequent project. **In fact, you could think about a large number of variants that could be built around this simple concept of transmitting a laser beam and then receiving it on the other end.** It becomes still more interesting for our community of electonics enthusiasts as laser source is available very cheap now in the form a laser pointer and the typical power level available from a laser pointer being more than adequate for building these gadgets for concept learning and demonstration purpose if not for actual field use.

CIRCUIT DESCRIPTION

Fig.43.1 shows the circuit diagram. As you can see, the circuit is divided into two parts i.e. the Transmitter-part and the Receiver-part.

Transmitter Part

The transmitter circuit is nothing but a laser diode driven by a battery connected to the diode through a series resistance R1. In order to ensure that the current through the diode remains constant irrespective of drop in battery voltage, a 3-terminal voltage regulator VR-1 has been used. This regulator produces a constant 5 volt output as long as input remains equal to or more than 7.5 volts thus ensuring a constant drive current for the laser diode. The drive current in this case would be (3500/47) mA. Remember that voltage across laser diode is of the order of 1.5 volt. The battery is connected to the circuit through switch SW-1.

The laser diode here can be the one typically used in laser pointers emitting in red. This would be more economical than buying one. If the experimenter so desires, he can use the laser pointer itself as a complete transmitter circuit. The pointer has in-built suitable series resistance and an ON/OFF switch and a battery. The given circuit would help when you want to go a step further and want to use an infrared laser diode so as to get an invisible laser beam, which would be a requirement in any intruder alarm system. I am recommending the use of a laser pointer only for the purpose of learning and demonstration.

Receiver Part

The receiver part basically comprises of a current-to-voltage converter section configured around IC-1 (OPAMP 356) feeding a positive edge triggered monoshot configuration built around IC-2 (Timer IC 555). The output of the monoshot feeds a buzzer that gives an audio beep during the time it get a HIGH input from timer IC 555. The receiver section operates from +5VDC generated from another 9V battery B-2 and a 3-terminal regulator VR-2. The battery can be connected to the circuit through switch SW-2.

The current-to-voltage converter secton converts the photocurrent produced by the photodiode PD-1 as result of laser light falling on it into an equivalent voltage across resistor R2. This voltage gets amplified by a factor of 23 in the non-inverting amplifier configuration provided by the opamp and resistors R3, R4. So, when the laser light is falling on the photodiode, the opamp output is some DC voltage. The component values have been so chosen as to produce about 5VDC for a laser power of 0.5mW, typical of a laser pointer. Otherwise the amplifier gain can be adjusted to produce 5VDC.

When the laser light is interrupted, the output of opamp goes to zero and then comes back to 5VDC when the laser light-photodiode link is restored. Thus the opamp output goes from HIGH to LOW and back to HIGH every time some one tries to walk through the laser light temporarily blocking the laser light.

This pulse feeds the positive edge triggered monoshot configuration. The output of the monoshot goes HIGH for time duration equal to approximately (R8.C5) every time it gets a pulse at its trigger input terminal (pin-2). The HIGH output pulse appearing at pin-3 of IC-2 feeds the buzzer. The time duration for the chosen values is 1 second.

CONSTRUCTION GUIDELINES

Figs.43.2(a) and (b) respectively show the PCB layout the transmitter and receiver sections. Figs. 43.3(a) and (b) show the components layout for the same. However, the circuits are simple enough so as to be constructed on general purpose PCBs.

TESTING GUIDELINES

1.   Switch ON the tramsmitter circuit, align the transmitter and receiver circuits so that the laser beam falls on the photodiode. You can use a small transmitter-receiver distance, even a few feet, for the purpose.

2.   If necessary, change the values of one or more resistors (R2, R3, R4) to get 5VDC at the opamp output.

3.   Block the laser radiation with your hand and again measure the opamp output. It should be near zero volt.

4.   If you have the services of an oscilloscope, observe the pulse appearing at opamp output. You would see a HIGH-to-LOW pulse every time you cut the laser beam.

5.   Also check the pulse at collector of the transistor Q1. You would see a very narrow HIGH-to-LOW pulse coinciding with the LOW-to-HIGH edge of the opamp output pulse.

6.   At pin-3 of IC-2, you would see a positive going 1-second duration pulse beginning with HIGH-to-LOW edge of the trigger pulse appearing at pin-2 of IC-2 or collector of transistor Q1.

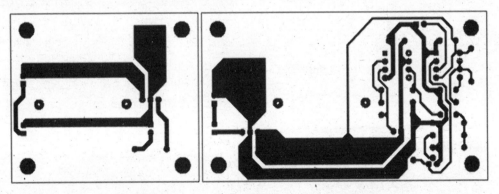

Fig. 43.2

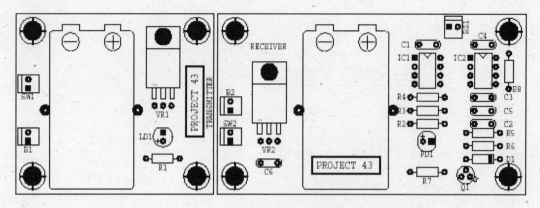

Fig. 43.3

PARTS LIST

Resistors

All resistors are carbon film or composition resistors unless specified otherwise

R1	:	47 ohms, 1/4W
R2,R3	:	1K, 1/4W
R4	:	22K, 1/4W
R5, R7	:	10K, 1/4 W
R6	:	47K, 1/4W
R8	:	1M, 1/4W

Capacitors

C1, C4, C6	:	0.1µF (ceramic disc)
C2, C3	:	0.01µF (ceramic disc)
C5	:	1µF (tantalum)

Semiconductor and ICs

D1 (Diode)	:	IN4001
PD-1 (Photodiode)	:	BPX-65 or equivalent
LD-1 (Laser Diode)	:	Can use a laser pointer
Q1 (Transistor)	:	2N2222
IC-1	:	OPAMP LM356
IC-2	:	Timer 555

Hardware and other Components

B-1, B-2 (Battery)	:	9V battery (Fig.43.4)
SW-1, SW-2	:	ON/OFF swich, SPST type
Buzzer	:	Suitable Piezo buzzer (Fig.43.5)

Multi-strand wire, Solder metal, General purpose PCB, if needed.

Fig. 43.4

Fig. 43.5

PROJECT: 44

LASER-BASED PERIMETER PROTECTION SYSTEM

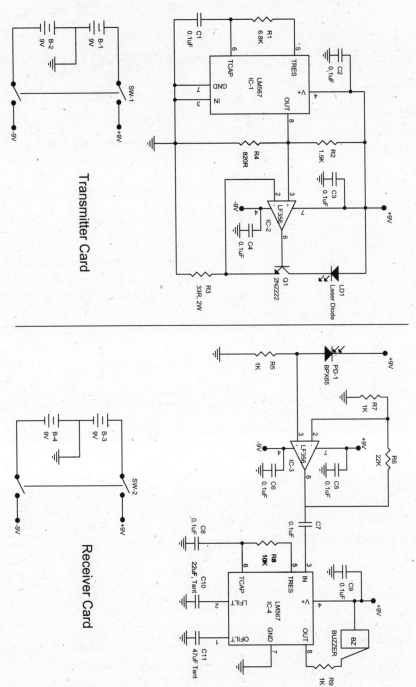

Fig. 44.1

OBJECTIVE

The objective of this exercise is to build a laser-based intruder alarm gadget that could very conveniently and effectively be used to provide protection from any unauthorized acess of a building or any other similar location. The suggested circuit is an improvement over the one discussed in project-43. The present circuit, instead of using continuous laser beam, uses a pulsed one. This feature, as we shall see in the following paragraphs, makes the system highly immune to false alarms resulting from birds cutting the laser beam.

The concept of this project, as you will see, can be extended further to build a perimeter protection system where this gadget would be used to protect the perimeter of a building or any other precious location from unauthorized intrusion. A cascade arrangement of multiple gadgets could also be used to extend the range of the system. All these ideas are separately discussed in subsequent projects.

In fact, you could think of a large number of variants that could be built around this simple concept of transmitting a laser beam and then receiving it on the other end. It becomes still more interesting for our community of electronics enthusiasts as laser source is available very cheap now in the form a laser pointer and the typical power level available from a laser pointer being more than adequate for building these gadgets for concept learning and demonstration purpose if not for actual field use.

CIRCUIT DESCRIPTION

Fig. 44.1 shows the circuit diagram. As you can see, the circuit is divided into two parts i.e. the Transmitter-part and the Receiver-part.

Transmitter Part

The transmitter circuit is nothing but a laser diode driven by a pulsed waveform produced by IC-1. IC-1 is basically a Tone Decoder IC. The inside of the IC has a current controlled oscillator (CCO) whose output feeds one of the inputs of a phase comparator. The other input of the phase comparator is used to feed an external signal

input. The output of phase comparator feeds some more circuit blocks which finally produce a HIGH output if there is an external signal input at the same frequency as that of CCO or if the input signal has a frequency different from the one being internally generated by CCO by an amount less than a certain value (called Detection bandwidth) chosen by the designer. The output goes to LOW state if there is no external input signal or if the input signal frequency is different from the CCO frequency by an amount greater than the capture range. In the transmitter part, only CCO portion of the IC has been used. The frequency of pulsed waveform is given by (1.1/RICI) and is approximately 1kHz for the chosen values. This pulsed waveform appearing at pin-8 of IC-1 feeds the output driver circuit comprising of IC-2 (OPAMP 356), transistor Q1 (2N2222) and R3. Resistor R2 is pull-up resistor for IC-1 output. R2-R4 combination produces pulse amplitude of 3V at their junction.

To simplify things, the laser diode LD-1 will be driven alternately by two current levels. The lower current level is given (VL/R3) and upper current level is given by (VH/R3). (VL) and (VH) are voltages correponding to lower and upper level of pulsed waveform appearing at pin-8 of IC-1. (VL) is approximately zero in the present case. Thus the laser beam produced by the laser diode switches between two power levels i.e. zero and a power level corresponding to upper drive current level. VH here is 3V. The transmitter circuit is powered by two 9V batteries B-1 and B-2, which can be connected to the circuit through a DPDT (Double Pole Double Throw) swich SW-1.

The laser diode here can be the one typically used in laser pointers emitting in red. This would be more economical than buying one. In this case, the laser diode terminals would need to be carefully brought out as the laser pointer would have an in-built series resistance, a battery and a switch.

RECEIVER PART

The receiver part basically comprises of a current-to-voltage converter section configured around IC-1 (OPAMP 356) feeding the input of another tone decoder IC. The CCO frequency of this IC (IC-4) is chosen to be the same as that chosen in the transmitter part. As a result of this, whenever the laser beam is falling on the photodiode, the current-to-voltage section would produce a pulsed output of the same frequency as transmitter CCO, which further equals receiver CCO frequency. Due to this frequency matching, pin-8 of IC-4 remains HIGH, which ensures that the buzzer is deactivated. The moment the laser beam is interrupted, pin-8 of IC-4 goes LOW activating the buzzer for the duration the beam remains interrupted. The bandwidth here is decided by C10 and is chosen to be 100 Hz around the center frequency i.e. 950 Hz to 1050 Hz. C11 is recommended to be equal to 2C10. The receiver also operates from its own two 9V batteries B-3 and B-4, which can be connected to the receiver circuit through another DPDT swich SW-2.

Please Note: *Duration of the alarm equals the time for which the laser beam is interrupted. Someone walking through the beam very fast may lead to alarm duration as small as fraction of a second, which would be inadequate as an alarm. The circuit could be modified to produce an alarm of given duration irrespective of the time duration for which the beam is cut as long as it is cut. This could be done by using HIGH-to-LOW transmition at pin-8 of receiver tone decoder IC to trigger a monoshot built around timer IC 555. The buzzer in that case would be connected to the output of monoshot. Pin-8 of IC-4 would have only the pull-up resistor and not a series combination of pull-up resistor and buzzer as shown. 555-based monoshot configurations have earlier been discussed in several projects.*

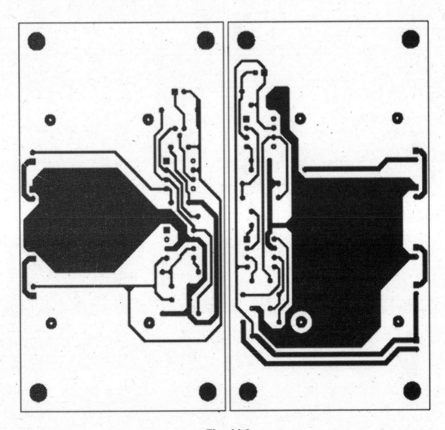

Fig. 44.2

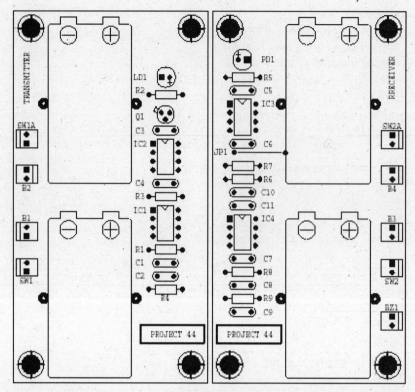

Fig. 44.3

CONSTRUCTION GUIDELINES

Figs. 44.2 (a) and (b) repetively show the PCB layout for the transmitter and receiver sections. Figs. 44.3(a) and (b) show the components layout for the same. However, the circuits are simple enough so as to be constructed on general purpose PCBs.

Perimeter Protection System: What is explained so fare is a Transmitter-Receiver link. The transmitter and receiver could be aligned in the line-of-sight with the fine laser beam linking the two and interruption of the beam leading to alarm. In such as case, transmitter and receiver are not co-located as shown in Fig.44.4. A perimeter protection system, for example to protect a building from unauthorized intrusion, could be built by having three additional near 100% reflecting mirrors to bend the beam as shown in Fig.44.5. In this case, the transmitter and receiver are co-located. Interruption of the laser beam in any part of the perimeter would cause an alarm.

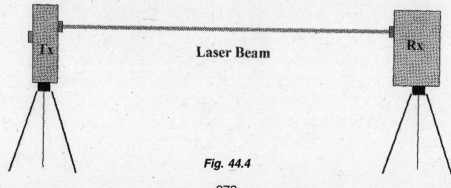

Fig. 44.4

TESTING GUIDELINES

1. Swich ON the transmitter ciruit. Align the transmitter and receiver circuits so that the laser beam falls on the photodiode. You can use a small transmitter receiver distance, even a few feet, for the purpose.

2. If necessary, change the value of one or more resistors (R5, R6, R7) to get a signal peak magnitude of 2 to 3 volts at opamp output.

3. Block the laser radiation with you hand and again measure the opamp output. It should be near zero volt.

4. If you have the services of an oscilloscope, observe the pulse waveforms appearing at pin-8 of IC-1 and pin-6 of IC-3. At pin-8 of IC-4, you would see a HIGH-to-LOW transition every time you block the laser beam.

PARTS LIST

Resistors

All resistors are carbon film or composition resistors unless specified otherwise

R1	:	6.8K, 1/4W
R2	:	1.5K, 1/4W
R3	:	33 ohms, 2W
R4	:	820 ohms, 1/4W
R5, R7, R9	:	1K, 1/4 W
R6	:	22K, 1/4W
R8	:	10K, 1/4W

Capacitors

C1, C8	:	0.1µF (Polyester/ Polystyrene/Mica)
C2 to C7 and C9	:	0.1µF (ceramic disc)
C10	:	22µF (tantalum)
C11	:	47µF (tanalum)

Semicoonductor Devices and ICs

PD-1 (Photodiode)	:	BPX-65 or equivalent
LD-1 (Laser Diode)	:	Can use a laser pointer
Q1 (Transistor)	:	2N2222
IC-1, IC-4	:	LM/NE 567
IC-2, IC-3	:	LF 356

Hardware and other Components

B-1, B-2, B-3, B-4 (Battery)	:	9V battery
SW-1, SW-2	:	DPDT swich
Buzzer	:	Suitable Piezo buzzer

Multi-strand wire, Solder metal, General purpose PCB, if needed

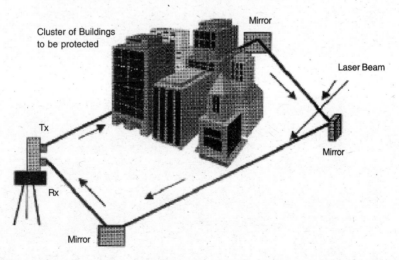

Fig. 44.5

273

Communicating with a Laser Beam

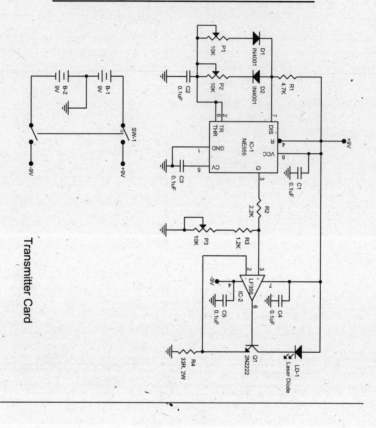

Transmitter Card

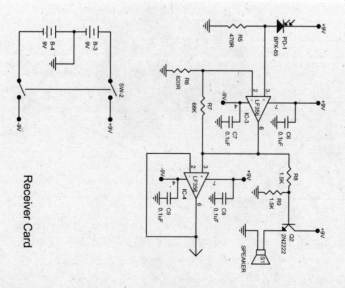

Receiver Card

Fig. 45.1

OBJECTIVE

Communicating with laser is not new. We are all familiar with fiber optic cables that carry our telephone signals from one place to another. The laser beam here is used as a carrier, which is modulated by the signal to be transmitted. On the receiver end, the desired signal is separated from the carrier. Here in the present project activity however, we are going to talk about a wireless laser link that could be used to transmit information from one end to another in its line of sight. The basic underlying principle of operation is the same whether we have the fiber optic link or the wireless link. I would also like to mention here that wireless laser communication links are very popular in space applications for providing inter-satellite communications.

In the present project activity, we shall demonstrate how a given electrical signal can be transmitted from one place to another riding over a laser beam. This will explain the basic principle of operation. We shall vary some parameters of the signal such as amplitude, frequency etc. and confirm that the received signal is a replica of the transmitted signal.

CIRCUIT DESCRIPTION

Fig.45.1 shows the circuit diagram. The circuit is broadly divided into transmitter part and receiver part. These are separately described in the following paragraphs.

Transmitter Part

The transmitter circuit basically comprises of an astable multivibrator generating pulse train which serves as modulation input for the laser diode circuit. The astable multivibrator circuit is built around famous timer IC 555 (IC-1). The output waveform appearing at pin-3 of this IC has a HIGH-time given by $0.69*(R1+P2)*C2$ and a LOW-time given by $0.69*P1*C2$. The frequency of this pulse train can be set to be around 1kHz. The potential divider arrangement of R2, R3 and P3 reduces the peak amplitude of the pulse train from about 8 volts to 3 volts. IC-2, transistor Q1 and associated components constitute the driver circuit for the laser diode LD-1. This type of driver cicuit has been described in projects 43 and 44. The laser diode current in this case switches from zero and about 90 mA. The upper current level in this configuration is given by voltage at pin-3 of IC-2, which due to virtual earth phenomenon of the operational amplifier also appears pin-2, divided by R4.

The transmitter is powered by two 9V batteries to provide both +9V and -9V outputs. These voltages can be connected to the transmitter circuit through DPDT switch SW-1.

Receiver Part

The receiver part is again like the two previous projects a current to voltage converter followed by a non-inverting gain stage. The gain stage is built around IC-3 with gain value given by $[(R6+R7)/R6]$. The gain for this stage can be chosen so as to get sufficient signal amplitude at its output. The output drives a mini speaker (S1) through an emitter follower arrangement configured around Q2. The unity gain buffer stage built around IC-4 is to facilitate viewing of received signal on oscilloscope if so desired.

The receiver circuit is powered by two 9V batteries to provide both +9V and -9V outputs. These voltages can be connected to the receiver circuit through DPDT switch SW-2.

Construction Guidelines

Figs. 45.2 (a) and (b) respectively show the PCB and components layout of the transmitter circuit. The same for receiver circuit are shown in Figs. 45.3(a) and (b). The two circuits are however simple enough to be assembled on general purpose PCBs.

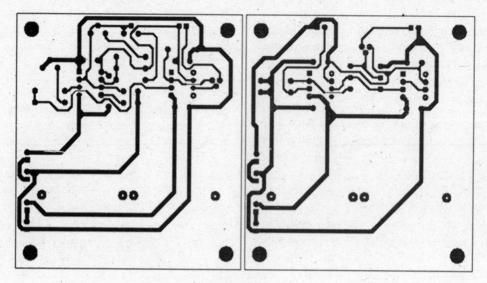

Fig. 45.2

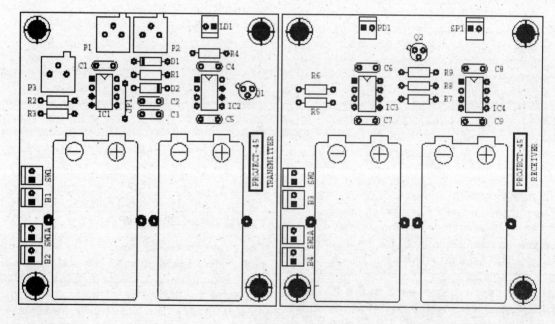

Fig. 45.3

Testing Guidelines

1. Adjust presets P1 and P2 to get approximately 1kHz pulse signal frequency at pin-3 of timer IC 555.

2. Adjust P3 to ensure that desired value of current flows through the laser diode.

3. Align transmitter and receiver cards to ensure that laser light falls on the photodiode.

276

4. Check the signal amplitude at the output of IC-3 (Pin-6 of the IC). The pulse amplitude should be in the range of 3 to 5 volts.

5. This will lead to an audio beep from the speaker.

6. You can observe change in the pitch of the audio beep by changing the frequency of the signal on the transmitter card.

PARTS LIST

Resistors

All resistors are carbon film or composition resistors unless otherwise stated

R1	:	4.7K, 1/4 watt
R2	:	2.2K, 1/4 watt
R3	:	1.2K, 1/4 watt
R4	:	33 ohms, 2 watt
R5	:	470 ohms, 1/4watt
R6	:	820 ohms, 1/4watt
R7	:	68K, 1/4 watt
R8, R9	:	1.5K, 1/4 watt

P1, P2 and P3 : 10K Presets

Capacitors

C1,C3,C4,C5,C6,C7, C8 and C9	:	0.1 µF (Ceramic Disc)
C2	:	0.1 µF (Polyster/Mica)

Semiconductor Devices and ICs

D1, D2 (Diodes)	:	IN4001
LD-1 (Laser Diode)	:	Laser Pointer Laser Diode/Any Laser diode With about 1 mW output power
PD-1 (Photodiode)	:	BPX-65
IC-1	:	Timer IC555
IC-2,IC-3, IC-4	:	LF356

Miscellaneous

Batteries B-1 to B-4	:	9V batteries
SW-1, SW-2	:	DPDT switch

Solder Wire, Solder Metal, General purpose PCB etc.

PROJECT: 46

DIFFERENT WAYS OF GENERATING CLOCK SIGNALS

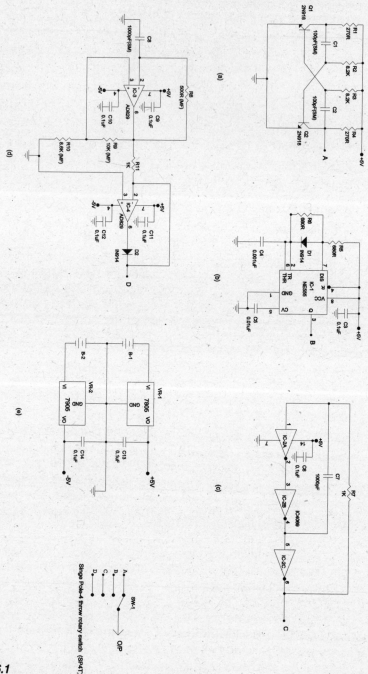

Fig. 46.1

278

OBJECTIVE

In majority of circuits involving digital integrated circuits, we invariably need a clock signal, which is nothing but a continuous train of pulses, for the proper functioning of the circuit. It is more so when the involved digital ICs include sequential logic devices like flip-flops, counters, registers and so on. Although some dedicated clock generator ICs are available for the purpose, yet it would, I suppose, be definitely a worthwhile exercise to look into some of the basic circuits that could also server as a clock. In this project activity, we shall build four different types of clock generators, each having its own limitations vis-a-vis maximum clock frequency that could be generated from the circuit. We shall make an attempt to generate a 1MHz clock signal with each one of those circuits and see for ourselves the quality of the signal products in each case. Another notable feature of this project activity is that we have tried all categories of devices such as discrete deveices, linear integrated circuits and digital integrated cicuits to build the clock generator.

CIRCUIT DESCRIPTION

Fig. 46.1 shows the complete circuit diagram. The circuit is divided into five different circuits. Four of the five circuits are different clock generator circuits and the fifth one generates the required DC voltages for the operation of these circuits. Each one of these circuits is described in the following paragraphs.

Astable Muiltivibrators Based Clock Generators using Discretes Devices (Fig.46.1a)

Fig. 46.1(a) shows the circuit. It is the basic astable multivibrator circuit configured around two bipolar transistors connected back to back. The output can be taken from either of the two collector terminals. In case, it is taken from the Q2-collector, the HIGH-time of the output waveform is governed by R2-C1 time constant ($= 0.69R2C1$) and LOW-time is decided by R3-C2 time constant ($= 0.69R3C2$). It will be the opposite if the output is taken across Q1-collector. In other words, Q1-collector waveform is inverted version of Q2-collector waveform. In the present case,

R2 =R3 = R (say) and C1 = C2 = C (say). Then the output signal frequency is given by $f = 1/(1.38RC)$. For the chosen component values, it turns out to be approximatelhy 1 MHz.

Remember that the bipolar transistors to be used here should be high speed switching transistors and that is how we have chose 2N918. If you try replacing this transistor by another switching transistor such as 2N 2222, you would notice that the waveform looks more like a triangle rather than pulsed one due to deterioration in the rising and falling edges of the waveform. However, 2N 2222 may be good enough up to frequency of a few tens of kHz.

Timer IC 555 Based Clock Generator (Fig.46.1B)

Fig.46.1(b) shows the circuit. It is the famous astable configuration built around timer IC 555. The HIGH-time of the waveform appearing at pin-3 of the IC is given by $(0.69R5C4)$ and the LOW-time is given by $(0.69R6C4)$. For the chosen component values, both HIGH and LOW time equals about 500 nano seconds and the frequency of the output waveform is therefore approximately 1MHz. Though the component values have been chosen to get a clock signal frequency of 1MHz, the signal wave shape as seen at pin-3 of the IC is far from satisfactory. The rising and falling edges of the waveform are far from being vertical. The waveform looks more like a triangle rather than square. This is because of limitation with internal circuitry of 555 timer IC. The idea behind choosing component values for 1 MHz output frequency was to bring home the point that 555 timer IC can not be used at that frequency. You can experiment with different component values and you would find that it produces a reasonably good clock signal wave shape up to 100 kHz.

Digital Inverter Based Clock Generator (Fig.46.1c)

There are a large number of clock generator configurations that can be built using a cascade arrangement of three inverters and an R-C circuit. One such simple configuration built around CMOS hex inverter IC 4069 is given here in Fig. 46.1(c). Both HIGH and LOW times are decided by R7-C6 time constant and given by $0.5R7C6$. The capacitor C6 charges through R7 when the output is HIGH and the charged capacitor discharges through R7 when the output is LOW. For the chosen component values, the output frequency is 1MHz.

OPAMP-Based Clock Generator (Fig.46.1d)
Fig.46.1(d) shows the circuit. The first part built around IC-3, resistors R8, R9, R10 and capacitor C7 is a square wave oscillator with the positive and negative half cycle peak amplitude of about 5 volts. It produces a symmetrical output waveform with a time period (T) given by $2R8*C7*Ln[(1+K/(1-K)]$ where $K = R10/(R9+R10)$. For the chosen component values $Ln[(1+K)/(1-K)] = 1$ and the frequency of operation equals $1/2R8*C7$), which further equals 1MHz. The second part configured around IC-4, resistor R11 and diode D2 is an active half wave rectifier

that passes only the positive half cycles. You would notice that during the positive part of the square waveform, diode D2 is reverse biased with the result that the positive part appears as such at the output. During negative half cycles, the diode becomes forward biased and the circuit reduces to an inverting amplifier configuration with a zero feedback resistance. The result is zero output. Remember AD829 is a high speed opamp and diode D2 (IN914) is also a high speed switching diode to ensure that you get a proper 1 MHz signal.

POWER SUPPLY
The power supply section is nothing but two voltage regulator ICs VR-1 and VR-2 that are used to generate +5 and -5 volt DC from the two 9 volt batteries as shown. C12 and C13 are decoupling capacitors.

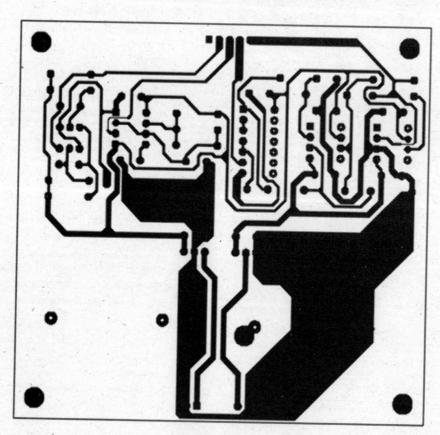

Fig. 46.2

The rotary switch SW-1 (single pole, 4-throw switch) can be used to select one clock generator circuit at a time for the purpose of analysis. The ouputs from various clock generating ciruits are connected to the four throws and the output is taken from the pole terminal of the switch.

CONSTRUCTION GUIDELINES

Figs. 46.2 and 46.3 respectively show the PCB and component layout diagrams. The circuit however is simple enough to be constructed even on a general purpose PCB. The circuit can be tested by selecting one waveform at a time and then analyzing it on an oscilloscope. Measured values can be compared with theoretically expected ones. Also, one should play a little with component values responsible for deciding the frequency and see that the output shows the expected trend.

PART LIST

Resistors

All resistors are of carbon film or carbon composition variety unless otherwise specified

R1, R4	:	270 ohms, 1/4 W
R2,R3	:	8.2K, 1/4 W
R5, R6, R11	:	680 ohms, 1/4 W
R7	:	1K, 1/4 W
R8	:	500 ohms, 1/4 W
R9	:	10K, 1/4 watt
R10*	:	8.6K, W

* R10 may be made by a series combination of 8.2K and 390 ohms and R8 as a parallel combination of two 1K resistors.

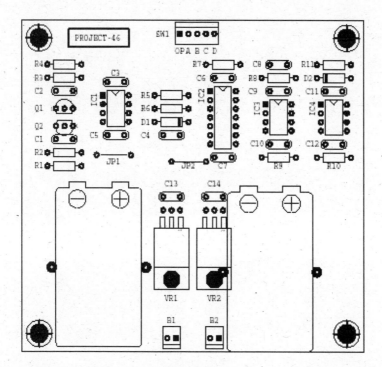

Fig. 46.3

Capacitors

C1,C2	:	100pF (Silver Mica)
C3, C5,C8,C9,C10, C11, C12, C13	:	0.1µF (Ceramic disc)
C4	:	0.001µF (Polyster/Mica)
C6, C7	:	1000pF (Silver mica)

Semiconductor Devices and ICs

Diodes D1 and D2	:	IN 914
Transistors Q1 and Q2	:	2N 918
Voltage Regulator VR-1	:	7805
Voltage Regulator VR-2	:	7905
IC-1	:	Timer 555
IC-2	:	CD 4069B
IC-3, IC-4	:	AD 829

Miscellaneous

Batteries B-1, B-2	:	9Volt batteries
SW-1	:	SP4T Rotary switch

Solder Wire, Solder Metal, General purpose PCB etc.

CANDLES GO ELECTRONIC

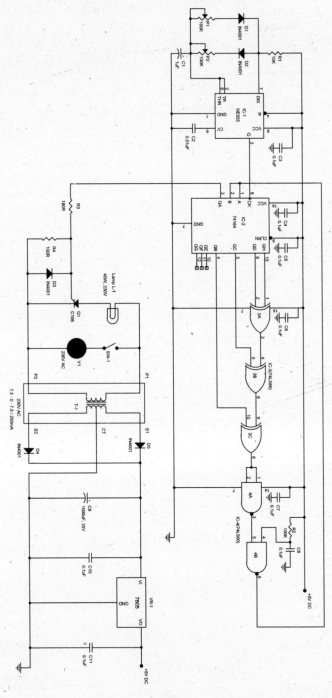

Fig. 47.1

OBJECTIVE

Construction of a simple circuit that can produce the effect of candle light in a normal electric bulb is the project activity here. A candle light as we all know resembles a randomly flickering light. The objective of this project activity is therefore to produce a randomly flickering light effect in an electric bulb.

CIRCUIT DESCRIPTION

Fig.47.1 shows the circuit. It is broadly divided into three parts. The first part comprising of IC-1, IC-2, IC-3, IC-4 and the associated components generates a randomly changing train of pulses. The second part comprising of SCR, the electric bulb in its anode circuit and gate trigger circuit components is basically a half wave AC power control circuit which controls the AC power being supplied to the electric bulb. The third part comprising of diode D3 (acting as half wave rectifier), the associated filter capacitors and voltage regulator VR-1 is the power supply circuit that generates +5VDC from 230 VAC mains for operation of random signal generator.

Looking at the random signal generator, the heart of this part of the circuit is the 8-bit shift register type 74164 (IC-2). Different outputs of the shift register pass through a set of logic gates (IC-3 and IC-4) and the final output appearing at pin-6 of IC-4 fed back to the input of the register. The theory of operation of this random signal generator would be beyond the scope of this book. The random signal appears at pin-3 of IC-2. IC-2 is clocked by an astable multivibrator configured around timer IC 555 (IC-1). The clock frequency is set at 100 Hz. It can be varied a bit around 100 Hz to get the best flickering effect.

The random signal triggers the gate of the SCR. The electric bulb gets AC power only for the period for which SCR is ON. In the present arrangement, the SCR can be ON only during the positive half cycles of the AC input. The period during the positive half cycles for which the SCR conducts would in turn depend upon the triggering instant of the SCR, which is random. Thus we see a flickering effect in the light output.

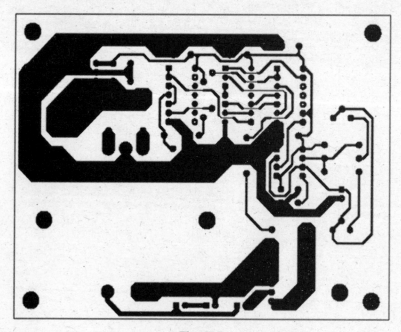

Fig. 47.2

The third part is the power supply section, which generates +5VDC from 230VAC mains. It consists of the conventional arrangement of a step-down transformer (T-1), full wave rectifier (Diodes D4 and D5), filter capacitor (C9) followed by a regulator (VR-1).

CONSTRUCTION GUIDELINES

Fig. 47.2 and 47.3 repectively show the PCB and component layout diagrams. Though the circuit can also be wired on a general purpose PCB, it would be desirable to use properly made PCB for the purpose.

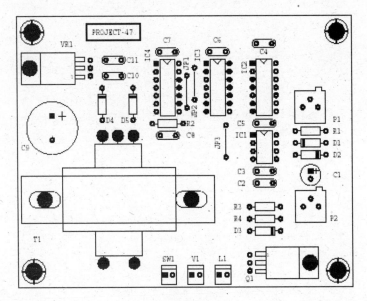

Fig. 47.3

PARTS LIST

Resistors and Potentiometers

All resistors are of carbon film or carbon composition variety unless otherwise specified.

R1, R2	:	10K, 1/4 W
R3	:	180Ω , 1/4W
R4	:	100Ω, 1/4W
P1, P2	:	100K PRESETS

Capacitors

C1	:	1µF (Tantalum)
C2	:	0.01µF (Ceramic disc)
C3, C4, C5,C6, C7,C8, C10, C11	:	0.1µF (Ceramic disc)
C9	:	1000µF/25VDC (Electolytic)

Semiconductor Devices and ICs

Diodes D1, D2,	:	IN 4001
D3, D4, D5		
SCR-1	:	C106M or equivalent
Voltage Regulator, VR-1	:	7805
IC-1	:	Timer 555
IC-2	:	76164
IC-3	:	7486
IC-4	:	7400

Miscellaneous

Transformer, T-1	:	230VAC (Primary) 7.5-0-7.5VAC/250mA SecondaryLamp L-1
	:	Electric Bulb, 40 W to 100 W
		230VAC
SW-1	:	ON/OFF switch

Solder metal, Multi-strand wires, PCB etc.

PROJECT: 48

BATTERY LOW INDICATOR

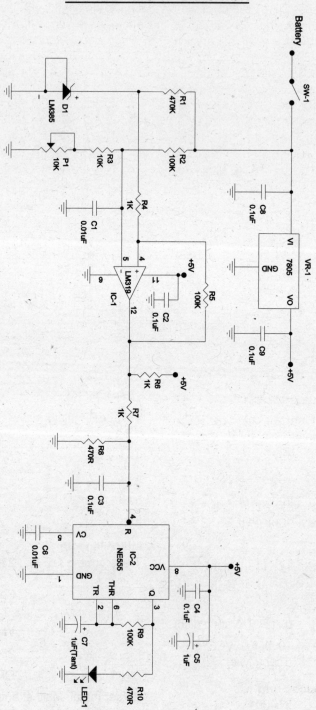

Fig. 48.1

OBJECTIVE

The objective of this project acitivity, as evident from the title of the project, is to build a circuit that can give an indication on the status of a battery in terms of battery voltage falling below a certain preset value. We all know that rechargeable battery irrespective of the type of the battery it is should not be allowed to discharge to a voltage below a certain value if it is to be efficiently recharged. The lower limit again would depend upon the type of battery being used. Also, for non-rechargeable batteries, there could be a requirement of knowing if the battery voltage has fallen below a certain value as a matter of status monitoring. This simple circuit can do that job for 12V and 9V batteries. The indication is in the form of flickering LED light.

CIRCUIT DESCRIPTION

Fig.48.1 shows the complete circuit diagram. The heart of the circuit is a voltage comparator built around IC-1 (LM319). LM319 is a dual comparator with a TTL, compatible output. We have used only one of the two available comparators for our purpose. The non-inverting input of the comparator is fed with a reference voltage of 1.2 volt generated by band gap reference diode D1 (LM385). The reference diode D1 is biased by resistor R1 (470K). The inverting input is fed with a voltage from the potential divider arrangement of R2 (100K) in the upper limb

and series combination of resistor R3 (10K) and preset P1 (10K) in the lower limb. P1 is so adjusted as to get a voltage at the inverting input equal to 1.2 volt when the battery voltage has fallen to the acceptable lower limiting value. Let us say we are using a 12 volt battery and we want an indication as soon as battery voltage reaches 11 volt. In that case P1 should be so adjusted as to get a voltage of 1.2 volt at pin-5 of IC-1 when the battery voltage is 11 volts. We can do a small calculation to find out that P1 would need to be set at 2.2K to achieve this. C1 (0.01μF) is a decoupling capacitor. R4 (1K) and R5 (100K) provide hysteresis to give a noise free operation. R6 (1K) is the recommended pull-up resistor.

Initially, when the battery is healthy, inverting input voltage is higher than the non-inverting input voltage with the result that the comparator output is LOW. The timer IC 555, which has been wired as an astable multivibrator, is reset. Consequently, its output is at zero level. When the battery voltage falls to a point that drives the inverting input voltage to a value less than the non-inverting input voltage, the output goes to HIGH state. The RESET pin is deactivated and the astable output appears at pin-3 of the IC. The astable output of about 10 Hz drives the LED. R7 (1K)-R8(470 ohms) potential divider ensures that during LOW output state of the comparator, the voltage appearing at RESET pin of timer IC is

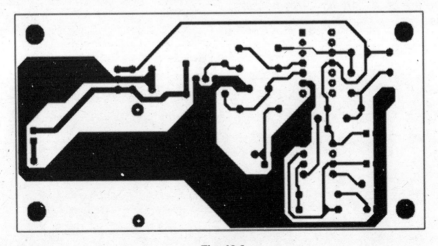

Fig. 48.2

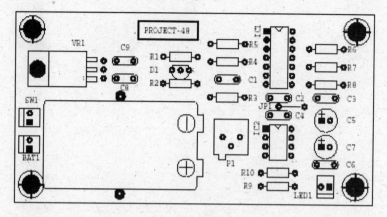

Fig. 48.3

below 0.4 volt, which is the requirement for the RESET function to be activated. Both IC-1 and IC-2 operate from regulated +5VDC generated by VR-1 (7805).

CONSTRUCTION GUIDELINES

Fig.48.2 and 48.3 respectively show the PCB layout and components layout diagrams. From these diagrams, it should not be difficult for you to make your own PCB and then place the components at their designated places. The circuit can also be conveniently wired on a general purpose PCB.

PARTS LIST

Resistors and Potentiometers

All resistors are of carbon film or composition type unless specified otherwise

R1	: 470K, 1/4 W
R2, R5, R9	: 100K, 1/4 W
R3	: 10K, 1/4 W
R4, R6, R7	: 1K, 1/4 W
R8, R10	: 470 ohms, 1/4 W
P1	: 10K PRESETS

CAPACITORS

C1, C6	: 0.01µF (Ceramic disc)
C2, C3, C4, C6,C8, C9	: 0.1µF (Ceramic disc)
C5, C7	: 1µF (Tantalum)

Semiconductor Devices and ICs

Diode D1	: LM 385 (Reference Diode)
LED-1	: Red colour miniature LED
Voltage Regulator, VR-1	: 7805
IC-1	: LM 319
IC-2	: Timer 555

Hardware Components

Switch, SW-1	: ON/OFF Toggle Switch

Multi-strand wires, Solder metal

General-purpose PCB (if required)

STAIRCASE LIGHT WITH AUTO-SWITCH-OFF FEATURE

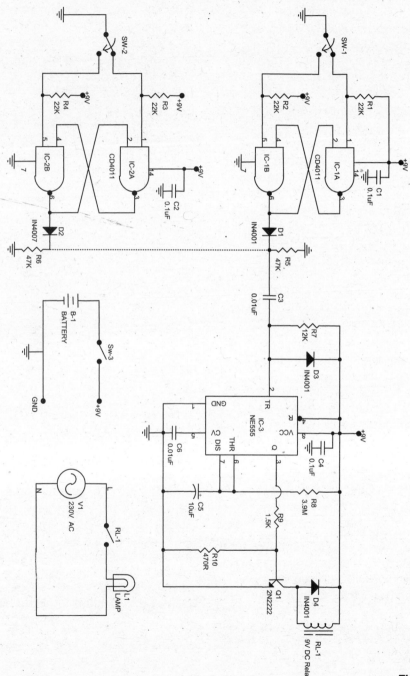

Fig. 49.1

OBJECTIVE

We are all familiar with the electrical wiring diagram that connects an electrical bulb with two switches with one of the swtiches placed at the bottom of a staircase and the other located at the top. The wiring is done in such a way that either of the two switches can be used to switch ON the bulb (if it is initially OFF) or switch it OFF (if it is initally ON) as the case may be. In such a wiring arrangement, while climbing up the staircase in dark, the switch located at the bottom of the staircase is used to switch ON the light. After you have the climbed the staircase, you use the switch located there to switch the light OFF.

The present circuit is an electronic counterpart of the electrical arrangement to get a similar facility. Also in the present gadget, you need to operate the switch only once. In the earlier arrangement of electrical wiring mentioned in the first paragraph, you may forget to switch OFF the light once you have already climbed up he staircase or gone down the same as the case may be perhaps because you were thinking something. In that case, the light would remain ON the whole night leading to wastage of electrical energy.

In the present case, we have two micro-switches, one located near the top and the other located near the bottom of the staircase. With every push of either of the two switches, the bulb lights up for a time period of about 40 seconds, which is considered adequate for climbing up or going down the staircase. The bulb extinguishes automatically after that. This ON-time can however be changed by the user by changing one resistance value depending upon the requirement.

CIRCUIT DESCRIPTION

Fig.49.1 shows the circuit diagram. SW-1 and SW-2 are the two micro-switches, which feed the inputs of their respective de-bouncing circuits. Each de-bouncing circuit is built around the famous back-to-back connection of two NAND gates. The de-bouncing circuit ensures a clean bounce free pulse at the output every time the micro switch is pressed. Since the two switches are to be located physically apart some distance, we have used separate NAND gate ICs (CD 4011) for each de-bouncing circuit. The outputs from the two de-bouncing circuits are ORed using diodes D1 (IN 4001) and D2 (IN 4001). So, every time we press either of the micro-switches, we get a positive going pulse at the junction of the cathodes of diodes D1 and D2. This pulse is used to trigger the monoshot circuit configured around IC-3 (Timer IC 555). The triggering occurs on the trailing edge of the pulse. The output of monoshot goes HIGH for a time given by 1.1R8*C5. This time period for the chosen values is 40 seconds. This 40-second pulse drives the transistor Q1 (2N 2222) wired as a switch. The relay RL-1 gets activated thus closing the normally open relay contact wired in series with the mains and the bulb. The bulb extinguishes when the relay gets de-activated after 40-second period has elapsed. Diode D4 (IN 4001) is to protect the transistor Q1 against transients during relay switch-OFF operation.

The circuit operates on 9VDC derived from a battery, which gets connected to the circuit through a toggle switch SW-3. In the actual set-up, this DC voltage could also be derived from AC mains voltage.

CONSTRUCTION GUIDELINES

Fig.49.2 and 49.3 respectively show the PCB layout and components layout diagrams. From these diagrams, it should not be difficult for you to make your own PCB and then place the components at their designated places. The circuit can also be conveniently wired on a general purpose PCB. The PCB layout shown here is for the complete circuit diagram to allow you to test the circuit as an experimenter. In real practice, if you have to actually implement the device in your house, you would need to make separate PCBs for the two switches along with their de-bouncing circuits and another PCB for the control circuit.

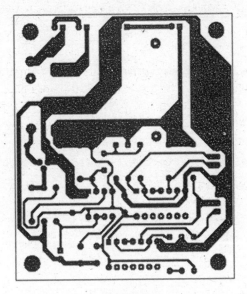

Fig. 49.2

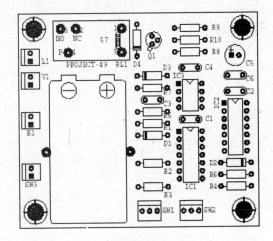

Fig. 49.3

PARTS LIST

Resistors and Potentiometers

All resistors are of carbon film or composition type unless specified otherwise

R1, R2, R3, R4	:	22K, 1/4 W
R5, R6	:	47K, 1/4 W
R7	:	12K, 1/4 W
R8	:	3.9K, 1/4 W
R9	:	1.5K, 1/4 W
R10	:	470 ohms, 1/4 W

Capacitors

C1, C2, C4	:	0.1µF (Ceramic disc)
C3, C6	:	0.01µF (Ceramic disc)
C5	:	10µF (Tantalum)

Semiconductor Devices and ICs

Diodes D1,D2,D3	:	IN 4001
Transistor Q1	:	2N 2222
Voltage Regulator, VR-1	:	7805
IC-1, IC-2	:	CD 4011
IC-3	:	Timer 555

Hardware Components

SW-1, SW-2	:	Micro-switch
SW-3	:	ON/OFF Toggle Switch
RL-1	:	9VDC/100 to 200 ohms Relay
		With at least one normally Open (NO) Contact*
L-1	:	Suitable 230 VAC Bulb 40 to 100 Watt rating

Multi-strand wires, Solder metal

General-purpose PCB (if required)

* Even a 6V/100 ohms or 12V/100 ohms DC relay would also work.

PROJECT: 50

REMOTE CONTROL OF HOME APPLIANCES

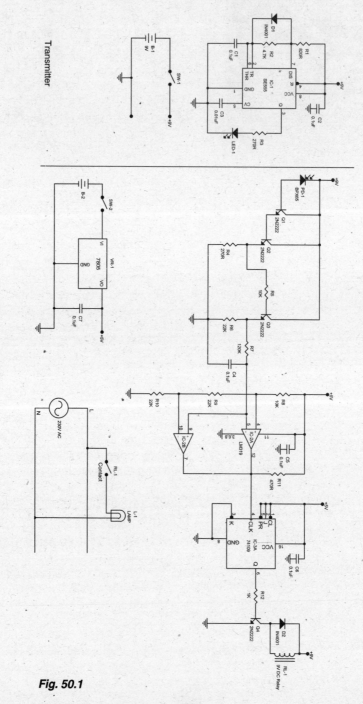

Fig. 50.1

OBJECTIVE

In the last project activity of this revised and enlarged edition of the book, we shall attempt yet another interesting gadget that would demonstrate a simple concept of remotely controlling the switch ON and switch OFF operation of AC mains operated electrical appliances. It may be mentioned here that the circuit is not the most optimum for the purpose and almost all remote control gadgets are built around dedicated chips with embedded technology meant for performing a certain intended function. The purpose of the project activity, as has been the case with most of the other project activities presented earlier, is to raise the technical level of the expermenter and motivate him to do something new with available general purpose devices.

CIRCUIT DESCRIPTION

Fig.50.1 shows the complete circuit diagram. The circuit has two distinct parts namely the TRANSMITTER and the RECEIVER. Both are separately described in the following paragraphs.

Transmitter

The transmitter circuit is nothing but an astable circuit built around timer IC 555. It produces a pulsed output waveform with an ON-time of 60 μs and an OFF-time of about 330 μs. The output of timer feeds the IR LED (LED-1). The IR LED used here is same as the one typically used in TV remotes. The experimenter can use any IR LED used in any of the TV remote control units. We are not recommending any particular type number as these IR LEDs are easily available and low cost. These are also highly suitable for the purpose. The circuit operates from a 9 volt battery (B-1), which can be connected to the circuit through switch SW-1.

Receiver

The input part of the circuit comprising of photodiode PD-1, Darlington connection made with transistors Q1 and Q2 and resistor R5 constitute the current-to-voltage converter, which converts the photocurrent generated by photodiode into an equivalent voltage. In fact, the photodiode and the Darlington connection together make a Photo-Darlington. The Darlington connection amplifies the photo current generated by the photodiode thus allowing even a feeble IR power to be detected. The equivalent photo voltage appears across R4. So, across R4, we get a replica of what we produce at timer IC output in terms of wave shape but not in amplitude. Amplitude would vary with distance and other factors such as the angle of arrival of the IR beam at the sensor and so on. Transistor Q3 is wired as a non-inverting switch. The low pass filter constituted by R7 and C4 produces a DC value of approximately 3 volts. This DC voltage feeds the junction of inverting input of IC-2A and non-inverting input of IC-2B. The two extremes of window comparator circuit are decided by the two reference voltages appearing at the inverting input of IC-2B and non-inverting input of IC-2A. These are 2 and 4 volts. This window comparator is so configured that whenever the input voltage lies within the window of 2 to 4 volts (greater than 2 V and less than 4V), the output goes to HIGH state. If the input voltage is less than equal to 2 volts or more than equal to 4 volts, the output goes to LOW state. The output of the window comparator feeds the clock input of the J-K Flip-flop, which is wired as a toggle flip-flop. The output of a toggle flip-flop toggles i.e. goes to HIGH-state if initially in LOW-state and to LOW-state if initially HIGH, every time it is clocked. Output of flip-flop feeds the transistor Q4 base terminal. Q4 is wired as a switch with relay coil as its collector load. The relay operates and its normally open contact closes every time the transistor Q4 is switched ON.

Initially, with no IR light falling on the sensor (photodiode), the DC voltage appearing at the input of the window comparator is near zero. The comparator output is in LOW-state with the result that transistor Q4 is in OFF-state and the relay remains inactivated. When IR light is made to fall on the sensor for a short period of time, a positive going pulse with amplitude of about 3 volts appears at the input of window comparator. The output of comparator goes to HIGH state, which in turn switches the transistor Q4 ON. Relay RL-1 gets activated and its normally open contact closes thus switching ON the intended gadget or appliance. The receiver operates from its own 9 volt battery (B-2), which can be connected to the circuit through switch SW-2. The same 9 volt is also used as an input to a 3-terminal regulator (VR1), which generates +5 volts for operating the timer and comparator ICs.

CONSTRUCTION GUIDELINES

Fig.50.2 and 50.3 respectively show the PCB layout and components layout diagrams. From these diagrams, it should not be difficult for you to make your own PCB and then place the components at their designated places. The circuit can also be conveniently wired on a general purpose PCB.

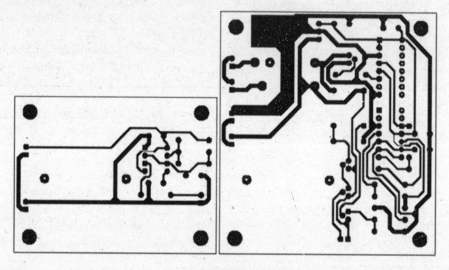

Fig. 50.2

PARTS LIST

Resistors

All resistors are of carbon film or composition type unless specified otherwise

R1	:	820 ohms, 1/4 W
R2	:	4.7K, 1/4 W
R3, R4	:	270 ohms, 1/4 W
R5, R8	:	10K, 1/4 W
R6, R9, R10	:	22K, 1/4 W
R7	:	120K, 1/4 W
R11	:	470 ohms, 1/4 W

Capacitors

C1, C4	:	0.1µF (Polyester/Mica)
C2, C5, C6,C7	:	0.1µF (Ceramic disc)
C3	:	0.01µF (Ceramic disc)

Semiconductor Devices and ICs

Diodes D1. D2	:	IN 4001
Photodiode	:	BPX-65 or equivalent
IR LED LED-1	:	IR LED used in TV Remote
Transistor Q1, Q2, Q3, Q4	:	2N 2222
Voltage Regulator, VR-1	:	7805
IC-1	:	Timer IC 555
IC-2	:	LM 319
IC-3	:	74109

Hardware Components

SW-1, SW-2	:	ON/OFF Toggle Switch
RL-1	:	9VDC/100 to 200 ohms Relay

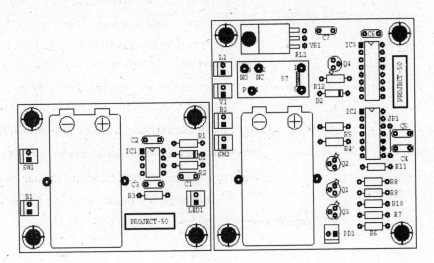

Fig. 50.3

With at least one normally Open (NO) contact*

L-1 : Suitable 230 VAC Bulb 40 to 100 Watt rating

B-1, B-2 : 9 Volt Battery, PP3 type

Multi-strand wires, Solder metal

General-purpose PCB (if required)

* Even a 6V/100 ohms cr 12V/100 ohms DC relay would also work